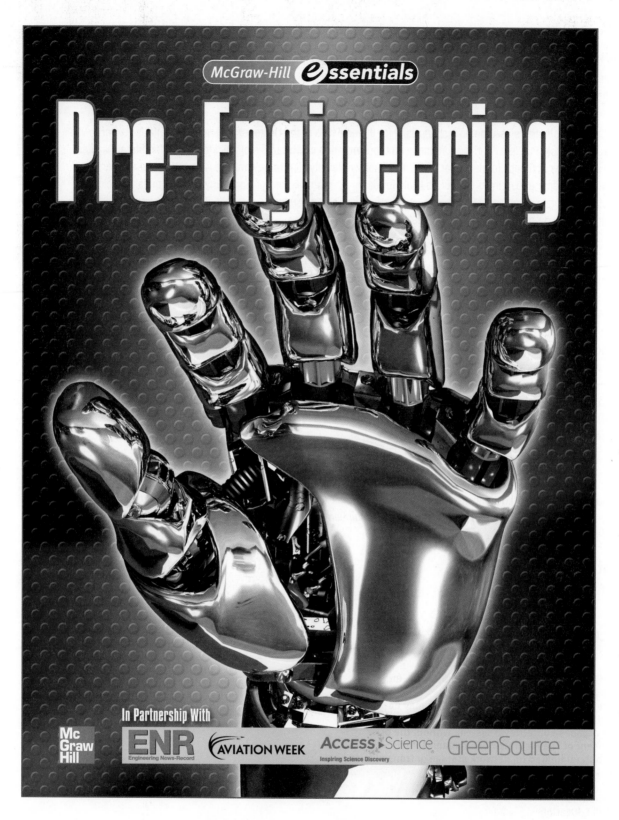

McGraw-Hill *e*ssentials

Pre-Engineering

In Partnership With

Mc Graw Hill

ENR Engineering News-Record

AVIATION WEEK

ACCESS Science Inspiring Science Discovery

GreenSource

Henry R. Harms | David A. Janosz, Jr.

Mc Graw Hill **Education**

Bothell, WA • Chicago, IL • Columbus, OH • New York, NY

Safety Notice

The reader is expressly advised to consider and use all safety precautions described in this book or that might also be indicated by undertaking the activities described herein. In addition, common sense should be exercised to help avoid all potential hazards.

Publisher and Authors assume no responsibility for the activities of the reader or for the subject matter experts who prepared this book. Publisher and Authors make no representation or warranties of any kind, including but not limited to, the warranties of fitness for particular purpose or merchantability, nor for any implied warranties related thereto, or otherwise. Publisher and Authors will not be liable for damages of any types, including any consequential, special or exemplary damages resulting, in whole or in part, from reader's use or reliance upon the information, instructions, warnings, or other matter contained in this book.

Internet Disclaimer

The Internet listings in this product are a source for extended information related to this title. We have made every effort to recommend sites that are informative and accurate. However, these sites are not under the control of Glencoe/McGraw-Hill, and, therefore, Glencoe/McGraw-Hill makes no representation concerning the content of these sites. We strongly encourage teachers to preview Internet sites before students use them. Many sites may eventually contain links to other sites that could lead to inappropriate material. Internet sites are sometimes under construction and may not always be available. Sites may also move or have been discontinued completely by the time you or your students attempt to access them.

Notice: Information on featured companies, organizations, and their products and services is included for educational purposes only and does not present or imply endorsement of the *Pre-Engineering* program.

mheonline.com

 Education

Send all inquiries to:
McGraw-Hill Education
4400 Easton Commons, Suite 200
Columbus, OH 43219

ISBN: 978-0-07-878336-4 (Student Edition)
MHID: 0-07-878336-4 (Student Edition)

Printed in the United States of America.

2 3 4 5 6 7 8 9 QDB 15 14 13 12 11

Meet the Authors

Henry R. Harms

Since 2008, Henry R. Harms has been the Manager of Engineering and Technology Education Programs in the Center for Innovation in Engineering and Science Education (CIESE) at Stevens Institute of Technology in New Jersey. He is responsible for managing projects that involve the development of curriculum materials and teacher training. He has B.S. and M.S. degrees from the State University of New York at Oswego. Prior to joining CIESE, he taught technology education at the middle school, high school, and college levels. He is a member of the Board of Directors of the Technology Student Association, and was Project Director of the New Jersey Technology Student Association for seven years.

Henry has served as Coordinator of the Stepping Up Recruitment for High Need Districts Program, 5 Star program for the New Jersey Technology Education Program, and the New Jersey Commission on Higher Education's Exploring Design and Engineering project. He has served as a co-author for multiple technology textbooks published by Glencoe/McGraw-Hill.

David A. Janosz, Jr.

David A. Janosz, Jr. is a supervisor in the Northern Valley Regional High School district in Bergen County, New Jersey. Prior to that, he taught Technology Education in Northern Valley – Old Tappan High School and at Fair Lawn High School, his alma mater, for a total of twelve years. He holds a Bachelor of Science degree in Industrial Education and Technology and a Master of Arts degree in Technology Education from Montclair State University. He also holds a Master of Education degree in Educational Administration and Supervision from Rutgers University.

David is a past President and former Executive Director of the New Jersey Technology Education Association, a statewide professional organization for those in the field of technology education. He has over fifteen years of experience designing and implementing education programs at all grade levels P-12. David has made presentations to local, national, and international audiences, including programs sponsored by the International Technology and Engineering Educators Association, New Jersey Technology Education Association, New Jersey Education Association, New Jersey School Boards Association, IEEE, American Foundryman's Society, Montclair State University, Ramapo College, The College of New Jersey, Liberty Science Center, and WNET/Thirteen. He also maintains a video blog and podcast about the study of technology and engineering called Education for Innovation, which can be accessed at educationforinnovation.org.

Contributing Writers, Reviewers, and Advisory Board

Advisory Board

Lynn Basham, *Ph.D.*
Virginia Department of Education
Richmond, VA

Gary R. Bertoline, *Ph.D.*
Purdue University
West Lafayette, IN

Todd Kelley, *Ph.D.*
Purdue University
West Lafayette, IN

Robert E. Lindberg, Jr., *Eng.Sc.D.*
National Institute of Aerospace
Hampton, VA

Cheryl Simmers
Appomattox Regional Governor's
*   School for the Arts and Technology*
Petersburg, VA

Cynthia Sims, *Ph.D.*
Southern Illinois University
Carbondale, IL

Nancy Study, *Ph.D.*
Virginia State University
Petersburg, VA

Contributing Writers

Greg Burnham
Estacado High School
Lubbock, TX

Brian Drelick
High Point Regional High School
Sussex, NJ

Laura J. Hummell, *Ph.D.*
California University of Pennsylvania
California, PA

David Niemierowski
Colts Neck High School
Colts Neck, NJ

Cheryl Simmers
Appomattox Regional Governor's
*   School for the Arts and Technology*
Petersburg, VA

Nancy Study, *Ph.D.*
Virginia State University
Petersburg, VA

Melanie Weiss
Earth Ed
Oak Park, IL

Reviewers

We wish to acknowledge the contributions of the following reviewers:

Bob Behnke
Hawkins High School
Hawkins, TX

Gil Burlew
Braden River High School
Bradenton, FL

Greg Burnham
Estacado High School
Lubbock, TX

Brian Drelick
High Point Regional High School
Sussex, NJ

Farley Ferrante
Southern Methodist University
Dallas, TX

Lila Hackett
Richlands High School
Richlands, NC

Brian Lien
School District of Manatee County
Princeton High School
Cincinnati, OH

Michael Miller
Kilbourne Middle School
Worthington, OH

Richard Platt
Braden River High School
Bradenton, FL

Ricardo Rodriguez
Science Academy
Mercedes, TX

Susan Sanford
Doherty High School
Worcester, MA

Cheryl Simmers
Appomattox Regional Governor's
*   School for the Arts and Technology*
Petersburg, VA

Nancy Taliaferro
Highland School of Technology
Grover, NC

Doug Wagner
School District of Manatee County
Manatee, FL

Our Partners at McGraw-Hill

Engineering News-Record provides the news, analysis, commentary, and data that construction industry professionals need to do their jobs more effectively. ENR products include a weekly magazine with more than 70,000 paid subscribers, a website with over 90,000 unique visitors a month, and a series of in-person events. The audience includes contractors, project owners, engineers, architects, government regulators, and industry suppliers—many of whom work around the world. ENR connects diverse sectors of the industry with coverage that everyone needs about issues such as business management, design, construction methods, technology, safety, law, legislation, environment, and labor.

Serving over 1.2 million professionals in 185 countries, AVIATION WEEK is the largest information and services provider to the global commercial, defense, maintenance/repair/overhaul (MRO), space, and business aviation communities, and plays a critical role in connecting industry professionals worldwide. Anchored by its flagship *Aviation Week & Space Technology*, AVIATION WEEK continues to grow and evolve its portfolio to meet the needs of the industry.

The new generation of AccessScience gathers and synthesizes vast amounts of information, and organizes it to give you fast, easy, and accurate access to authoritative articles in all major areas of science and technology. It's easier than ever to find what you're looking for and put it to use quickly.

AccessScience puts the most useful and up-to-date technology to work for you: in addition to fast, sophisticated search capability, you'll find RSS feeds, Flash® animations, image galleries, podcasts, videos, and more, with an enhanced search engine making discovery of this wide range of information easier than ever.

GreenSource

GreenSource is developed with a process similar to the integrated design process undertaken for sustainable buildings. Our collaborative team members meet to brainstorm and debate about ideas and projects worthy of occupying the pages of the magazine and page views of the website. The McGraw-Hill team has the active participation of four of *Architectural Record's* editors. In addition, GreenSource's editorial partners BuildingGreen have nearly two decades of experience publishing *Environmental Building News* and the *GreenSpec Directory*.

Contents in Brief

Table of Contents

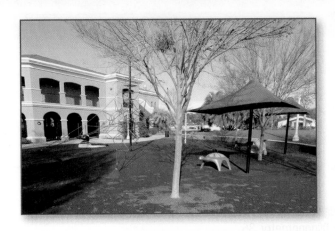

Chapter 4

Design and Modeling   68

Chapter 9   Mechanical Engineering   168

Chapter 10   Manufacturing Engineering   184

Table of Contents *continued*

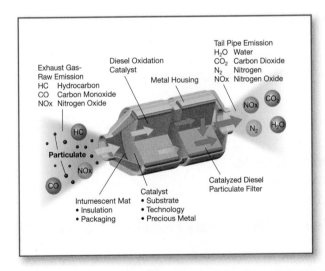
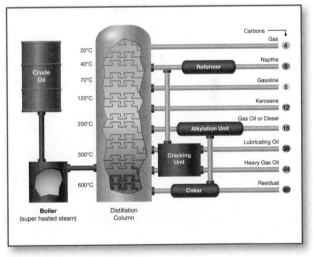

Table of Contents *continued*

FEATURES Table of Contents

 Green reSource

Virtual Lab

Career Center

STEM CONNECTION

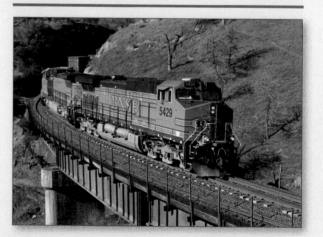

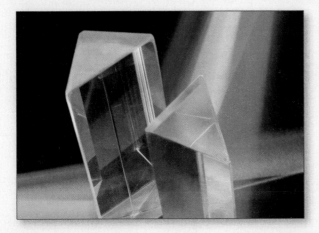

Visualization

Welcome to McGraw-Hill essentials Pre-Engineering!

Pre-Engineering is a comprehensive program that introduces you to the world of engineering. This text and its integrated online companion, Connect, address engineering with a focus on project-based learning. Completing this program will help you make an informed decision about preparing to be a member of the engineering team: an engineering technologist, a technician, a skilled worker, or a practicing engineer.

This program will challenge you to think critically, and use technology and tools effectively and safely. You will learn skills to communicate clearly, cooperate within teams, and solve mathematical, scientific, and logistical problems. Accomplishing these goals will help to prepare you for the exciting world of engineering.

Unit Objectives This is an outline of your goals for each unit. Use the unit objectives to help you keep track of the skills and concepts you will need to successfully complete the Challenge Project.

Essentials Icon This lets you know that you will be going online to complete this activity.

Challenge Project The Challenge Project Video Launcher introduces you to concepts that you will learn throughout the unit, and helps you start thinking about how you will apply these concepts.

The Engineer's Blog This is an interactive tool that allows you to communicate and collaborate with your peers as you work on engineering projects throughout the program.

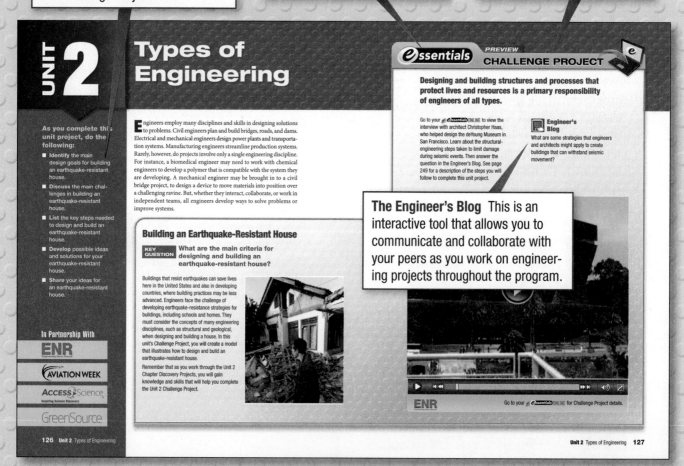

Unit Review and Challenge Project

Each unit concludes with a hands-on project that explores an important aspect of engineering. To complete each project, you will work with your team to evaluate and plan your resources, conduct research, complete the project steps as outlined, and share your results with your teacher and your class. These projects show you what it is like to be a member of an engineering team, completing a project from start to finish. Specially designed Chapter Discovery Projects will help you build the skills and knowledge you need to complete the Unit Challenge Project.

Challenge Project Using skills that you have developed throughout the Chapter Discovery Projects, you will complete the hands-on Challenge Project after watching an online video and following the steps of the engineering process.

Critical Thinking Every unit contains key concepts that help you develop critical thinking skills.

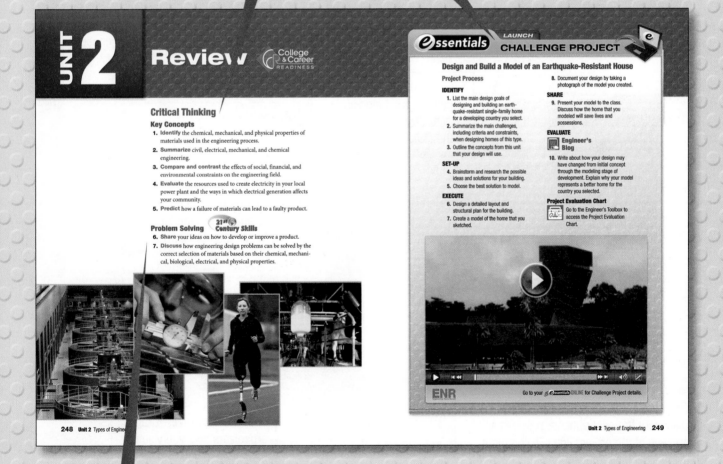

21st Century Skills In every unit, you will have the opportunity to communicate and collaborate with other members of your class.

Chapters

Pre-Engineering chapters are organized around the topics and processes that help you discover, learn about, and apply the essential skills of engineering. Visual cues direct you to the online site in Connect where you will collaborate with your classmates on activities and projects.

Reading Guide Each chapter begins with a reading guide to give you a preview of content and academic vocabulary and the industry and academic standards you will cover.

Essential Question An essential question leads you to key inquiries within the field of engineering that you will consider throughout the chapter.

Before You Read A pre-reading question or statement will help you connect with what you read in the chapter.

Chapter Objectives These objectives will help you preview what you will learn in the chapter.

Academic Standards *Pre-Engineering* helps you gain proficiency in Technology, Mathematics, Science, and Career & College Readiness. The chapter reading guides list the academic standards that the chapter will cover.

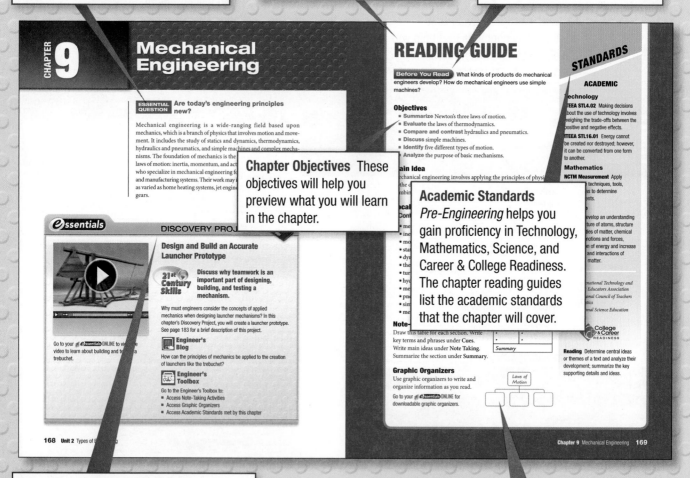

Discovery Project Launcher The Discovery Project Launcher provides a preview of the project you will complete using skills and knowledge you gain in the chapter. You will watch a video and record your ideas in a blog as you consider the engineering design process.

Graphic Organizer Graphic organizers give you visual tools to help you organize and remember new content.

In-Chapter Features

The features help you check your understanding of what you are reading and extend your knowledge of engineering concepts.

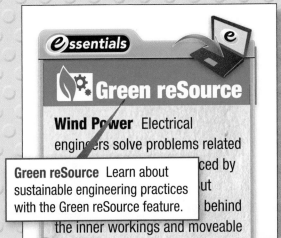

Green reSource Learn about sustainable engineering practices with the Green reSource feature.

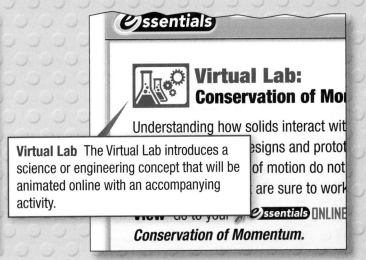

Virtual Lab The Virtual Lab introduces a science or engineering concept that will be animated online with an accompanying activity.

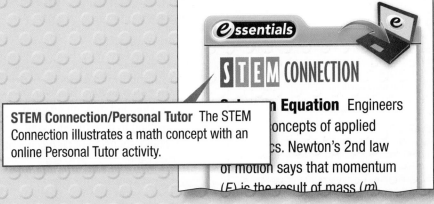

STEM Connection/Personal Tutor The STEM Connection illustrates a math concept with an online Personal Tutor activity.

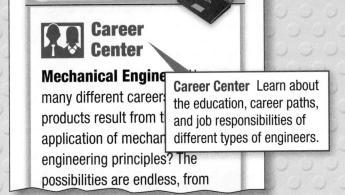

Career Center Learn about the education, career paths, and job responsibilities of different types of engineers.

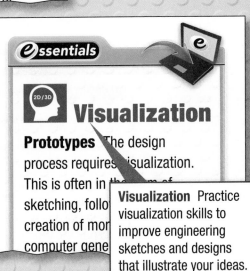

Visualization Practice visualization skills to improve engineering sketches and designs that illustrate your ideas.

Section Assessments

Assessing what you have learned is a critical part of the learning process. Use the review questions to check your understanding, apply this new knowledge to activities and projects, and get ready to show your mastery of these concepts.

its simplest forms, an egg-shaped cam can translate rotary movement to reciprocating or intermittent movement. This type of cam is most commonly applied in a camshaft in an internal combustion engine. Cams along the rotating shaft are used to open and close intake and exhaust valves intermittently.

When a cam is used in conjunction with a third-class lever, it can create oscillating movement. This movement is found in many wind-up and other mechanical toys.

Cranks

A crank effectively combines a wheel and axle with a lever. Consider the example of a bicycle crank set at the pedals. In a way, simply bending an extension of the axle at two points combines the two simple machines. Moving the pedals (on which feet will apply the force) farther from the axle allows for more mechanical advantage.

Another common application of a crank is found in the crankshaft of an internal combustion engine. As the pistons in the engine reciprocate, this movement translates into the rotary movement of the crankshaft.

Ratchet and Pawl

The ratchet and pawl is a common mechanism, used when motion in one direction is desired and movement in the opposite direction is undesired. A ratchet and pawl is found in devices that tie down heavy loads to the bed of a truck, or in devices that hoist heavy items.

A ratchet looks like a gear with its teeth curved slightly in one direction. The pawl slips over each tooth as it moves in one direction. Then it locks, to prevent movement in the other direction.

Complex Mechanisms

Clutches, watch escapements, mechanical switches, winches, differentials, and transmissions are all examples of complex mechanisms. Complex mechanisms are simple mechanisms that have been optimized for different applications. It is important to remember that engineers use all mechanisms, regardless of their complexity, to control and translate movement, directionality, and power.

essentials

Visualization

Prototypes The design process requires visualization. This is often in the form of sketching, followed by the creation of more complex computer generated 2D drawings and 3D models. Virtual prototypes can also be made and tested in simulated conditions using computer tools before creating physical prototypes.

Go to your **e**ssentials ONLINE to learn more about developing models.

Engineer's Blog

Plan out the modeling process and visualize and sketch all the steps necessary in creating a finished model.

> **Reading Check** Reading Checks are located throughout each section to help monitor your comprehension of core concepts.

 Reading Check Describe how mechanical engineers use simple machines to create mechanisms.

Check Your Understanding

SECTION **9.2**

After You Read Perform the following tasks.

1. **Identify** an example of each of the three classes of levers.
2. **Describe** what kind of motion gears usually transmit.
3. **Analyze** why cams are used.

> **After You Read** Reviewing your reading is a powerful study skill. After You Read will help you organize and process your understanding of what you have read.

Chapter Review and Assessment

Use end-of-chapter activities to assess your learning and reach your goals.

Problem-Solving Process Sharpen your problem-solving skills with your classmates by using the engineering design process.

Key Concepts Take time to determine how well you have met the chapter objectives by completing the activities outlined here.

Activity Center Use the online activities to review and apply what you have learned, and to prepare for tests and competitive events.

CHAPTER **9**

Review and Assessment

College & Career
READINESS

Problem-Solving Process

Identify

The XYZ Toy Design Company wants to develop simple mechanical toys for 3- to 5-year-olds. Of 10 models, three will be chosen. Your team will develop one model.

Set Up

1. Ground yourself in information about the project. Ask: *"What is really important about this project?"* and *"What criteria will make for a successful project?"*
2. Gather related background information. Research existing toys and disassemble some toys to see how they work.
3. Brainstorm potential solutions. Remember, there are no "bad" ideas in a brainstorming session. Record all thoughts on paper.
4. Choose the best solution. Base decisions on your previous criteria for success.

Execute

5. Plan the building of the solution with your team.
6. Keep sketching and recording ideas. These may become references later.
7. Build mock-ups of the solution, using different ways to carry out the building. You may try many ways of doing something before you find the best way.
8. Meet with your team at the end of each session to discuss accomplishments and set goals.

Evaluate

Determine which mock-up is best by testing the prototype with a group of children, your class, or a group of teachers. If your project is not successful, reevaluate your steps. Ask: *Did your group communicate effectively? Did you understand the project at the start?*

Share

Share your views on the importance of this project and the criteria that determined the success of the project. Discuss how well your team communicated and any difficulty you had with the project.

Critical Thinking

Key Concepts

1. **Identify** three different kinds of systems that mechanical engineers use.
2. **Summarize** Newton's three laws of motion.
3. **Compare and contrast** hydraulic and pneumatic systems.
4. **Evaluate** Newton's third law of motion and the first law of thermodynamics. Then discuss why and how they are related.
5. **Analyze** how mechanical advantage is achieved with a wheel and axle.

Teamwork   21st Century Skills

6. **Share** with your project team what you have learned about applied mechanics and how that information relates to your Discovery Project.
7. **Discuss** the use of simple machines in various systems and how to apply simple machines to solve a design problem in your Discovery Project.

Activity Center

Go to the **Activity Center** to review chapter vocabulary and key concepts.

Engineer's Toolbox

Go to the **Engineer's Toolbox** to:
- Access Academic Activities
- Access the Test-Prep Activity
- Access the Competitive Event Prep Activity

DISCOVERY PROJECT

Design and Build an Accurate Launcher Prototype

In this chapter's Discovery Project, you will create a launcher prototype that can launch a marshmallow at a target. Your team's launcher should be reliable and predictable. It should be able to adjust to targets at different ranges.

Go to your *Essentials* ONLINE to view the video to learn about building and testing a trebuchet. Then complete the Discovery Project.

182   **Unit 2** Types of Engineering

Chapter 9 Mechanical Engineering   **183**

21st Century Skills Communicate what you have learned with your peers.

Discovery Project Go to your Essentials Online to apply your new skills and knowledge to the chapter project.

How to Use the *McGraw-Hill* **essentials** Pre-Engineering Program

The *Pre-Engineering* Student Edition introduces key engineering concepts. Connect allows you to extend and apply your engineering skills with activities and projects.

Projects, Activities, and Assignments in Connect These help you apply what you have learned.

connect

Section 1

Discovery Project

Instructions:

Goal: Design and Build an Accurate Launcher Prototype

Why must engineers consider the concepts of applied mechanics when designing launcher mechanisms? View the video from AviationWeek to learn about the application of catapult mechanisms for launching cutting-edge unmanned aircraft.

IDENTIFY

1. List the main goals of designing and building an accurate launcher.
2. Summarize the main challenges, including the criteria and constraints, of designing and building a launcher.
3. Outline the key concepts from this chapter that you will use to design and build the launcher prototype.

SET-UP

4. Brainstorm and research possible ideas and solutions for designing and building your launcher, forming small groups as directed by your teacher.
5. Choose the best solution that you will use to design and create the launcher, considering the main challenges of the design.

EXECUTE

6. Design a detailed sketch of the launcher.
7. Create a model of the launcher, using the tools and materials listed.
8. Test your launcher. For final testing, place the target at three random points somewhere between five and 10 feet away from the machine. You will take three "shots" from each distance. The target footprint will cover an area of one square yard.

SHARE

9. Present and demonstrate your launcher to the class. In your presentation, discuss why you think your launcher achieves the goals of the project.

EVALUATE

10. Write one or two paragraphs about how well your sketch represents the actual model you built. Describe what changes (if any) you made to the model to make it function as required. Summarize why you think your model represents an accurate launcher.

Tools & Materials:

Integrating the Book, eBook, and Connect

For the *Pre-Engineering* program, McGraw-Hill Connect houses the chapter projects and resources for students and instructors. McGraw-Hill ConnectPlus houses the eBook.

- McGraw-Hill Connect is a Web-based assignment and assessment platform that links students with their coursework.

- The eBook is the electronic version of the textbook. It is only available on ConnectPlus.

After students have registered in a McGraw-Hill Connect course, they may sign in at the course's Web address to access the corresponding program materials.

The library section of a student's account provides shortcuts to these and other resources. This is where you will find course projects, assignments, and activities.

home · **library** · **reports**

McGraw-Hill Essentials *Pre-Engineering* features projects that allow students to apply the concepts they have learned in the textbook. They can be completed using videos and the Engineer's Blog within Connect.

To move seamlessly within Connect, students follow these steps:

1. Open the course library page.

2. Navigate to the desired project, feature, or assignment.

In ConnectPlus, students can move seamlessly between the eBook and other resources by following these steps:

1. Open the eBook in ConnectPlus.

2. When you encounter a feature with a laptop icon or  essentials online logo, click on it to go to that feature in Connect.

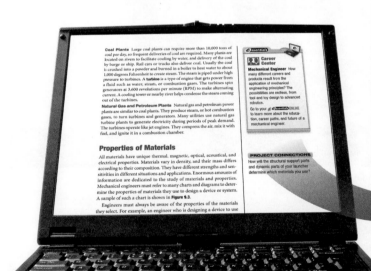

essentials

Career Center

Mechanical Engineer How many different careers and products result from the application of mechanical engineering principles? The possibilities are endless, from tool and toy design to advanced robotics.

Go to your **e**ssentials ONLINE to learn more about the education, career paths, and future of a mechanical engineer.

Easy to access! Easy to use!
Connect to McGraw-Hill Pre-Engineering at mcgrawhillconnect.com/k12

CONNECT

Use Connect to access your *Pre-Engineering* course home page.

Access your Materials

- Watch videos and complete projects.
- Create portfolios to highlight skills you learn.
- Use the Engineer's Blog to complete projects and interact with team members.

LEARN

Access additional resources

- Project Videos
- Virtual Labs
- Personal Tutors
- eFlashcards
- Engineer's Blog
- Chapter Activities
- Engineer's Toolbox
- Green reSource Videos
- Career Center Videos

Access your eBook anywhere!

- Store class notes.
- Highlight and bookmark material online.

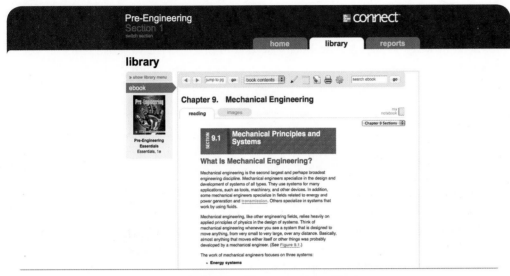

With ConnectPlus

SUCCEED

- Complete your homework online.
- Get immediate feedback on your work.
- Link back to sections of the book to review core engineering concepts.
- Collaborate with your peers on course projects.

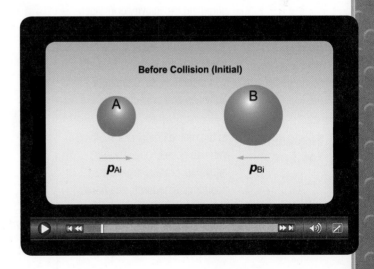

McGraw-Hill Essentials *Pre-Engineering* is the first truly integrated text and online learning program. Reading the textbook will introduce you to the history, principles, and types of engineering, and will help you to understand the knowledge, skills, and vocabulary needed in this field. At various points throughout the text, you will be directed online to apply what you have learned in activities, hands-on projects, and practice tests. Become familiar with the key icons shown below to know when to go online:

Icon Key

Every time you see an **Essentials** box or the **Essentials Online** logo, your assignment will involve going online to watch a video or animation, blog, participate in a project, or complete another activity.

 Laptop Icon
When you see the laptop icon, read the text in the **Essentials** box, and then go online to complete the activity or project.

 Group Workspace
The Group Workspace icon lets you know that you should go online to write about your activities and projects.

Engineer's Toolbox
In the online Engineer's Toolbox, you can access note-taking activities, graphic organizers, academic standards, academic activities, competitive event prep activities, and project evaluation charts.

 Personal Tutor
The Personal Tutor helps you learn about and practice important math concepts.

McGraw-Hill Connect™ is a web-based assignment and assessment platform that helps you connect to your course and success beyond the course.

 Virtual Lab
The Virtual Lab brings science and engineering concepts to life through animation.

 Career Center
The Career Center will help you learn about the education, career paths, and daily responsibilities of different kinds of engineers.

 Visualization
Practicing Visualization skills will help you communicate your engineering ideas to others through sketches and drawings.

 Activity Center
The Activity Center will help you master vocabulary and key concepts from the text.

What Are Standards?

Being prepared for college or a career includes developing a wide range of skills that you will need to meet future educational and employment needs and expectations. Standards are an established and agreed upon set of measures or guidelines for the knowledge, processes, and practices that you as a student should know or be able to do to succeed in your academic and professional careers.

Pre-Engineering meets key academic and professional standards. At the beginning of each chapter Reading Guide is a list of the standards that are covered in that chapter. With these standards as your foundation, you will ensure that you are taking important steps toward your college career and goals. Go to page 311 for an appendix of academic standards.

READING GUIDE

Before You Read What kinds of products do mechanical engineers develop? How do mechanical engineers use simple machines?

Objectives
- **Summarize** Newton's three laws of motion.
- **Evaluate** the laws of thermodynamics.
- **Compare and contrast** hydraulics and pneumatics.
- **Discuss** simple machines.
- **Identify** five different types of motion.
- **Analyze** the purpose of basic mechanisms.

Main Idea
Mechanical engineering involves applying the principles of physics to the design of machines and systems. Mechanical engineers combine simple machines to create more complex machines.

Vocabulary

Content Vocabulary

- mechanics
- inertia
- momentum
- statics
- dynamics
- thermodynamics
- turbine
- hydraulics
- mechanical advantage
- pneumatics
- simple machine
- mechanism

Academic Vocabulary

- transmission
- alternative
- nuclear
- complex
- transfer
- vehicle

Note-Taking Activity
Draw this table for each section. Write key terms and phrases under **Cues**. Write main ideas under **Note Taking**. Summarize the section under **Summary**.

Cues	Note Taking
•	•
•	•
Summary	

Graphic Organizers
Use graphic organizers to write and organize information as you read.

Go to your *e*ssential ONLINE for downloadable graphic organizers.

 Laws of Motion

STANDARDS

ACADEMIC

Technology

ITEEA STL4.02 Making decisions about the use of technology involves weighing the trade-offs between the positive and negative effects.

ITEEA STL16.01 Energy cannot be created nor destroyed; however, it can be converted from one form to another.

Mathematics

NCTM Measurement Apply appropriate techniques, tools, and formulas to determine measurements.

Science

NSES B Develop an understanding of the structure of atoms, structure and properties of matter, chemical reactions, motions and forces, conservation of energy and increase in disorder, and interactions of energy and matter.

ITEEA *International Technology and Engineering Educators Association*
NCTM *National Council of Teachers of Mathematics*
NSES *National Science Education Standards*

College & Career READINESS

Reading Determine central ideas or themes of a text and analyze their development; summarize the key supporting details and ideas.

Academic Standards Take note of the Technology, Mathematics, and Science standards under the Academic Standards heading at the beginning of each chapter in the Reading Guide. You will practice these specific academic skills as you move through the chapter.

College & Career Readiness Standards Each section Reading Guide highlights the chapter's content in relation to meeting important academic and professional standards in engineering. Knowing these standards will help you prepare for your future after high school.

Chapter 9 Mechanical Engineering **169**

What If English Is Not Your First Language?

Today's diverse classrooms offer wonderful opportunities for you as a student to learn and enhance a variety of skills, including language arts. Whether you are a native English speaker or not, there are many opportunities to practice your English language speaking, writing, and listening skills with your teacher and your classmates. Practicing these skills will help you to communicate effectively in your academic and future professional careers.

Use these tips as you read and learn from this textbook:

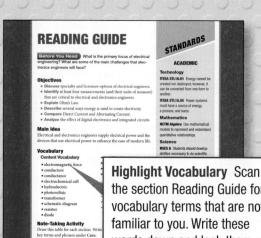

Highlight Vocabulary Scan the section Reading Guide for vocabulary terms that are not familiar to you. Write these words down and look them up in the glossary at the back of the book or practice with online vocabulary flash cards in Connect.

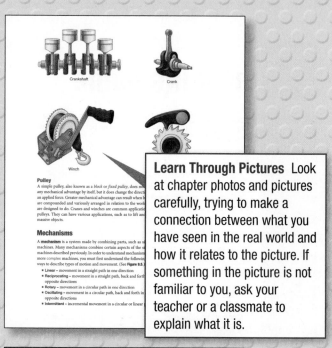

Learn Through Pictures Look at chapter photos and pictures carefully, trying to make a connection between what you have seen in the real world and how it relates to the picture. If something in the picture is not familiar to you, ask your teacher or a classmate to explain what it is.

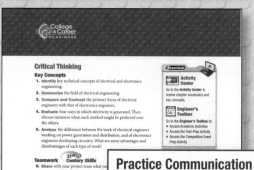

Practice Communication Study, blog, and complete projects with classmates. At the end of each chapter, you can review together what you have learned in that chapter. Start by discussing what you have learned in the chapter, and how it applies to the Discovery Project.

Connect to Your World You will have the chance to show what you have learned by working on projects such as the Unit Challenge Project. When working on or writing about a project, think of your culture, experiences, and skills and how these might apply to your tasks. Relate your project to your world!

What Is Collaborative Learning?

Engineers often work in an interdisciplinary team when working on projects. Learning to work with others will better prepare you for this type of environment when you enter college and the world of work. Collaborating with your classmates on projects and activities will give you the chance to improve your communication, presentation, and teamwork skills. Partnering with your team members will give you a deeper understanding of the engineering process, and you are likely to retain more of what you learn. *Pre-Engineering* offers numerous opportunities for collaboration.

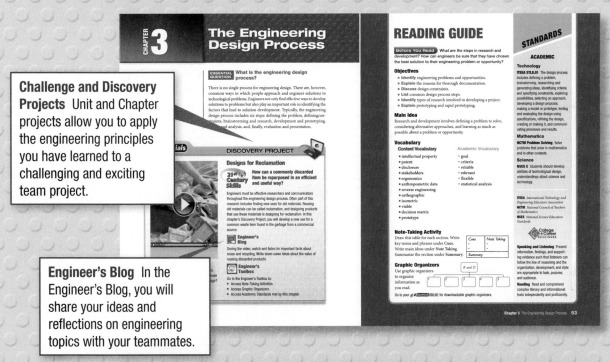

Challenge and Discovery Projects Unit and Chapter projects allow you to apply the engineering principles you have learned to a challenging and exciting team project.

Engineer's Blog In the Engineer's Blog, you will share your ideas and reflections on engineering topics with your teammates.

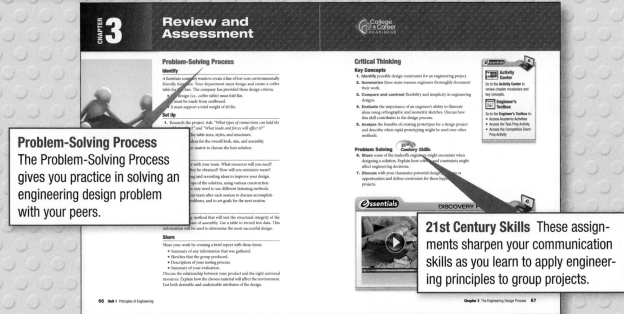

Problem-Solving Process The Problem-Solving Process gives you practice in solving an engineering design problem with your peers.

21st Century Skills These assignments sharpen your communication skills as you learn to apply engineering principles to group projects.

What Are Work Ethics?

Behaving ethically is an important factor in both student and professional life. A career in engineering will present numerous opportunities to make ethical choices, such as thinking of ways to benefit the planet by making engineering activities more sustainable. Since engineers often work on teams, it is also important that each person contributes to the team and receives proper credit for ideas and other contributions. Project Evaluation Charts, which you can download from Connect, will guide you in providing objective feedback on the work of your teammates.

In this class, you will be doing a lot of work with your peers, and you will also be doing a lot of work on the Internet. It is important for you to do research and discuss your ideas with your peers, but it is also important that you only take credit for your own ideas, and give credit to the ideas of others that may have inspired you.

What Is Plagiarism?

By now you probably know that you should not copy another student's work, or cut and paste something from the Internet and present it as your own. Those are obvious cases of plagiarism. However, you also should not use or paraphrase someone else's ideas (that is, using their ideas, but putting them into your own words) without giving credit for them. It is also unacceptable to use someone else's writing and just change some of the words. You *should* learn and gather ideas from every source you can—written sources, your teacher, your peers, and even television. These sources can provide inspiration, but you must remember to give credit for ideas that were not your own. Your teacher may suggest a style guide for written work that will show you how to give credit to sources.

Finally, while you have surely learned by now that plagiarism is ethically wrong because it is a way of stealing others' ideas, the problems with plagiarism go well beyond this. Someone who copies the work of others, whether purposely or inadvertently, will have trouble developing ideas and solving problems independently. A good engineer must be a creative problem-solver. Throughout this program, you will have many opportunities to solve problems creatively with your peers. By engaging in these hands-on team activities, you will not only gain a sense of what it is like to be a member of an engineering team, but you will also discover that communication, collaboration, and problem-solving can be fun and challenging experiences.

What Is the NSPE Code of Ethics?

 As you begin your work in the engineering classroom, you should become familiar with the National Society of Professional Engineers (NSPE) Code of Ethics for Engineers. Engineers are bound to consider these ethical guidelines when working on projects. This code has fundamental canons that must be followed if you are working as an engineer. These canons include concepts such as considering safety above any other concern, performing within your personal level of expertise, and acting honorably. The code expands into general rules of practice with which engineers should be intimately familiar. You should review and apply the NSPE Code of Ethics for Engineers as you work on team projects. This code will help in identifying constraints within which you should work when considering alternative solutions for problems.

How Do I Prepare For Competitive Events?

Have you pictured your future? Competition in the real world is strong, so you need to be prepared. One of the best ways to gain experience and develop leadership skills is to participate in local, state, and nationwide competitive events. Competitive events for high school students are popular, but a few of the most notable ones are sponsored by Technology Student Association (TSA), SkillsUSA, and FIRST Student Chapters.

 Technology Student Association

TSA is a nationwide organization serving over 150,000 middle and high school students who are enrolled in or have completed technology education courses. TSA members attend state and national conferences and compete in events at state and national levels.

TSA activities are correlated to the International Technology and Engineering Educators Association's (ITEEA) Standards for Technological Literacy. TSA student members develop leadership and teamwork skills and meet STEM (Science, Technology, Engineering, and Mathematics) requirements while engaging in fun and exciting activities and competitions.

 SkillsUSA

SkillsUSA is a national organization serving teachers and high school and college students, who are preparing for careers in technical, skilled, and service occupations. More than 300,000 student and instructors join SkillsUSA annually. SkillsUSA has served more than 9.9 million members since 1965.

One of the most visible programs of SkillsUSA is the annual SkillsUSA Championships. This competition program serves as a showcase for some of the best career and technical students in the nation. Contests begin locally and continue through the state and national levels.

 FIRST

Founded in 1989, FIRST (For Inspiration and Recognition of Science and Technology) was established to heighten young people's engagement with science and technology. The FIRST Robotics Competition is designed to help students understand the experience of working on a real engineering team.

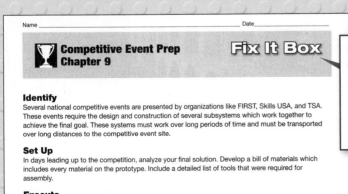

Name _____ Date_____

🏆 **Competitive Event Prep Chapter 9**   **Fix It Box**

Identify
Several national competitive events are presented by organizations like FIRST, Skills USA, and TSA. These events require the design and construction of several subsystems which work together to achieve the final goal. These systems must work over long periods of time and must be transported over long distances to the competitive event site.

Set Up
In days leading up to the competition, analyze your final solution. Develop a bill of materials which includes every material on the prototype. Include a detailed list of tools that were required for assembly.

Execute
Locate and pack a "Fix It Box". This box should include all necessary replacement tools and materials. Do not forget additional supplies like extension cords and adhesives that may not be on your finished prototype.

Competitive Events These require the design and construction of several subsystems which work together to achieve the final goal. Every chapter helps you prepare efficiently for these events.

UNIT 1

Principles of Engineering

As you complete this unit project, do the following:

- **Identify** the main design goals for building a wind-powered generator.
- **Explain** the main challenges in building a wind-powered generator.
- **List** the key steps needed to design and build a wind-powered generator.
- **Develop** possible ideas and solutions for your wind-powered generator.
- **Share** your ideas for a wind-powered generator.

In Partnership With

Engineering News-Record

Inspiring Science Discovery

GreenSource

With science, technology, and mathematics as its foundation, the engineering process has transformed our world. The homes in which we live, the ways in which we travel and communicate, and the products that we use were all developed to some degree by engineers. There are several activities that are important to the creation of engineered products: analysis, research, design, testing, development, management, consulting, and sales. Engineers must understand the processes of drawing and sketching, modeling, and prototyping. They must also be knowledgeable about the materials that play a part in determining the design of a product. Those materials bring their own constraints to the fabrication process, whether in manufacturing or in on-site construction. Engineering uses technology to build the systems that meet our needs.

Building a Wind-Powered Generator

KEY QUESTION What elements must be included in the design of a wind-powered turbine generator?

One of the most promising sources of sustainable electrical power is the wind, a form of renewable energy. New materials and advances in wind power technology improve the efficiency of each new generation of machines that comes into use. In this unit's Challenge Project, you will use found materials to design and develop a wind-powered turbine generator. You will need to optimize materials and make all appropriate electrical connections so that the output can be monitored. A fan will act as the wind power source for testing.

Remember that as you work through the Unit 1 Chapter Discovery Projects, you will gain knowledge and skills that will help you complete the Unit 1 Challenge Project.

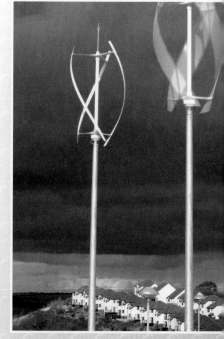

Engineers must know the fundamentals of mathematics and science as well as the steps of the engineering design process to create and improve products and systems.

Go to your *essentials* ONLINE to view the video about wind power. Learn about one of the world's fastest-growing sources of electric power. Then answer the question in the Engineer's Blog. See page 125 for a brief description of the steps you will follow to complete this unit project.

Group Workspace

How do engineers decide on the ideal site for a wind turbine?

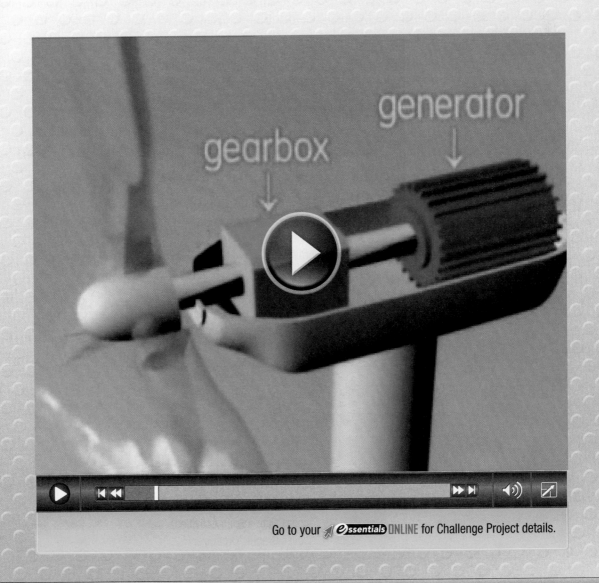

Go to your *essentials* ONLINE for Challenge Project details.

Introduction to Technology and Engineering

| ESSENTIAL QUESTION | **How has engineering affected the world in the past and the present?** |

Throughout history, engineering has affected the world's people, economies, and environments. Engineered items are all around us. For instance, services such as energy, water, and the Internet all resulted from great achievements in engineering.

Science, technology, and mathematics form the core of the engineering process. There are also several activities that are important to the creation of engineered products, regardless of the engineering discipline. These are analysis, research, design, testing, development, management, consulting, and sales.

essentials

DISCOVERY PROJECT

Go to your **essentials** ONLINE for Discovery Project details.

Design and Build a Solar Thermal Plant

 21st Century Skills

Discuss why teamwork is an important part of designing, building, and testing.

Energy is one of the key resources of technology. In this chapter's Discovery Project, you will construct a model solar thermal plant. Some solar thermal plants use mirrors to focus sunlight on a receiver tower. Others use parabolic mirrors to heat a liquid that flows through pipes. The model solar thermal plant you construct will demonstrate that sunlight focused by mirrors can heat liquid.

 Group Workspace

Go to your **essentials** ONLINE to view the video. Watch and listen for important facts about energy and power. Write down some ideas about the importance of renewable energy.

 Engineer's Toolbox

Go to the Engineer's Toolbox to
- Access Note-Taking Activities
- Access Graphic Organizers
- Access Academic Standards met by this chapter

READING GUIDE

Before You Read What is engineering? What are some of the major activities of engineering?

Objectives

- **Discuss** the definition of engineering.
- **Summarize** the connections among science, technology, engineering, and mathematics.
- **Identify** several early examples of engineering.
- **Evaluate** great engineering achievements of the past century.
- **Compare and contrast** the major engineering activities.

Main Idea

Engineering involves the use of science and mathematics to develop products, processes, and systems. Engineering involves many different activities.

Vocabulary

Content Vocabulary

- electronic
- science
- technology
- mathematics
- engineering
- electrification
- biomedical
- prosthetic
- manufacturer
- quality control
- consultants

Academic Vocabulary

- design
- process
- concepts
- resources
- energy
- constraints
- research

Note-Taking Activity

Draw this table for each section. Write key terms and phrases under **Cues**. Write main ideas under **Note Taking**. Summarize the section under **Summary**.

Cues	Note Taking
•	•
•	•
Summary	

Graphic Organizers

Use graphic organizers to write and organize information as you read.

Go to your  ONLINE for downloadable graphic organizers.

Major Engineering Tasks

STANDARDS

ACADEMIC

Technology

ITEEA STL01 Students will develop an understanding of the characteristics and scope of technology.

ITEEA STL07 Students will develop an understanding of the influence of technology on history.

Mathematics

NCTM Problem Solving Solve problems that arise in mathematics and in other contexts.

Science

NSES E Students should develop abilities of technological design, understanding about science and technology.

ITEEA *International Technology and Engineering Educators Association*
NCTM *National Council of Teachers of Mathematics*
NSES *National Science Education Standards*

College & Career READINESS

Reading Determine central ideas or themes of a text and analyze their development; summarize the key supporting details and ideas.

Reading Analyze how and why individuals, events, and ideas develop and interact over the course of a text.

The World of Engineering

Green reSource

LEED (Leadership in Energy and Environmental Design)
A building's LEED designation ("Certified," "Silver," "Gold," or "Platinum") identifies its energy efficiency, as well as the level of environmentally responsible materials implemented during the design and construction process.

Go to your *essentials* ONLINE to view the innovative features of the Downtown Tempe Transportation Center.

 Group Workspace

Research Adding green features to a construction project often increases the upfront costs. Give examples of some of the benefits that make a LEED certification desirable.

What is Engineering?

Engineering is all around us. Most of the things that we come into contact with every day are engineered. Engineers design almost everything we use, from computers to automobiles. Engineering plays an important role in our daily lives.

Imagine that it is a school day. You wake up with the help of an alarm clock or clock radio. You take a shower, brush your teeth, dry your hair, get dressed, and sit down to a breakfast that is cooked in a microwave or toaster oven. You drink a glass of milk or juice that was kept cold in a refrigerator. To help make your school bus ride more productive, you take along your laptop computer. Your day has just begun, and you have already benefited from the work of many different kinds of engineers.

Electrical engineers developed the appliances and electronic products (products based on or operated by the flow of electrons) that you used. Civil engineers designed the water treatment and distribution systems that brought clean water to your home, and planned the roads on which you rode to school. Mechanical engineers designed the refrigerator in your home and your school bus. Electrical engineers designed your laptop. Engineers from several specialties designed the systems needed to process the foods you ate for breakfast. (See **Figure 1.1.**)

Fig. 1.1 Engineered Products
All day long we use products designed by engineers. *What engineered products do you find essential to your daily routine?*

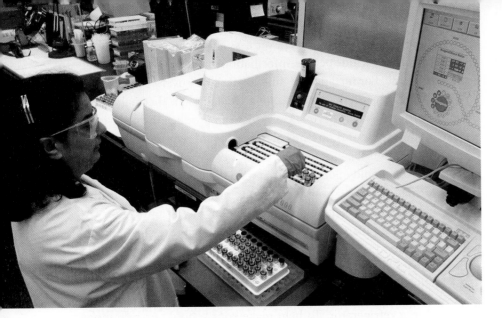

Science, Technology, Engineering, and Mathematics (STEM)

Schools and colleges throughout the United States are working to improve the number and quality of the science, technology, engineering, and mathematics courses they offer. This combination of courses is often referred to as STEM education. Government, business, and educational leaders agree that improving STEM education should be a priority for the long-term welfare of the United States. The goal is to promote student interest in preparing for technical careers and help reduce the shortage of engineers, scientists, and mathematicians. As our daily lives become more and more connected to new technologies and devices, it is important for all of us to have a working knowledge of key STEM concepts.

Science

Science involves the search for a better understanding of the natural world. Scientists make observations and conduct tests in order to learn more about this world. They make new discoveries, which must be verified before being added to the body of accepted laws and principles. Scientists get their initial education in disciplines such as biology, chemistry, astronomy, geology, and physics before selecting an area of specialization. In Chapter 2 you will learn about some of the specific connections between engineering and science. (See **Figure 1.2.**)

Technology

Technology is often misunderstood. When many people hear the word "technology," they immediately think of computers. However, technology is much more than computers. Computer hardware and software are important, but they are only a part of technology. Technology is the use of resources to solve problems and create the things that people need and want. It is important to remember that needs and wants are different. Food, shelter, clothing, and medical care are examples of human needs. Most of us have many wants, such as the latest video games, smart cell phones, or products endorsed by celebrities. These products can add to our lives, but they are not basic human needs.

Accomplishing a task requires resources. The resources required to create technology include people, information, materials, tools, energy, capital, and time. For instance, in this chapter's Discovery Project, you will work on a team that will build a model solar thermal plant. Building an actual solar thermal plant that can produce the electricity needed for hundreds or thousands of homes would require people who could select a good location for the plant, people who could build it, and people who would operate and maintain the plant after its completion. Information about how to design, construct, and operate the plant would come from plans prepared by engineers and others. A variety of building materials, including steel, concrete, pipe, mirrors, and electrical and electronic components, would be needed. Heavy equipment would be used to prepare the site, and many different tools and machines would be needed to construct the plant. Energy in the form of human labor, fuel to operate the equipment, and electrical energy to operate tools and machines would be required. Essential capital would include the land for the plant, money to purchase materials, and money to pay workers. Time is another important resource. Completing the plant on time is important for staying within budget and making the plant operational on schedule.

Technological problems can be simple or complex. Choosing the best wrench to remove a wheel from a bicycle so that a tire can be patched is a simple problem. Repairing a bicycle tire is not a difficult

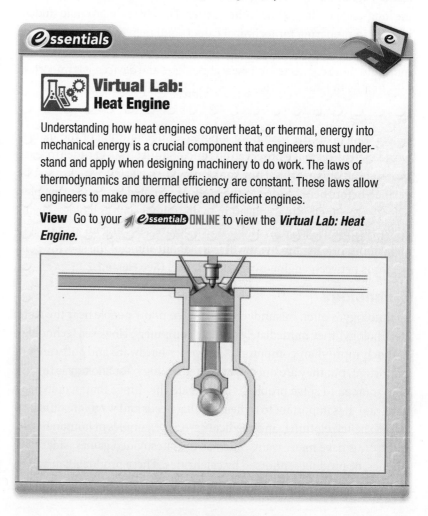

essentials

Virtual Lab: Heat Engine

Understanding how heat engines convert heat, or thermal, energy into mechanical energy is a crucial component that engineers must understand and apply when designing machinery to do work. The laws of thermodynamics and thermal efficiency are constant. These laws allow engineers to make more effective and efficient engines.

View Go to your **essentials** ONLINE to view the *Virtual Lab: Heat Engine.*

task, and only limited resources are required. Planning and building a solar thermal plant is an example of a complex problem that would require extensive resources, including years of work, hundreds of people, and millions of dollars.

Mathematics

Mathematics is the study of the relationships among numbers, shapes, and quantities. It is an essential tool for scientists, engineers, and many other professionals. It involves counting, measuring, calculating, analyzing, and reasoning. We know that people have used mathematics for thousands of years and that it has many practical applications. You have probably studied algebra, geometry, and perhaps calculus. All of these subjects have important applications in science, technology, and engineering. In Chapter 2 you will learn about some of the specific connections between engineering and mathematics.

Engineering

Engineers apply their knowledge of science, technology, and mathematics to produce useful products, processes, and systems, and to improve those that already exist. Innovation refers either to an entirely new product or process, often called an invention, or to an improvement on something that already exists. Engineering involves solving problems and looking for opportunities. Determining whether to repair or replace an aging bridge is an example of an engineering problem. Designing a new, easy-to-use smart phone that appeals to senior citizens is an example of an engineering opportunity. (See **Figure 1.3.**)

PROJECT CONNECTIONS

Designing and building a power plant is a complex engineering problem. Identify some of the constraints likely to apply to building an actual solar thermal plant.

Reading Check Explain why it is important for engineers to understand science, technology, and mathematics.

Another way to describe engineering is to say that it is "design under constraint." **Constraints** include limits or restrictions, such as on the resources that may be used. An engineer might be told that the bridge he has been assigned to design must be built for $2.5 million or less and completed in 18 months. These two requirements are examples of constraints. Natural laws also impose constraints. Newton's Three Laws of Motion, which are discussed in Chapter 9, explain some of the major constraints that govern the work of mechanical engineers. Constraints will also be specified for Challenge and Discovery Projects included in this textbook.

As you read this textbook, work on projects, and use the online support materials, you will learn a lot more about engineering, including how engineering affects people, the nature of various engineering disciplines, and how to prepare for an engineering career. Next, you will learn about both early and more recent engineering achievements.

Early Engineering

Engineering has a long and fascinating history. Simple machines were developed during ancient times. Imhotep, the first engineer known by name, designed and supervised the construction of the Pyramid of Djoser (the Step Pyramid) around 2600 B.C. The Egyptians, Romans, and Greeks used mathematics in the design and building of all types of structures. The Romans built the Colosseum, aqueducts, and roads. These and many other Roman structures are still largely intact. The Chinese built the Great Wall from the mid-1300s to the mid-1600s to help protect China's borders. Much of the 5,500 mile long wall still stands today. Those who designed, built, and maintained these structures pioneered the use of important engineering concepts; however, they were not called "engineers." (See **Figure 1.4.**)

Fig. 1.4 Roman Aqueduct The Romans built systems of bridges, tunnels, pipes, and canals to bring water to their cities. *How does water reach your own home?*

Fig. 1.5 Sputnik 1 In 1957, the Russian satellite Sputnik 1 became the first human-made object to orbit the Earth. *What effect did the launching of Sputnik 1 have on engineering in the United States?*

Modern Engineering

Engineering as we know it today began during the Renaissance, when it was used for military purposes. For the first time, there was a division of labor between the designing and the building of military fortifications and weapons. Designers used mathematics in the planning and design of structures and weapons, and skilled craftspeople built those structures and weapons. During the mid 1700s the term "civil engineering" was used for the first time. It referred to the planning and building of projects such as roads and bridges that were intended for civilian use rather than military use. The first formal institutions for preparing engineers were established in France in the mid 1700s; however, most engineers at that time were educated on the job rather than in formal institutions. Mechanical engineering started in England and Scotland with the invention of steam engines and other machines needed for the textile (clothing) industry.

After the American Civil War, the education of engineers became more formal. Training programs for civil, mechanical, and electrical engineers were established in the United States, as were professional organizations for the engineers working in those fields. The importance of engineering continued to increase throughout the twentieth century. In 1957, the Soviet Union launched the Sputnik satellite. (See **Figure 1.5.**) This notable event focused American attention on the need to improve science and mathematics education. Also in response to Sputnik, the National Aeronautics and Space Administration (NASA) was established in 1958. This created the need for thousands of engineers to work on the space program. Products and systems initially developed by engineers for the space program that have been used for other commercial applications are referred to as "spin-offs." There have been thousands of spin-offs, including the artificial heart, solar panels, and water purification systems.

Great Engineering Achievements

The National Academy of Engineering was established by the United States Congress and given the responsibility of promoting the technological welfare of the United States. Recently it brought together more than 25 engineering societies in an effort to identify the engineering achievements that had the most important impact on humankind during the past century. Each organization asked its members to nominate achievements related to its field. A National Academy committee discussed nominations, narrowed down the list, and identified the following engineering achievements as those with the most positive impact during the twentieth century.

PROJECT CONNECTIONS

Why is it important for power plants to develop new ways of producing electricity?

Electrification

The process of making electricity readily available within a region or country is called **electrification**. The National Academy of Engineering committee considered electrification to be the greatest single engineering achievement of the twentieth century. Most of the other great achievements would not have been possible without it.

Getting electricity to where it is needed involves generating power, transmitting it, and then distributing it to homes, factories, and businesses. Thomas Edison built the first commercial power plant in 1882. That plant produced direct current (DC), a system in which the electricity needed to be generated close to the home or business using that electricity. Such systems soon proved themselves to be impractical, especially in rural areas.

It soon became apparent that alternating current (AC), which makes use of transformers and lower voltages than DC systems, was an easier

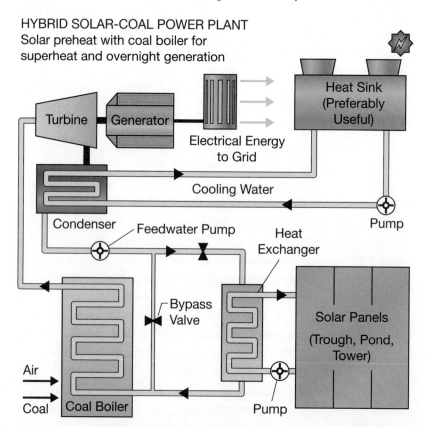

Fig. 1.6 Hybrid Power Plant
Today's power plants produce electricity by using several sources. *What sources of power are used to create electricity in your area?*

and more economical way of transmitting power over long distances. For that reason, AC became the preferred system. Today most power companies use a combination of sources to produce electricity, including coal, gas, hydroelectric power, nuclear power, and alternative energy. (See **Figure 1.6.**)

Transportation

The past century has witnessed dramatic developments in the way people and goods move from place to place. Thanks to developments in automotive, air, and space travel, people are now able to travel to places beyond the limits of their ancestors, at speeds never before possible.

Automobiles At the beginning of the twentieth century, most Americans relied on horses for transportation. Henry Ford, an engineer for an electric light company, believed that there would be demand for automobiles in the U.S. if good, affordable vehicles could be built. In 1903 he formed the Ford Motor Company.

Ford Motor Company engineers used standardized parts and efficient machine tools. They greatly improved the use of the assembly line, where each worker performed a specific task as a component or vehicle passed by on a conveyor belt. After about 10 years of fine-tuning the process, the company was able to reduce the time needed to assemble a vehicle from 12 hours to under 2 hours. At one point, more than 40 companies were manufacturing automobiles in the United States. Over time, the industry became extremely competitive, and many of those companies went out of business.

Automobiles have had a major impact on individuals and society. Millions of workers are employed in automobile manufacturing and related industries. The automobile contributed to the growth of suburbs and to shopping centers, motels, and other conveniences.

Automobiles have also created problems, such as traffic congestion, air pollution, injuries and deaths from crashes, and a tremendous need for gasoline and other petroleum products. Hybrid vehicles powered by a combination of an electric motor and gasoline engine may reduce petroleum product consumption if they continue to grow in popularity. All-electric vehicles may also help to reduce air pollution.

Highways The success of the automobile created the need for paved highways. By the early twentieth century, the U.S. had millions of miles of roads, but most of them were unpaved. The federal government began to experiment with paving materials and trained engineers in the basics of highway design. World Wars I and II created the need to move increased amounts of heavy materials by truck. This did extensive damage to the existing roads and helped to bring about the development of limited-access highways. The first section of the Pennsylvania Turnpike opened in 1940 and incorporated major engineering improvements such as reinforced concrete and entrance and exit ramps.

President Dwight D. Eisenhower signed into law the Federal-Aid Highway Act of 1956. This authorized the creation of the Interstate Highway System, one of the largest civil engineering projects in the world. Currently the system includes more than 46,000 miles of roads.

Airplanes Aviation pioneers found that designing and building an airplane required solving several engineering challenges: structure, aerodynamics, control, and propulsion. The Wright brothers studied the work done by others and conducted many experiments, including testing wing shapes in a wind tunnel. Their early flights began in 1903, and by 1905 they had produced the first practical airplane suitable for human flight. Today four million people travel on fifty thousand commercial flights every day.

Spacecraft The U.S. entered the space age in 1958 with the launch of its first satellite, Explorer 1, which contained instruments used to study radiation. Human spaceflight began in 1961. Other space missions have included the Apollo program, which completed several successful moon landings; the Space Shuttle program; and the International Space Station. We now rely on the use of satellites for global communication, weather forecasting, and GPS locating devices.

Water Supply and Distribution

At the beginning of the twentieth century, the demand for safe water in American cities greatly exceeded the available supply. Most people did not have indoor plumbing, and raw sewage was commonly dumped onto public streets. Diseases caused by poor sanitation caused thousands of deaths. Adding chlorine to the water supply eliminated most of the diseases. Engineers also recognized that sewage needed to be treated rather than just dumped into lakes and rivers.

Today most communities in the U.S. have modern water supply, treatment, and distribution systems. A related engineering challenge stems from the fact that water shortages are becoming increasingly common. This is encouraging the development of new technologies such as those used by large-scale desalination plants, which turn salt water from our oceans into safe, clean drinking water. (See **Figure 1.7.**)

Electronics and Communication

Alexander Graham Bell invented the telephone in 1876. By the early twentieth century, telephone systems had made long distance voice communication possible. Eventually this technology would provide the foundation for other communication devices and systems such as Telex, fax, and computer networks.

Prior to the 1950s, most electronic products were based on the use of vacuum tubes. The transistor, which replaced vacuum tubes in most applications, was invented in 1947 and refined for several years. This development proved to be so important to electronics that in 1956 its inventors were awarded the Nobel Prize. Continued research and development in electronics led to the development of additional components, including integrated circuits, that were smaller, faster, and less expensive than anything previously available. The cell phones, computers, televisions, and other electronic devices that are part of our everyday lives today depend on these integrated circuits.

The ability to transmit sound instantly over long distances through the air became possible in the 1920s as the result of research and

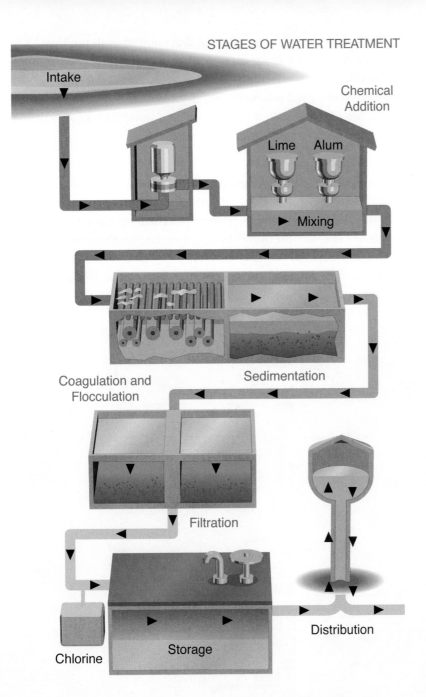

STAGES OF WATER TREATMENT

Intake

Chemical Addition

Lime   **Alum**

Mixing

Coagulation and Flocculation

Sedimentation

Filtration

Chlorine   **Storage**

Distribution

Fig. 1.7 Water Treatment This drawing shows several stages of water treatment and processing. *Which stages help purify water?*

experimentation on transmitters, amplifiers, and receivers. By the 1930s, most American families had radios. Networks to bring news and entertainment to the public were created. The next major communication advance was the television. Within a few years of its invention, millions of sets were in use.

Computers and the Internet The first successful electronic computer, ENIAC, which was based on the use of vacuum tubes and weighed over 30 tons, was introduced in 1946. Computers for business applications—and the languages needed to operate them—were first developed in the 1950s. In 1977 Apple introduced the first successful personal computer, the Apple II. Several years later, the first laptop computer was designed for use in NASA's space program.

PROJECT CONNECTIONS

How will computers and the Internet be used to help operate a solar thermal plant?

The Internet began as an effort to link computers in multiple locations, in order to facilitate communication among military facilities. By the 1990s, the World Wide Web had been created. Since then, Web browsers, high speed networks, and devices such as laptops and smart telephones have revolutionized the business world and the way people obtain and share information.

Agriculture

Until the twentieth century, agriculture was driven by human and animal labor. The successful work of internal combustion engineers led Ford and others to design tractors for planting and hauling. Later on, combines (machines that can do things like picking and shelling corn) greatly increased productivity. Today virtually every crop can be planted and harvested mechanically, often by multi-million-dollar, air-conditioned machines guided by satellite technology. (See **Figure 1.8.**)

Fig. 1.8 High Tech Farm Equipment Global Positioning System (GPS) devices are now common on farming equipment. *How has technology affected the routines of many farmers?*

Air Conditioning and Refrigeration

Air conditioning and refrigeration are related technologies. Before refrigeration, it was difficult to store foods at home for long periods and even more difficult to transport them over long distances. In the 1970s, affordable air conditioning spurred heavy migration to the Southern states known as the Sun Belt. Air conditioning helps make homes and businesses comfortable year round. It is also essential in some industries, such as a software company's large computer labs.

Medical Imaging

Engineering has created some of the physician's most valuable tools. X-ray imaging and computed tomography (CAT) scans are invaluable diagnostic tools. One disadvantage is that they use radiation to create images. Magnetic Resonance Imaging (MRI) machines have the advantages of not using radiation and producing higher quality images that reveal details about the functioning of internal organs. Similar imaging technologies are also useful for industrial applications, such as the x-raying of metal pipes to verify that they have been properly welded together. (See **Figure 1.9.**)

Materials

Many great achievements in engineering were made possible by a period of unprecedented development in both new and improved materials. Twentieth-century improvements to materials included the creation of stronger and more durable metals, some of them alloys (made by adding other materials to a basic metal such as steel or aluminum). A few new materials, such as Pyrex (used for laboratory glassware and cooking) and several plastics, were discovered accidentally.

Another category of new materials is composites, or combinations of materials. Fiberglass boat hulls and bathtubs are examples of items produced with a composite made from plastic materials strengthened by glass fibers. Small airplanes and commercial airlines are now being made from composite materials to reduce weight and increase fuel efficiency.

Fig. 1.9 Industrial Imaging
X-rays are used to examine this connection between two pipes. *What are some other non-medical uses for x-rays?*

✓ **Reading Check** **Discuss** how different your daily life would be if one or more of the great engineering achievements of the twentieth century had not occurred.

Check Your Understanding

SECTION **1.1**

After You Read Perform the following tasks.

1. **Identify** items you have used today that were designed by engineers.

2. **Determine** what types of engineering were involved in creating those items.

3. **Prioritize** which engineering achievements have had the greatest impact on our world. Give reasons to support your answer.

The Major Activities of Engineering

Major Activities of Engineering

In Unit 2 of this textbook, you will learn about the major disciplines of engineering and about specialty fields. One way to understand engineering is to think about some of the major activities that engineers perform. All engineering disciplines and specialties have some similar characteristics, including tasks that are performed every day. Analysis, research, design, testing, development, management, consulting, and sales are examples of those tasks.

Analysis

Analytical engineers play an important role at the beginning of new projects. They apply mathematics and use engineering software to answer important questions. For example, a company designing cell phone towers would need to know if its latest design was structurally sound. Rather than building and testing a physical model of the tower, it would be more efficient and cost-effective to use software to analyze the design and pinpoint changes that are needed. The use of such software saves time and money, and makes it possible to correct problems early in the design process.

essentials

Virtual Lab:
The Engineering Design Process

Engineers need to understand how the engineering process works if they are to solve problems safely, effectively, efficiently, and appropriately. The engineering design process is a complex series of steps that is cyclical. One step leads to another until the entire process either ends or is repeated. The engineering process may continue until the optimum solution is achieved.

View Go to your *e*ssentials ONLINE to view the *Virtual Lab: The Engineering Design Process.*

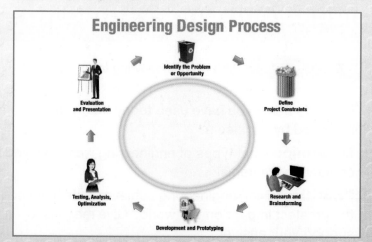

Engineering Design Process

Identify the Problem or Opportunity

Define Project Constraints

Research and Brainstorming

Development and Prototyping

Testing, Analysis, Optimization

Evaluation and Presentation

Ⓔssentials

Visualization

Spatial Ability The ability to visualize and make mental pictures of your creative ideas is one of the most important skills an engineer can possess. You need to be able to form mental pictures of your ideas and make technical sketches or computer-aided design and drafting (CADD) drawings from them so your ideas can be made real.

Go to your **Ⓔssentials** ONLINE to learn more about developing your spatial abilities.

Group Workspace

Look at a technical drawing online. Describe what dimensional object or objects the drawing represents.

PROJECT CONNECTIONS

What kind of research needs to be done by an engineering company tasked with designing a solar thermal plant?

Research

Research engineers, like scientists, are involved in the search for new knowledge within a particular field. The research they conduct is often supported by government or corporate grants. They usually have advanced degrees and may hold faculty positions in engineering programs at colleges and universities. For example, a **biomedical** engineer at a university, teaching engineering related to both biology and medicine, might conduct research to develop new materials that can reduce infections in people who have knee replacement surgery. New knowledge discovered during the research can be used in several different ways. It can be passed on to students at the university. It can also be shared with, and possibly sold to, biomedical companies that make **prosthetic** devices (artificial body parts, such as an artificial arm, leg, or heart). (See **Figure 1.10**.)

Design

Design engineers take new ideas and concepts and develop formal plans for creating products and processes. When evaluating the possibility of making a new product, they consider a wide range of factors such as cost, the materials that might be used, possible manufacturing processes, and recyclability. It is important for the design engineer to determine if a concept is worth pursuing.

PROJECT CONNECTIONS

What kinds of tasks are engineering managers likely to face during construction of the solar thermal plant?

Testing

Test engineers need to know the best way to test a product or process to determine if its specifications and performance requirements are being met. For example, a test engineer working for a paint **manufacturer** (the individual or company making the paint) may be asked to determine if a new product will perform well after exposure to bright sunlight and extreme temperatures. The engineer is responsible for determining what tests should be performed. The engineer or other members of the engineering team conduct the tests and report the results. Test engineers are also responsible for conducting **quality control** tests (tests relating to the process of ensuring quality) on manufactured products. (See **Figure 1.11.**)

Development

Development engineers help design and test engineers bring ideas to reality. They review the proposed designs and test results, coordinate the building of prototypes, and make sure that models meet all requirements and specifications. Prototypes are tested and the results evaluated. In some cases, those results may indicate a need for design changes.

Management

Engineering managers need good leadership and communication skills. Project management involves supervising a team of engineers working on a particular project. The project manager is given the responsibility of making sure that a project is successfully completed, on time and within budget. Most projects encounter challenges as they are carried out, so project managers need to be good problem solvers. A Gantt chart is a valuable tool for engineering managers. Gantt charts show the planned start and completion dates for various aspects of projects. They help engineers monitor progress and identify changes that may be needed to complete the project as planned. (See **Figure 1.12.**)

Fig. 1.11 Structural Testing This model of a bridge is being subjected to structural tests. *What can testing on a model reveal about a structure before it is actually constructed?*

Building Redesign Project

Start date: 1/1/2012

Weeks / Tasks	Current Week														
	01/01 to 01/08	01/08 to 01/15	01/15 to 01/22	01/22 to 01/29	01/29 to 02/05	02/05 to 02/12	02/12 to 02/19	02/19 to 02/26	02/26 to 03/05	03/05 to 03/12	03/12 to 03/19	03/19 to 03/26	03/26 to 04/02	04/02 to 04/09	04/09 to 04/16
Preliminary design	■														
Final design		■													
Budgeting						■									
Remodelling							■	■							
Utilities and networking									■	■					
Equipment installation											■	■			
Integration and testing													■		
Final acceptance															■

Fig. 1.12 Gantt Chart This is a typical Gantt chart. *What other resources can be used to assist engineering managers in assuring the efficiency of a project?*

Consulting

Consulting engineers may be self-employed, or they may work for firms that specialize in providing engineering talent on a contract basis. Consulting engineers are hired because they have the specific skills needed for certain tasks or projects. Many companies hire **consultants** (individuals or companies engaged to provide expert advice or assistance) when a particular skill will only be needed for a limited time. Consulting assignments can last a day or months or even years. Consulting may be good for engineers who enjoy travel, since overseas assignments have become increasingly common.

Sales

A sales engineer needs to have a good understanding of the products or services offered by his or her company. Good communication skills and a persuasive personality are important requirements. The sales engineer must be able to explain how a product works and convince the client that the product will meet the client's specific requirements. If successful in persuading the client to purchase the product or service, the sales engineer must stay in touch with the client to ensure customer satisfaction and thus increase the possibility of future sales.

Reading Check **Compare and contrast** the roles of analytical engineers and research engineers.

Check Your Understanding

After You Read Perform the following tasks.

1. **Identify** the eight common engineering tasks.
2. **Justify** why testing is a necessary engineering task.
3. **Decide** which engineering tasks you would most enjoy conducting.

Review and Assessment

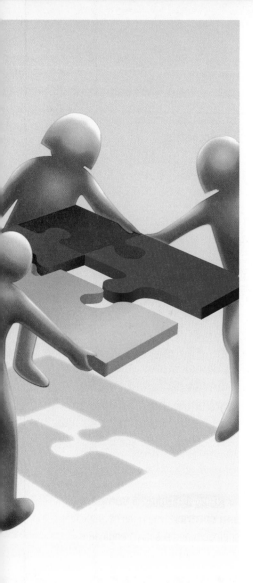

Problem-Solving Process

Identify

The ACME novelty company wants to develop a themed coin sorter for children. Your team must present a prototype to the executive board. Below are the criteria for designing and producing your prototype.

- The device must be able to sort various coins accurately.
- It must appeal to a target audience of 3- to 6-year-olds.
- It must have an appealing visual theme or interactive feature.

Set Up

1. Research the project criteria and the target audience.
2. Study existing coin sorters and analyze how they work. Identify the components that they share and the purpose that each serves.
3. Brainstorm potential solutions. Include information about possible materials and dimensions. Record all thoughts on paper.
4. Choose the best solution based on your previous criteria for success. Use a table to list the pros and cons of each design.

Execute

5. Plan the solution with your team. Identify and assign the various roles needed in engineering and designing this product.
6. Keep sketching and recording ideas for later reference.
7. Build mock-ups of the solution. You may need to try various materials and production processes to find the best approach.
8. Discuss progress, problems, and new goals with your team.

Evaluate

Test the prototype with your class, or a group of children or teachers. If your project is not successful, reevaluate your steps. Ask: *Did your team communicate effectively? How can your device be improved?*

Share

Create a brief report on the activity that includes the following items:

- Summary of any information that was gathered.
- Sketches that the group produced.
- Description of your testing process.
- Summary of your evaluation.

Discuss how the major activities of engineering relate to the roles played by the team members.

Critical Thinking

Key Concepts

1. **Identify** the eight great engineering achievements of the twentieth century.

2. **Summarize** the importance of science, technology, and mathematics in engineering.

3. **Compare and Contrast** development engineers and consulting engineers.

4. **Evaluate** the ways in which major engineering achievements have had impact on the history of our world and our own daily lives.

5. **Compare and Contrast** the major activities and fields of engineering.

Information Literacy

6. **Share** the ways in which electronics have affected the world. Discuss why and how they paved the way for new engineering innovations.

7. **Discuss** three ways in which science and technology were used in the engineering of automobiles.

essentials

Activity Center

Go to the **Activity Center** to review chapter vocabulary and key concepts.

Engineer's Toolbox

Go to the **Engineer's Toolbox** to:
- Access Academic Activities
- Access the Competitive Event Prep Activity

---

essentials

DISCOVERY PROJECT GOAL

Design and Build a Solar Thermal Plant

In this chapter's Discovery Project, you will create a Solar Thermal Plant prototype that uses mirrors and sunlight to produce energy. Your team's solar thermal plant should be able to heat water successfully.

Go to your **essentials** ONLINE to view the video to learn about solar power.

Math and Science Connections

ESSENTIAL QUESTION Why are math and science important to the daily tasks of engineers in all disciplines?

Engineers apply mathematics, from basic to advanced, in their daily work. Mechanical, civil, and electrical engineers apply the science of physics on a regular basis, while chemical engineers concentrate on the concepts of chemistry. Agricultural and biomedical engineers apply their knowledge of biology as well as their knowledge of earth science and geology to practical problems.

The intention of this chapter is to explain the application of specific concepts in an engineering context, not necessarily to explain the concepts of mathematics and science in great detail. The concepts discussed here vary in complexity, from basic to advanced.

essentials

DISCOVERY PROJECT

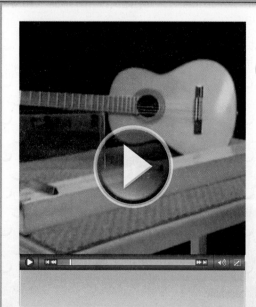

Design and Build a Musical Instrument

 21st Century Skills How are math and science involved in the way musical instruments work?

In this project, you will design a musical instrument from commonly found materials. In order to complete this task, you will need to research appropriate physics and mathematics concepts and be able to explain some musical concepts.

 Group Workspace

During the video, watch and listen for important facts about the constraints of the project. Write down some ideas on where you might find the items you need to complete the project and how you might apply some of the ideas from the video.

 Engineer's Toolbox

Go to the Engineer's Toolbox to

- Access Note-Taking Activities
- Access Graphic Organizers
- Access Academic Standards met by this chapter

Go to your **essentials** ONLINE to view the Chapter 2 Discovery Project Launcher Video to learn about how to produce sound waves using various materials.

READING GUIDE

Before You Read What are some basic to advanced math concepts that engineers use in the regular course of their work, and what are four science disciplines that are addressed in this chapter?

Objectives

- **Describe** four levels of mathematics that engineers use.
- **Discuss** how probability and statistics affect the choices applied to engineers' designs.
- **List** applications of geometry and trigonometry in engineering.
- **Describe** how engineers work within four fields of science.
- **Identify** five main physics topics of interest to engineers.

Main Idea

Regardless of the field of engineering, one or more fields of science, along with various levels of mathematical concepts, are applied in the design and analysis of products and systems.

Content Vocabulary	Academic Vocabulary
• probability	• ratio
• quadratic	• indicator
• iteration	• rational
• space	• deviations
• waveforms	• compounds
• derivatives	
• potential energy	
• kinetic energy	
• force	
• fluid mechanics	
• hydrology	
• hydrocarbons	

Note-Taking Activity

Draw this table for each section. Write key terms and phrases under **Cues.** Write main ideas under **Note Taking.** Summarize the section under **Summary.**

Cues	Note Taking
•	•
•	•
Summary	

Graphic Organizers

Use graphic organizers to organize information as you read.

Go to your **essentials ONLINE** for downloadable graphic organizers.

Science Connections

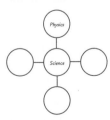

ACADEMIC

Technology

ITEEA STL02 Students will develop an understanding of the core concepts of technology.

ITEEA STL3.04 Technological progress promotes the advancement of science and mathematics.

Mathematics

NCTM Problem Solving Build new mathematical knowledge through problem solving.

Science

NSES E Students should develop abilities of technological design, understandings about science and technology.

ITEEA *International Technology and Engineering Educators Association*
NCTM *National Council of Teachers of Mathematics*
NSES *National Science Education Standards*

College & Career READINESS

Reading Integrate and evaluate content presented in diverse formats and media, including visually and quantitatively, as well as in words.

Speaking and Listening Draw evidence from literary or informational texts to support analysis, reflection and research.

Math Connections and Applications

Basic Mathematics

Engineers employ mathematical concepts throughout their work. Among the more basic concepts are ratios, reciprocals, and algorithms. Engineers must also be adept at measuring and converting units, and possess a firm understanding of statistics.

Ratios

A ratio is a comparison of two numbers and is most commonly expressed as a fraction. Virtually all fields of engineering are concerned with ratios. For example, an automotive engineer may seek to optimize the air-to-fuel ratio for an internal combustion engine, and an aerospace engineer may search to find an ideal thrust-to-weight ratio for an aircraft.

In aircraft design, the thrust-to-weight ratio is an indicator, or something which reveals the aircraft's performance. It is found by dividing the thrust provided by the engine or engines by the weight of the aircraft. This value is expressed as a rational number, such as 0.84 or 1.14. A commercial aircraft might have a thrust-to-weight ratio of about 0.25 or 0.30 while a jet fighter has a ratio between 0.85 and 1.15.

Gear ratios are used by mechanical engineers to optimize the speed and/or torque of a power transmission. Gear ratios are usually expressed with two numbers separated by a colon, such as 1:2 or 1:8. In this ratio, the number before the colon represents the number of turns of a gear and the number after represents the number of turns a second gear meshed with the first will take relative to the first.

Most motor vehicles contain a power transmission that uses gears to change the engine output speed and torque as needed. Gear ratios for a five-speed manual transmission automobile are shown in **Table 2.1**.

Gear	Ratio
1st gear	2.89:1
2nd gear	2.09:1
3rd gear	1.49:1
4th gear	1.02:1
5th gear	0.85:1

Table 2.1 Five-Speed Manual Transmission Gear Ratios

Using the above as an example, a car uses first gear to start moving from a stop, where more power or torque is required to start the vehicle moving. First gear in this case increases the natural torque of the engine by a value of 2.89:1, which means that the torque is increased by 2.89 times. When in fifth gear, the vehicle requires less power from the engine, so the transmission reduces the natural torque from the engine but provides enough power to maintain speed.

A civil engineer may focus on finding the ideal water-to-cement ratio for a mixture of concrete. A smaller ratio will yield higher strength and durability but will not be as workable as a higher water-to-cement ratio. Strength improves with a lower water-to-cement ratio. The water-to-cement ratio is calculated by dividing the weight of the water in one cubic yard of a concrete mix by the weight of the cement in the mix. For example, if one cubic yard of the mix contains 240 pounds of water and 480 pounds of cement, the mix has a .50 water-to-cement ratio. The compressive strength of a mix with a .45 water-to-cement ratio might reach about 4500 PSI (pounds per square inch), where a mix with a .50 ratio might only reach about 4000 PSI. So, while more water in the mix may make it more workable before it cures, it also reduces its strength significantly. The engineer will need to evaluate which mixture is needed for the specific project.

Reciprocals

In electricity, the properties of resistance and conductance of a material have a reciprocal relationship. In a reciprocal, the numerator of a fraction becomes the denominator and the denominator becomes the numerator. The resistance of a material is its ability to oppose electron flow, and conductance is the ability to allow electron flow.

The formula for electrical resistance is

$$R = \frac{V}{I}$$

where V is the voltage and I is the current

The reciprocal, for electrical conductance, is

$$C = \frac{1}{R} \text{ or } C = \frac{I}{V}$$

Logic and Algorithms

Logic is the study of mathematical reasoning, and can be applied to various engineering problems, including the drawing of a map, the planning of a delivery route, or the design of a computer program. Engineers often have to create a step-by-step process (or algorithm) with which to complete their tasks. Engineers also use mathematical logic to optimize a control system or to automate a factory process. Computer engineers use algorithms as they create computer programs.

Logic The following is a sample logic problem as illustrated in **Figure 2.1**. A person wants to take a five-foot-long fishing rod on an airplane, but the airline will not allow any baggage that measures more than three feet in any direction. Through mathematical reasoning, the person has calculated the length of one of the diagonals of a three-foot square, which is approximately 4.24 feet, or the square root of 18.

Next, the person uses that known value along with the known length of one of the sides to figure out that the diagonal distance within the cube would be more than five feet. Therefore the fishing rod could fit inside a cube that still meets the airline regulations. This type of reasoning is applied regularly in engineering, such as in the design of packaging.

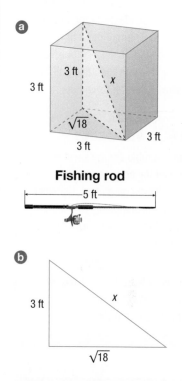

Fig. 2.1 Diagonal Measure of a Cube *What is the length of the diagonal inside the cube? Will the fishing rod meet airline regulations?*

Fig. 2.2 Control System Algorithm An algorithm is essentially a logic diagram that is especially useful in programming and other projects in which a systematic approach is used to solve a problem. *Develop steps and draw an algorithm that can be used to solve the engineering problem that is your chapter Discovery project.*

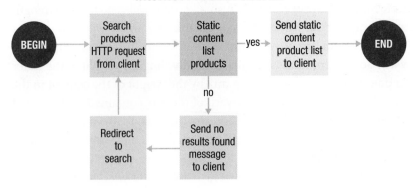

Internet Product Search

PROJECT CONNECTIONS

Describe how the dimensions of the component parts of your musical instrument affect the sound it makes.

Algorithms An algorithm is a process for performing a task and is closely related to mathematical logic. Engineers use algorithms in systems design when they find their way to a solution using a systematic method. Algorithms can be applied more directly in the writing of computer programs and in determining the efficiency of electrical circuits. (See **Figure 2.2**.)

Dimensions and Units

Engineers in all disciplines must be highly competent in mathematical computations. Extremely accurate measurements are vital to engineering projects, whether these are measurements of physical distances and sizes, or the quantities used in a chemical compound.

A prime example of the importance of accurate measurements in engineering happened in 1999. That year NASA lost a $125 million Mars orbiter at least in part because one part of the engineering team used English units of measurement while other parts of the team used the metric system. This has become a famous example of an engineering failure. Most notably, this was one that was based on very simple mathematics. Engineers often convert measurements from one unit to another mathematically. Some common conversion factors used by engineers are shown in **Table 2.2**.

Statistics

Engineers use statistics to help analyze and interpret data. **Probability** is the number of times an event occurs, divided by the total number of occurrences in the sample. It is an important concept, because it relates to risk assessment and management, which is a major component of the work of some engineers. Picture a team of civil engineers about to design a new road approach to an existing bridge. They will collect data about the traffic, weather, and other factors in the area, and apply that knowledge as they design an effective system. With this data, they may be able to predict the needs of the roadway based upon the volume of traffic it receives, or the lifespan of the new road. This is all based on the application of statistical analysis.

At the heart of the study of statistics is an understanding of the normal distribution, also known as Gaussian distribution, or the law of errors. Normal distribution was used by German mathmetician and scientist Johan Carl Friedrich Gauss to model errors in astronomical

To Convert From	To Convert To	Multiply By
lb$_f$/in^2 (psi)	pascal (Pa)	6894.757
pascal (Pa)	lb$_f$/in^2 (psi)	1.4504E-4
g/cm^3	lb/ft^3	62.427974
lb/ft^3	kg/m^3	16.01846
lb/in^3	kg/m^3	27,679.90
lb/ft^3	g/cm^3	0.01601846
volts/mil	kV/mm	0.039370
mil (0.001 inch)	cm	2.54E-3
cm	mil	393.70
MPa(m$^{1/2}$)	psi(in$^{1/2}$)	910.06
J/(g-°C)	BTU/(lb-°F)	0.239006
BTU/(lb-°F)	J/(g-°C)	4.184000
joule (J)	cal (thermochemical)	0.2390057
cal (thermochemical)	joule (J)	4.184000
joule (J)	BTU (thermochemical)	9.4845E-4
BTU (thermochemical)	joule	1054.350
cm^3/Kg	in^3/lb	0.027680
in^3/lb	cm^3/kg	36.127
W/(m K)	BTU in /(hr ft^2 F)	6.9334713
BTU in /(hr ft^2 F)	W/(m K)	0.1441314
(J m)/(min m^2 C)	W/(m-K)	0.016667
W/(m-K)	(J m)/(min m^2 C)	60

Table 2.2 Typical Engineering Conversions

observations. The bell curve in **Figure 2.3** on page 30 illustrates the concept of normal distribution. Within the typical normal distribution there are three standard deviations.

A standard deviation is a departure from the norm. The bell curve represents the normal distribution graphically. If the normal distribution is within one standard deviation of the mean score, it is within 34.1% of the mean. Therefore, 68.2% (34.1 + 34.1 = 68.2) of the population is within 1 standard deviation +/− of the mean. The second standard deviation from the mean encompasses the next 13.6% of the population which is beyond the first standard deviation on either side of the mean score. This group includes 27.2% (13.6 + 13.6 = 27.2) of the population. Statistically, 95.4% (27.2 + 68.2 = 95.4) of the population lies within 2 standard deviations of the mean.

One of the most common applications of statistics in engineering is in the use of anthropometric data in design ergonomics. As a rule of thumb, devices are generally designed to fit 95–98% of the human population based on anthropometric data. According to the normal distribution, this percentage is covered within two standard deviations of the mean. (See **Figure 2.4**.)

Statistical methods are also applied in quality control. Engineers use statistics to determine the quality of parts coming off an assembly line and also to determine the reliability of the system that is being used to produce the parts. Industrial engineers often use statistical methods to determine if a process is within the control limits set by the design process. The key statistical concept in quality control is probability. Probability is the likelihood that something will occur given a statistical sample.

$$\text{Probability} = \frac{\text{number of times an event occurs}}{\text{total number of occurrences in the sample}}$$

To determine probability, begin by taking a random sample. Engineers should determine an appropriate size of the random sample from the level of accuracy they wish to obtain. If an engineer wants to determine the probability of defects in a manufactured product such as a mechanical toy, he could take a random sample from the assembly line, and inspect and test the sample for defects. If the random sample is 250 toys and the engineer finds that 246 or them have no defects, he can predict the probability that 98.4% of the toys will not have defects (246 ÷ 250 = .984, or 98.4%).

This information can help an engineer and a company in planning. If the company produces 100,000 toys, it might anticipate that 1.6 % (1600) of them will be defective. This would help it plan for returns and replacements of the items. In other situations, this information might help an engineer determine if the safety level of a process is or is not acceptable.

Reading Check **Describe** the concept of a normal distribution and two ways in which this concept can be used in engineering.

Fig. 2.3 The Bell Curve This bell-shaped curve represents the normal distribution. The theory is that for any statistic, 68% of the population is within 1 standard deviation of the mean, and 95% is within two standard deviations. *How much of the population is within three standard deviations of the mean?*

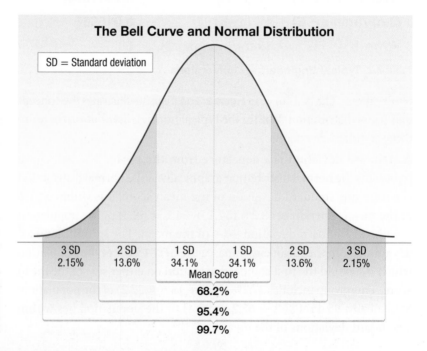

The Bell Curve and Normal Distribution

SD = Standard deviation

| 3 SD 2.15% | 2 SD 13.6% | 1 SD 34.1% | 1 SD 34.1% | 2 SD 13.6% | 3 SD 2.15% |

Mean Score

68.2%

95.4%

99.7%

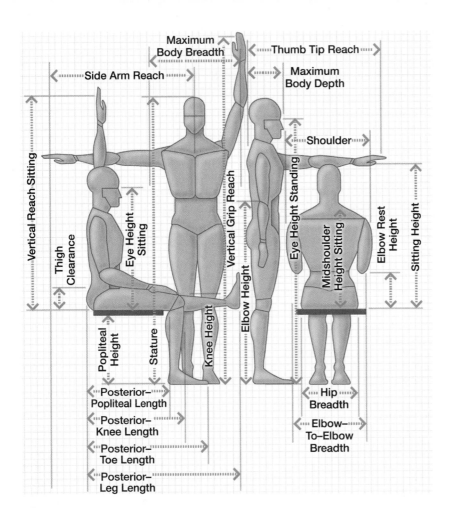

Algebraic Applications

Engineers regularly use algebraic applications such as inverse and quadratic functions. Inverse functions are used every time a value is converted to another unit, and quadratics represent certain ratios and shapes.

Inverse Functions

Inverse functions are apparent throughout many fields of mathematics. For example, the inverse of addition is subtraction. In algebra, the inverse of squaring a number is to find its square root. In more advanced formulas, the domain, x, becomes the range, y, and the range becomes the domain.

Engineers use inverse functions to determine values. If one formula can be used to convert pounds to kilograms, then the inverse can convert kilograms to pounds. Certain formulas can be used to detect voids in a structure and determine properties of materials, and in various acoustic, electromagnetic, and aerodynamics problems.

Quadratic Functions

The term quadratic relates to a polynomial function involving a square of unknown value. The equation in standard form of a quadratic function is $y = ax^2 + bx + c$, where x is the independent variable, y is the dependent variable and a, b, and c are constants. In mathematics, a function means that one quantity is related to and determines another quantity. Two ways to describe a function are algebraically and graphically.

A quadratic function is a specific type of calculation that is commonly applied in mathematics and engineering. The graph of a quadratic function is a parabola, and there are many instances in which parabolic shapes are applied in engineering. The flight of a projectile follows a parabolic curve. Parabolas are used in communications and optics. Parabolic arches may be found in bridges and other structural shapes. (See **Figure 2.5**.)

Other engineering and architectural applications and phenomena are based on quadratic equations. The golden ratio, also known by the Greek letter phi (φ), is applied in many designs and is based on a quadratic equation. Phi is an irrational number, and expressed in numeric form is approximately 1.618:1. This concept is sometimes applied in architecture and engineering using the golden rectangle, which is a

Fig. 2.5 Graphing Math A parabola is the graph of a quadratic function. The formula for this graph is $f(x) = x^2 - x - 2$. *Name some places in your home or town where parabolic shapes are used in designs.*

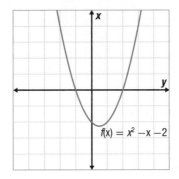

$$f(x) = x^2 - x - 2$$

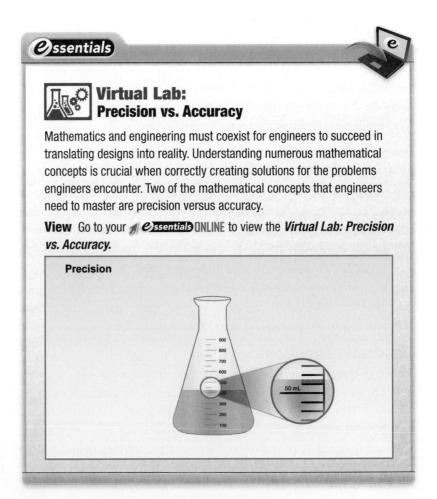

Virtual Lab: Precision vs. Accuracy

Mathematics and engineering must coexist for engineers to succeed in translating designs into reality. Understanding numerous mathematical concepts is crucial when correctly creating solutions for the problems engineers encounter. Two of the mathematical concepts that engineers need to master are precision versus accuracy.

View Go to your **essentials ONLINE** to view the *Virtual Lab: Precision vs. Accuracy.*

Precision

rectangle of that proportion, because its proportions have been studied and found to be pleasing to the eye. (See **Figures 2.6** and **2.7**)

$$\varphi = \frac{1 + \sqrt{5}}{2} \approx 1.618033887...$$

The Golden Ratio

1. Construct a simple square, then bisect it with a horizontal line.

2. Draw a line from the midpoint of one side of the square to an opposite corner

3. Use that line as the radius to draw an arc that defines the height of the rectangle

4. Complete the golden rectangle

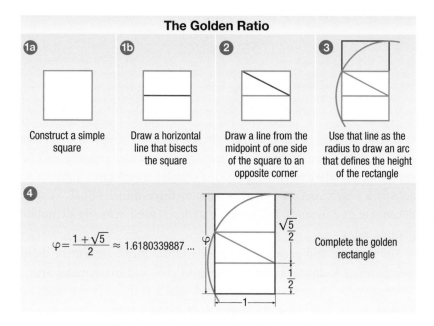

The Golden Ratio

1a Construct a simple square

1b Draw a horizontal line that bisects the square

2 Draw a line from the midpoint of one side of the square to an opposite corner

3 Use that line as the radius to draw an arc that defines the height of the rectangle

4 $\varphi = \frac{1 + \sqrt{5}}{2} \approx 1.6180339887 ...$ Complete the golden rectangle

Fig. 2.6 Constructing a Golden Rectangle A golden rectangle can be created using only a straightedge and a compass. *Following the steps shown to the left, create a golden rectangle.*

(a)   (b)   (c)

Fig. 2.7 Golden Ratio Applications The golden ratio can be identified in many classic forms. Artists apply the ratio to the dimensions of a model's features (a). The ratio has also been recognized in ancient architecture (b) and modern design (c).

Geometry and Trigonometry Applications

Geometry concepts are regularly applied in an engineer's work. Modern antennas are based on fractals, which are repeated **iterations**, or representations of a visual image. An fractal is a geometric concept in which a succession of approximations is used to develop accuracy. In a fractal, each part of a geometric shape is like the whole shape, but smaller. (See **Figure 2.8**.)

Fig. 2.8 A Fractal Antenna
This fractal pattern is used in communications devices. *How many iterations of the shape are included in this pattern?*

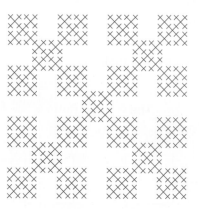

The sensitivity of an antenna is based upon its length and surface area. In the fractal antenna, the surface area of the antenna can be maximized relative to its length. This enables an effective antenna to occupy a much smaller overall **space**, or three-dimensional volume. Because of its efficiency, this type of antenna is used in nearly all mobile phones today.

Simple lines and geometric shapes and the measurement of them are common to the work of engineers in civil and mechanical areas. More complex shapes such as a cycloid, which is the curve defined by a point on the edge of a circle as it rolls along a straight line, can be found in many historical structural designs. (See **Figure 2.9**.) Galileo once theorized that the cycloidal arch was the strongest possible structural shape. Later studies revealed that this was not the case, and that a catenary or parabolic arch was actually stronger.

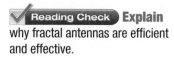
Reading Check **Explain** why fractal antennas are efficient and effective.

Fig. 2.9 The Cycloid A cycloid is defined by a point on the edge of a circle as it rolls along a straight line. *What are some examples of cycloids used in engineering design?*

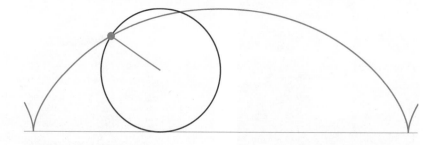

Area and Volume

Many engineers seeking to optimize surface area and volume of three-dimensional spaces call upon simple, and sometimes more complex, mathematical formulas. Imagine the complex geometric shape of a modern boat hull. An engineer must be able to figure out its water displacement and the buoyancy it will provide, which are based upon defining it as a measurable shape.

An example of this is a barge to transport containers. The relatively simple hull shape of a barge is perhaps most similar to that of a trapezoidal prism such as the design shown in **Figure 2.10**. The volume of the barge can, therefore, be calculated using the formula for volume of a trapezoidal prism: $\frac{1}{2}(A + B)(Y)(Z)$

(a) Barge

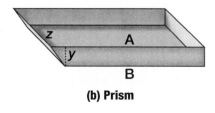

(b) Prism

Fig. 2.10 Trapezoidal Prisms
The hull shape for a barge might be a trapezoidal prism as shown here. *What is the volume of the barge represented by figure (b), if A = 36 ft, B = 30 ft, Y = 4 ft, and Z = 12 ft?*

Vectors

When applied in physics, engineering science, and mechanics, a vector represents quantities such as force that have both magnitude and direction. This mathematical and physical concept has several applications in structural and mechanical designs. For example, an engineer must be able to calculate the deflection of the structural members of a bridge when force is applied. This information is vital to make sure the bridge is strong and safe for use.

A simple way to calculate force vectors is by using graph paper. To find the combined effect of two forces, we can draw the forces to scale in the appropriate direction. For instance, to find the resulting force from two forces originating at the same point and extending out at a right angle, one should make use of the Pythagorean Theorem, $a^2 + b^2 = c^2$. (See **Figure 2.11**.)

Trigonometry

Wherever there are triangles in the world of engineering there is trigonometry, which is the study of the relationship between sides and angles of triangles. Engineers often use standard trigonometric functions such as sine, cosine, and tangent to make calculations using triangular shapes. The most common engineering application of a triangular shape is in the design of structures.

Trigonometry can be used to determine distances both directly and indirectly. It is used frequently in mapping and surveying, especially in places that are not ordinarily accessible. Global Positioning Satellite, or GPS technology, is based on trigonometry, as positions on earth are triangulated with satellites. (See **Figure 2.12**.)

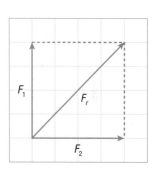

Fig. 2.11 Combining Forces A vector diagram showing a force, F_1, of 4.0 newtons north and a force, F_2, of 4.0 newtons east. *What is F_r, the resulting force derived from F_1 and F_2?*

Fig. 2.12 Global Positioning
The U.S. GPS system uses triangulation to find position using three or more of the satellites that comprise the system. *What type of math is used in the triangulation employed by the U.S. GPS system to calculate location?*

To begin to understand how GPS works, it is helpful to understand how to apply trigonometry in determining a distance indirectly. The height of a building can be determined indirectly by using trigonometry. From the ground, it is most practical to measure two values; the distance to the building, and the angle from the ground to the top of the building. With these values. the height of the building can then be determined by using the tangent ratio, $\tan x = \dfrac{opposite}{adjacent}$. (See **Figure 2.13**.)

Fig. 2.13 Indirect Measurement
To determine the height of a building indirectly, employ trigonometry and apply the formula *opposite = adjacent × tan x*. If the distance to the building is 300 feet, and the angle from the ground to the top of the building is 65°, what is the height of the building?

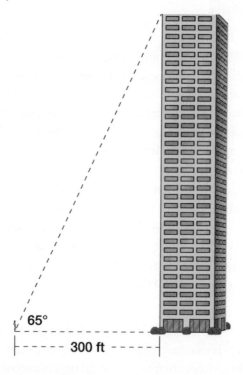

65°

|– – – – – 300 ft – – – – –|

PROJECT CONNECTIONS

How will various frequencies be used to make music through your device?

Trigonometry is also applied in the analysis of **waveforms**, or the shapes and forms of signals moving through a solid, liquid, or gas. Sine waves vary in amplitude (one cycle measured vertically on a coordinate grid from zero) and frequency (the reciprocal of one cycle measured horizontally), but maintain the same basic shape. (See **Figure 2.14**.) Waveforms are critical to acoustical, optical, and electrical engineers. Vibration of machinery or structural elements can be described using trigonometry. Applications, including Fourier analysis, are also based in trigonometry. Trigonometry is also critical to the study of heat flow and diffusion and the compression of digital information.

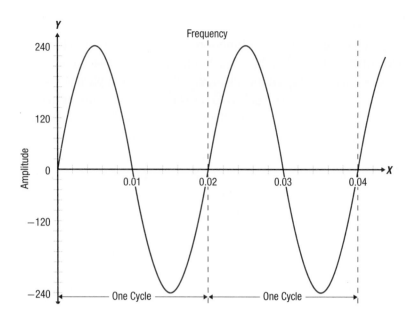

Calculus Applications

Because engineers are concerned with changing conditions, they must also be skilled in applications of calculus. Calculus can be defined as the study of rates of change. Whether working with computer memory or the variance in speed of a moving object, engineers use mathematics to predict the behavior of their designs.

Exponents and Logarithms

Exponents and logarithms (the inverse functions of exponents) are at the heart of the study of calculus. The base-2 logarithm is the basis for computer science and engineering. This is even used to describe the exponential increases in memory in computers. Today's 128 gigabyte device will become tomorrow's 256 GB, then 512 GB, and so on.

Differential Equations

Differential equations, which are part of advanced mathematics, are also applied in engineering contexts. Differential equations are used to predict continuous change such as exponential growth or decay. Agricultural engineers can use equations to predict the growth rate of a new crop. Nuclear engineers can forecast the decay of radioactive material over time. Concrete also experiences both exponential growth and decay, in that it reaches its full strength within a matter of a few weeks then slowly deteriorates over the next several decades or even centuries, depending on conditions. (See **Figure 2.15** on page 38.) Mechanical vibrations, which involve continuous change, can also be described using differential equations.

Another application of differential equations includes Newton's Law of Cooling, one of the laws of thermodynamics. Newton's Law of Cooling states that the rate of change of the temperature of an object is proportional to the difference between its own temperature and the temperature of its surroundings. The differential equation for Newton's Law of Cooling is $\frac{dT}{dt} = -k(T - T_a)$.

PROJECT CONNECTIONS

How are musical octaves logarithmic in nature?

Derivatives

Derivatives describe how a function changes as its input changes. A derivative is the result of how much one quantity changes as a result of another quantity or quantities changing. This can be applied to distance-time optimization work, such as in transportation systems, or to define the volume and area of various shapes. The stopping distance for a car can be predicted based on a number of known variables including road-tire friction and the force applied by the vehicle's brakes. The fact that these variables may be constantly changing makes the mathematics behind these calculations complex.

Derivatives are also used to predict atomic behavior, which is critical to nanotechnology and micro-scale computing applications. It is significant to nanotechnology, for example, because nanotechnology involves controlling things at a molecular level. To be able to control matter at this scale, it is important to be able to predict its behavior.

Reading Check **List** four types of calculus equations that are commonly important to engineers.

Fig. 2.15 Strength of Concrete
This graph shows the compressive strength of concrete, at various temperatures, for the first month after pouring. *At about 21°C, what is the compressive strength of concrete on day 14?*

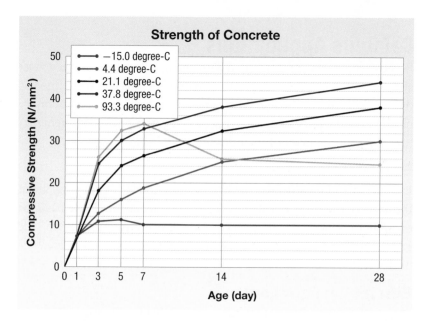

SECTION 2.1

Check Your Understanding

After You Read Perform the following tasks.

1. **Identify** the four main areas of math used by engineers.

2. **Explain** the key statistical concept used in quality control and why it is used.

3. **Analyze** how a GPS works in the mathematical sense.

Physics Concepts

Concepts of physics are routinely applied in mechanical, civil, and electrical engineering, but all fields of engineering rely on physics knowledge to some extent. Newton's laws of motion and projectile motion equations, as shown in **Table 2.3**, are common in certain fields. These laws are explored in more detail in Chapter 9, Mechanical Engineering.

Law	Formula
Projectile Motion	$d = vt$
Newton's Second Law	$F = ma$
Velocity of an Object in Freefall	$v = at$

Table 2.3 Common Formulas for Motion Calculations

The laws that describe electricity and electronics are based on the study of physics. The science of electromagnetic waves led to the development of modern communications systems, including radio and television, and is also the basis for digital communications.

The electromagnetic spectrum describes all frequencies of electromagnetic radiation. In theory, the wavelength of electromagnetic waves ranges from the atomic level to the size of the universe. However, engineers have found applications for only certain parts of the spectrum. Electromagnetic waves are used mostly in communications but are also applied to other technologies.

Radio, microwave, and infrared frequencies are used mainly in communications systems. Microwave frequencies are also used to cook food. Visible light is applied in electricity, such as in physical lighting applications, in lasers, and in many other technological applications. X-rays are used in many photographic applications, such as in medical imaging as well as structural testing.

Digital technology makes efficient use of electromagnetic bandwidth in communications applications. This is because digital signals can operate without electromagnetic interference, or "noise," or of rays from other areas of the spectrum. Digital transmissions require less bandwidth than older methods of transmission by allowing signals to be more precise and compressible.

Work, Energy, and Power

Work is the product of force and displacement. Energy is the potential of a system to do work. Power is the rate at which work is performed. An engineer may perform calculations for work, energy and power using the formulas and units in **Table 2.4** on page 40.

essentials

STEM CONNECTION

Speed/Momentum
Engineers may have to work with objects that are stationary, but often will be working with objects in motion. They will need to be well-versed in physics theories to solve problems with objects in motion. Engineers may also have to solve problems that involve multiple objects and how they interact with one another. This may require knowledge of speed and momentum.

 **Personal Tutor**

View
Go to your *essentials* ONLINE to view the *Personal Tutor: Speed/Momentum.*

Concept	Formula	SI Units
Work	$W = Fd$ F = force, d = distance or displacement	Joule
Potential Energy	$PE = mgh$ m = mass, g = gravity, h = height	Joule
Kinetic Energy	$KE = \frac{1}{2}mv^2$ m = mass, v = velocity	Joule
Total Energy	$TE = PE + KE$	Joule
Power	$P = W/t$ $P = E/t$ W = work, E = Energy, t = time	Watt

Table 2.4 Common Formulas for Work, Energy, and Power

Potential energy is stored and is based on an object's position. The potential energy of an object can be either gravitational or elastic, such as when it is stored in a spring. When the energy is due to motion in any direction, it is called kinetic energy.

Using the above formulas, we can conclude that an object on earth (where gravity is constant) has more potential energy if it has a greater mass and/or if it is held at a greater height. An object has more kinetic energy if it has a greater mass and/or if it is traveling at a greater velocity.

Much of an engineer's work relates to the transformation of energy, or the design of systems to do work, and the optimization of the power required to do the work. Some engineers focus on designing systems to convert electrical energy into mechanical energy, such as in an electric motor. Other engineers design systems that strictly change energy from one form into another, such as in a nuclear power plant, where nuclear energy is converted first to heat energy and then to electrical energy. (See **Figure 2.16**).

Consider that some of the power for the devices in our daily lives comes from a relatively small amount of radioactive material. Radioactive material is used to create heat. Turbines convert heat into mechanical energy and then into electrical energy. The electrical energy may then be carried to a destination where it will be used to power a motor to do work, which again is mechanical in nature. Because of all of these transfers of forms of energy, engineers are often concerned with efficiency. Efficiency is the ratio between the input energy and the useful output energy.

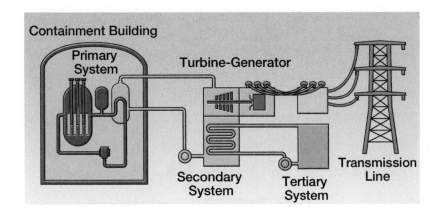

Fig. 2.16 Nuclear Power Plant Nuclear power plants generate electricity in much the same way as other power sources generate energy, except that nuclear energy is the original source. *What does a nuclear power plant have in common with power generation methods that use coal or oil?*

Thermodynamics

Thermodynamics is the study of the conversion between thermal energy and mechanical work. Variables in this conversion are temperature, volume, and pressure. Those studying thermodynamics examine how these variables change over time, and how they change with the conversion of heat to mechanical energy and vice versa. The study of thermodynamics has many applications including various methods of electric power generation such as nuclear, geothermal, or solar thermal. Thermodynamics is explored in more detail in Chapter 9, Mechanical Engineering.

essentials

Virtual Lab:
Conservation of Mechanical Energy

Engineers must understand and apply numerous scientific concepts in order to create safe, effective, and efficient solutions to design challenges. The conservation of mechanical energy is an essential scientific concept that engineers must apply.

View Go to your **essentials** ONLINE to view the *Virtual Lab: Conservation of Mechanical Energy.*

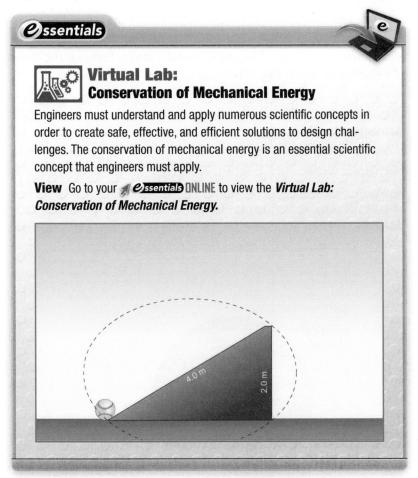

Laws of thermodynamics shown in **Table 2.5** are applied in nearly all fields of engineering. In addition to power generation, the design and optimization of power conversion systems, combustion engines, heating systems, refrigeration systems, fuel systems, and air conditioning systems all apply the laws of thermodynamics.

Thermodynamic Law	Principle	Equation
Zeroth Law	Equilibrium	$A \sim B \wedge B \sim C \Rightarrow A \sim C$
First Law	Conservation of Energy	$dU = \delta Q - \delta W$
Second Law	Entropy	$\int \frac{\delta Q}{T} \geq 0$
Third Law	Absolute Zero of Temperature	$T \Rightarrow 0, S \Rightarrow C$

Table 2.5 **Equations for Thermodynamic Laws**

Forces and Motion

Kinematics is the study of the motion of objects. Kinematic equations can be used to solve for distance, velocity, and the acceleration of objects, including falling objects and objects that are rotating.

While kinematics does not ordinarily consider the causes leading to motion, mechanics is the study of forces applied to physical objects. Mechanics has two branches, statics and dynamics. Statics is the study of forces on an object that is in equilibrium or at rest (see **Figure 2.17**), and dynamics is the study of objects in motion due to an outside force. Engineers often calculate the forces exerted upon each structural member and node.

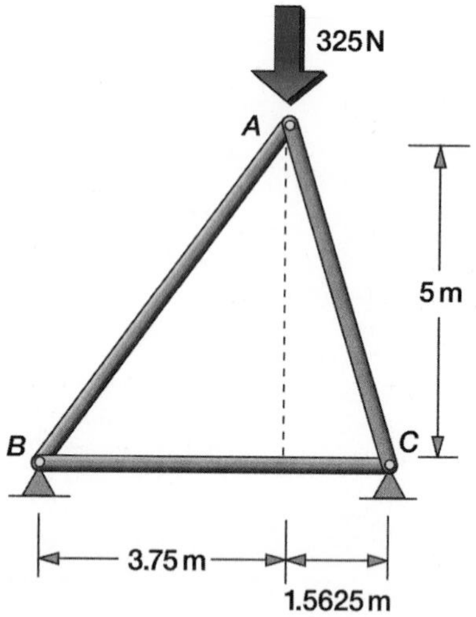

Torque is the measure of the turning force acting on an object. In mechanical engineering, torque is referred to as "moment." Torque is measured in foot-pounds in English units and in newton-meters in SI, or International System, units. Torque is dependent upon three variables; the applied force, the length of the lever arm, and the angle between the force and the lever arm. (See **Figure 2.18**.)

Fig. 2.17 How Vectors Are Applied This diagram of a bridge support shows truss members AB and AC under compression. This means that the structural member is being pushed together. Truss member BC is under tension, which means the structural member is being pulled apart. *What branch of mechanics is relevant to this diagram?*

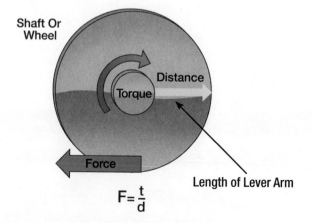

Fig. 2.18 Elements of Torque Torque is dependent upon three variables; the applied force, the length of the lever arm, and the angle between the force and the lever arm. *What might you do to loosen a nut that you have not been able to loosen using a standard wrench?*

$$F = \frac{t}{d}$$

Optics

Optics is the study of the behavior and properties of light. While many engineers apply concepts of optics in their work, optical engineers design instruments including lenses, cameras, microscopes and telescopes. Some engineers apply optics in the design of communications systems, including fiber optics, and optical digital memory storage systems.

Digital data information tracks on a DVD are etched by a laser as "pits" and "bumps" into photosensitive material on the disk. Those pits and bumps represent the "0s" and "1s" of binary information. A laser is also used to read the material from the disks. Since the reading and writing are based in large part on the disks' reflective and semi-reflective material, a thorough understanding of optics is required to design such an application. Optical disks have varying characteristics, which determine the storage capacity of the disk. The more layers contained on a disk, the greater the capacity (See **Figure 2.19**.)

PROJECT CONNECTIONS

An understanding of overtones, frequencies, and harmonics is regularly applied to the design of acoustical systems. Discuss how these concepts are applied in the design of your musical instrument.

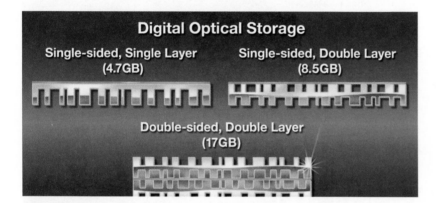

Digital Optical Storage

Single-sided, Single Layer (4.7GB)

Single-sided, Double Layer (8.5GB)

Double-sided, Double Layer (17GB)

Fig. 2.19 Optical Disks The data on CDs and DVDs is in the form of pits, bumps and layers in an optical disk. *What device both reads and writes the data on optical disks?*

Acoustics

Acoustics is the study of sound waves. Acoustical engineers may work on the reduction of undesired sounds, such as in noise reduction systems. Noise-control systems like noise-canceling headphones are products of engineering and draw upon a thorough knowledge of acoustics.

In noise-canceling headphones, an internal microphone, noise-canceling electronics, and a speaker actively match waveforms from the sound being played by the headphone speaker to those created by external sources. This effectively cancels out undesired external interference. (See **Figure 2.20**.)

Reading Check **List** three types of engineering in which physics concepts are most routinely applied.

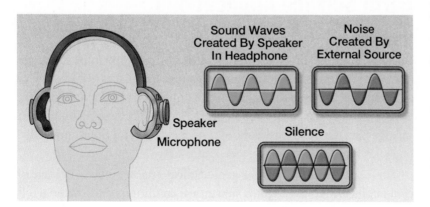

Sound Waves Created By Speaker In Headphone

Noise Created By External Source

Speaker

Microphone

Silence

Fig. 2.20 Noise-Canceling Headphones In addition to playing music, some headphones are able to reduce outside noise. *How are noise-canceling headphones able to reduce annoying outside noise?*

Fig. 2.21 The Big Dig Boston's "Big Dig" changed the landscape of one of America's most historic cities. The "before" image (inset) shows an area of raised highway before the project, and the "after" picture shows the same area after the project relocated the highway underground. *What were some of the many engineering challenges of the Big Dig?*

Earth Science Applications

Geology

Boston's "Big Dig" project was unprecedented not only in its scope but also in the nature of the work. Tunnels were dug in places that previously could not be tunneled through. Foundations were placed in places that were previously not able to handle them. This project was accomplished in large part thanks to the work of civil engineers and their knowledge of geology and earth science. (See **Figure 2.21**.)

The relatively new field of geotechnical engineering, a branch of civil engineering, investigates subsurface conditions and materials. It assesses the risks of digging foundations and tunnels based on soil

properties, and design foundations that are rooted deep in the earth, such as those needed for skyscrapers and tunnels. Looking at the New York City skyline, one may notice groupings of tall buildings far downtown in Manhattan and more in midtown, with shorter buildings in between. This is due to the geology of Manhattan Island. The bedrock can support larger structures only in certain spots. (See **Figure 2.22**.)

Fields of engineering other than civil engineering are concerned with the extraction of useful minerals and other materials from the earth. An in-depth knowledge of where these materials naturally occur is crucial to the understanding of how to extract them. Petroleum, natural gas, coal, and various minerals and ores are all removed from under the earth using designs created by engineers. Engineers also design systems that are used to image subterranean spaces. In areas of the U.S.A. and the world that are more seismically active, engineers may design and install seismic monitoring equipment. They might also become expert in seismic design and/or the seismic retrofitting of buildings and other structures in these areas.

Water

A scientific knowledge of water and its behavioral and material properties is important to the work of many engineers. A civil engineer might specialize in the application of environmental **fluid mechanics** and **hydrology**, so that people can have access to water resources. Fluid mechanics is the study of fluids and the forces that act upon them. Hydrology is the study of water and its occurrence, circulation, and distribution on earth.

Ocean engineers apply knowledge of tidal waters. Coastal engineering, a related branch of engineering, designs structures, including undersea foundations and erosion management systems.

Many civil engineers work on designs for flood control systems. In Louisiana during Hurricane Katrina, much attention was drawn to the

Fig. 2.22 Bedrock of a City
Due to varying subsurface geology, the New York City skyline has tall buildings in midtown and downtown, where the bedrock can support them, and shorter buildings in the middle. *In addition to building foundations, why would engineers other than civil engineers need to be knowledgeable about geology?*

Reading Check **Explain** why it is valuable for engineers to know about the subterranean make-up of a site before completing the design for a structure.

PROJECT CONNECTIONS

What material properties are most important to the parts of your musical instrument that directly produce sound?

failure of the levee system in the affected region. Engineers were involved in the repair of the breaches. They continue to design better systems to handle floodwaters and storm surges around the country. (See **Figure 2.23**.)

Chemistry Concepts

Concepts of chemistry are applied in chemical engineering especially, but aspects of this science are also applied in other engineering fields. Important concepts of chemistry that are applied in engineering include those of fluid mechanics, chemical kinetics, and chemical thermodynamics. Some engineers design the instruments that are used to analyze chemical properties.

Atomic and Molecular Structure

An understanding of the phenomena that take place on an atomic and molecular level are key to the work of some engineers. They must understand the way that atoms, along with their electrons, protons, and neutrons, behave. They must also understand how molecules and compounds are formed, and how bonding and chemical reactions take place. The application of these concepts in engineering is explored in more detail in Chapter 12, Chemical Engineering.

Materials Science

The field of materials science is closely aligned to the study of chemistry. Knowledge gained in materials science allows plastic polymers to be formed synthetically, thus creating useful new materials. Ceramics and composites can also be formed and modified to desirable shapes. In addition, the science of metallurgy can be applied in the development of new metal alloys. An understanding of material properties, including their corrosive or reactive properties, is also helpful in deciding which materials to use in certain projects and products.

Chemistry and materials science has led to the development of new engineered products such as those used as lubricants, as adhesives and coatings, and as explosives. Knowledge of compounds and how they

Fig. 2.23 Flood Control This flood wall was designed to hold back flood waters. *In addition to flood control systems, what are two other water-related specialties in civil engineering?*

react has led to new applications of concrete, the most widely applied human-made material on earth.

Organic Chemistry

While organic chemistry is viewed as an integral part of biological science, this field also has applications in engineering. **Hydrocarbons** are molecules that consist of only hydrogen and carbon atoms and are the basis for many naturally-occurring fuels such as petroleum and natural gas. Methane and propane are fuels commonly used in vehicles, cooking, and other applications. Octane is the key component of gasoline. All of these substances are hydrocarbons. (See **Figure 2.24.**)

Engineers seek to optimize the performance of fuels. This includes using additives to purify or to stabilize the fuel. Many fuels such as gasoline use stabilizers to enhance their shelf life because without them these compounds naturally break down rather quickly.

Electrochemistry

Chemical reactions that take place between an electrolyte and a conductor define the field of electrochemistry. In an electrical cell, commonly known as a battery, a chemical reaction takes places between an anode and a cathode that are placed in contact with an electrolyte. This is the electrochemical foundation for almost all commercial batteries, including lead-acid, nickel-cadmium, and lithium rechargeable batteries.

In fact, though, a common commercial AA "battery" is actually a single electrochemical cell. A true battery is a series of electrochemical cells connected to one another. The lithium-ion battery used in laptop computers is an example of a true battery, as it is a series of interconnected cells. (See **Figure 2.25.**)

The science applied in the development of electrochemical cells is advanced. Much of the time and money invested by companies that develop them is spent in research. The development of new battery chemistry that can even slightly increase the life, durability, or capacity of a cell would translate into a great deal of profit.

Environmental Chemistry

Chemistry also has several applications in the field of environmental engineering. The basis for the work of environmental engineers lies in environmental chemistry, which relates to the chemical make-up of air, water, and soil. This science is applied in water treatment, air pollution management, and hazardous waste management.

Biological Applications

Applications of biology that are common in engineering include botany, genetics, anatomy and physiology, and the concept of bioremediation.

Botany

Botany has many applications in the field of agricultural engineering. Knowledge of plants and how they grow is key to being able to grow them in large quantities. Plants need water, light, and nutrients. Some engineers seek to optimize these factors to increase food crop yields.

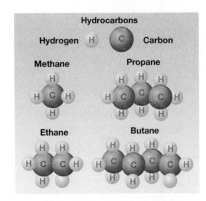

Fig. 2.24 Sample Hydrocarbons These hydrocarbon molecules consist of only hydrogen and carbon atoms. In chemistry, each atom of a given element is capable of accepting a finite number of bonds. *How many bonds does each carbon atom accept?*

Reading Check **Explain** the difference between an electrochemical cell and a true battery.

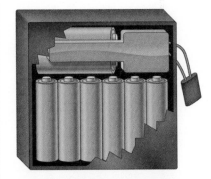

Fig. 2.25 A Battery This image of the inside of a lithium-ion battery for a laptop shows a series of interconnected electrochemical cells. *How many interconnected electrochemical cells are shown in this laptop battery?*

Knowledge of plants and how they function can also help in modifying them. Plant hybridization has resulted in new plant species. The grapefruit is a hybrid of pomelo and Jamaican sweet orange. Durum wheat comes from hybrids of wild grasses. Modifications also reduce stresses or increase nutritional qualities.

Genetics, Anatomy, and Physiology

Basic biology, organic chemistry, and human anatomy and physiology are essential to the work of engineers, including biomedical engineers. Biomedical engineers study cells and tissue and create artificial versions of them. An understanding of immunology is important to engineers who are involved in the design of pharmaceutical products. Some engineers also apply biomechanics to design artificial limbs. (See **Figure 2.26**.)

Knowledge of genetics, chromosomes and heredity, and DNA/RNA is crucial to the ability to manipulate these items. Somewhat controversial when applied to humans, biotechnology and biological engineering have led to new food sources, medicines, and gene therapies. Biological engineers attempt to mimic natural biological systems, and to modify plants and microorganisms for useful purposes.

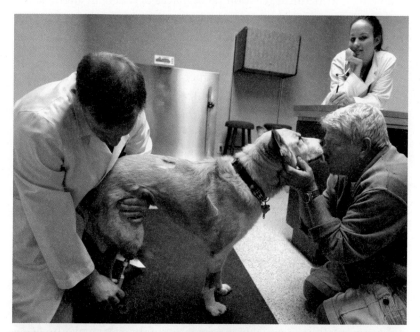

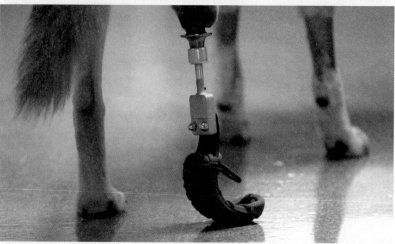

Fig. 2.26 Artificial Limbs The study of biomechanics has enabled engineers to develop functional artificial limbs for people and animals. *What is the focus of the work of biomedical engineers?*

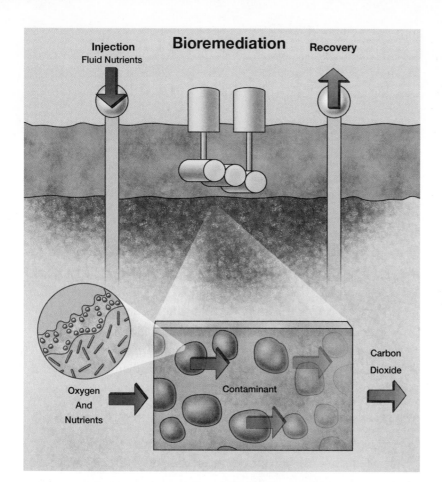

Bioremediation

Injection **Fluid Nutrients** **Recovery**

Oxygen And Nutrients

Contaminant

Carbon Dioxide

Fig. 2.27 The Bioremediation Process Bioremediation involves injecting fluid and nutrients into contaminated environments to return them to their natural state. *What is injected into the ground to decontaminate the soil in the diagram?*

Bioremediation

Bioremediation is the use of microorganisms, fungi, and/or enzymes to clean contaminated environments and return them as much as possible to their naturally occurring state. Bioremediation methods can remove crude oil and some soil contaminants, but not all of them. This process will not work to remove several of the most harmful contaminants such as heavy metals and radioactive materials. (See **Figure 2.27**.)

☑ Reading Check **List** three biological specialties that employ the work of engineers.

SECTION 2.2

Check Your Understanding

After You Read Perform the following tasks.

1. **Describe** what is studied in the science of thermodynamics.

2. **Analyze** why knowledge of geology is important to engineers.

3. **Justify** why groups of electrochemical cells are often used together in a device.

Review and Assessment

Problem-Solving Process

Identify

The Pikes Peak International Hillclimb is perhaps the premier hill-climbing event in North America. Each year hundreds of drivers brave the 12.4 mile course. TopGear Enterprises, an automotive fabricator specializing in off-road vehicles, wants to enter the competition. Your job is to develop a vehicle using the following constraints and criteria:

- The vehicle must handle well on a straight 45° slope.
- It must function on at least two different surfaces.
- It must be constructed to scale and no more than 10" in length.
- It must use an electric motor, 1.5 – 3.0 V, as its power source.

Set Up

1. Ground yourself in information. List characteristics of climbing vehicles. How can you overcome grade and varied friction?
2. Research gear ratios and motor output. How does weight distribution affect performance?
3. Brainstorm solutions. Develop sketches of components. Calculate gear ratios that provide the best power-to-speed ratio.
4. Use a decision matrix to choose a solution. Consider criteria and constraints.

Execute

5. Plan the solution. What gears will provide the best power to the wheels? What techniques can be used to produce the prototype?
6. Keep sketching and recording ideas to improve your design.
7. Prepare models of the solution, using various types of production. Optimize the gear ratio to obtain the desired outcome.
8. Discuss the prototype with your team. Analyze your design.

Evaluate

Test your design on a sloped surface. Simulate pavement and dirt roads. Complete several runs. Observe performance from one surface to another.

Share

Create a presentation, website, or wiki to guide building hill-climbing vehicles. The guide should include information on hill climbing, gear ratios, and weight distribution. Describe the process you followed for your prototype, as well as the testing procedure that was used.

Critical Thinking

Key Concepts

1. **Identify** the approximate percentages associated with the first and second standard deviations from the mean in a normal distribution.

2. **Describe** how to construct a Golden Rectangle using a straight-edge and a compass.

3. **Explain** how you would go about indirectly finding the height of a tall building.

4. **Evaluate** the importance of the study of optics to modern communication systems.

5. **Explain** why materials science is important to advancements in engineering.

Communication

21st Century Skills

6. **Explain** how developments in areas such as electrochemistry affect potential developments in other fields.

7. **Discuss** with a classmate at least three engineering areas that were likely involved in Boston's "Big Dig" project and the probable role of each.

essentials

Activity Center

Go to the **Activity Center** to review chapter vocabulary and key concepts.

Engineer's Toolbox

Go to the **Engineer's Toolbox** to

- Access Academic Activities
- Access the Competitive Event Prep Activity

essentials

DISCOVERY PROJECT

Design and Build a Musical Instrument

The sound waves produced when you strum a guitar or bang a drum are the product of scientific and mathematical concepts. Have you ever moved or bumped into something that made a pleasant sound when you did? In this project, you will design a musical instrument from commonly found materials. In order to complete this task, you will research related physics and mathematics concepts, as well as some musical concepts.

Go to your *essentials* ONLINE to collaborate with your team on this Discovery Project.

The Engineering Design Process

What is the engineering design process?

There is no single process for engineering design. There are, however, common ways in which people approach and engineer solutions to technological problems. Engineers not only find effective ways to develop solutions to problems but also play an important role in identifying the factors that lead to solution development. Typically, the engineering design process includes six steps: defining the problem, defining constraints, brainstorming and research, development and prototyping, testing and analysis, and, finally, evaluation and presentation.

DISCOVERY PROJECT

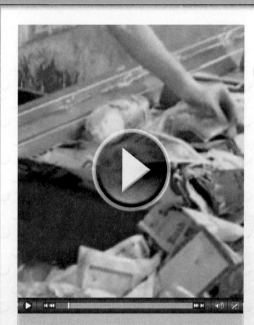

Go to your **essentials** ONLINE to view the Chapter 3 Discovery Project Launcher Video. What are some ways in which you might reuse products that are commonly found in garbage?

Designs for Reclamation

21st Century Skills

How can a commonly discarded item be repurposed in an efficient and useful way?

Engineers must be effective researchers and communicators throughout the engineering design process. Often part of this research includes finding new uses for old materials. Reusing old materials can be called reclamation, and designing products that use these materials is designing for reclamation. In this chapter's Discovery Project, you will develop a new use for a common waste item found in the garbage from a commercial source.

Group Workspace

During the video, watch and listen for important facts about reuse and recycling. Write down some ideas about the value of reusing discarded products.

Engineer's Toolbox

Go to the Engineer's Toolbox to:
- Access Note-Taking Activities
- Access Graphic Organizers
- Access Academic Standards met by this chapter

READING GUIDE

Before You Read What are the steps in research and development? How can engineers be sure that they have chosen the best solution to their engineering problem or opportunity?

Objectives

- **Identify** engineering problems and opportunities.
- **Explain** the reasons for thorough documentation.
- **Discuss** design constraints.
- **List** common design process steps.
- **Identify** types of research involved in developing a project.
- **Explain** prototyping and rapid prototyping.

Main Idea

Research and development involves defining a problem to solve, considering alternative approaches, and learning as much as possible about a problem or opportunity.

Vocabulary

Content Vocabulary

- intellectual property
- patent
- disclosure
- stakeholders
- ergonomics
- anthropometric data
- reverse engineering
- viable
- decision matrix
- prototype

Academic Vocabulary

- goal
- criteria
- reliable
- relevant
- flexible
- statistical analysis

Note-Taking Activity

Draw this table for each section. Write key terms and phrases under **Cues.** Write main ideas under **Note Taking.** Summarize the section under **Summary.**

Cues	Note Taking
•	•
•	•
Summary	

Graphic Organizers

Use graphic organizers to organize information as you read.

R and D
1 2 3 4 5

Go to your  ONLINE for downloadable graphic organizers.

ACADEMIC

Technology

ITEEA STL8.01 The design process includes defining a problem, brainstorming, researching and generating ideas, identifying criteria and specifying constraints, exploring possibilities, selecting an approach, developing a design proposal, making a model or prototype, testing and evaluating the design using specifications, refining the design, creating or making it, and communicating processes and results.

Mathematics

NCTM Problem Solving Solve problems that arise in mathematics and in other contexts.

Science

NSES E Students should develop abilities of technological design, understandings about science and technology.

ITEEA *International Technology and Engineering Educators Association*
NCTM *National Council of Teachers of Mathematics*
NSES *National Science Education Standards*

College & Career READINESS

Speaking and Listening Present information, findings, and supporting evidence such that listeners can follow the line of reasoning and the organization, development, and style are appropriate to task, purpose, and audience.

Reading Read and comprehend complex literary and informational texts independently and proficiently.

Development

Research and Development

The process of designing a solution to a problem is often referred to in business and industry as "R&D," or research and development. In the engineering sense, research and development for products and systems is an ongoing process where continuous research leads to new ideas for new and improved products and systems. These new products and systems lead to additional research, and so on. The goal of research and development in business is often long-term improvement rather than immediate profit. Research and development processes will be explored in more detail in Section 3.2. The first step in research and development is to develop a clearly defined problem or opportunity.

Defining Engineering Problems

In order for a person or team to perform design work and solve a problem, they must clearly define problems and opportunities, identify stakeholders and design constraints, and conduct appropriate research. Defining the problem is perhaps the most important step of the process. Without an effectively defined problem, the process may not be successful.

The Engineering Design Process (also called the Engineering Design Loop) has six steps.

- Identify Problem or Opportunity
- Define Project Constraints
- Research and Brainstorming
- Development and Prototyping
- Testing, Analysis, Optimization
- Evaluation and Presentation

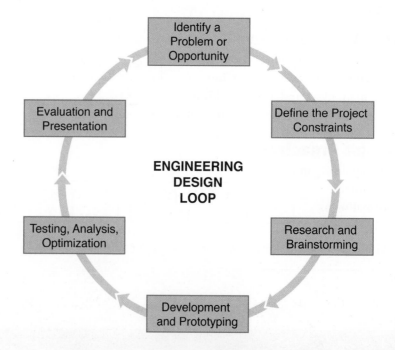

Fig. 3.1 The Engineering Design Process Engineering design is not a step-by-step process. *Why do engineers often need to repeat steps as they design a solution?*

Documenting Your Work

Once the problem is established, documentation of work completed during a project becomes a critical part of the processes of engineering design and research and development. This is important for two reasons. First, documentation is absolutely critical when trying to a patent a device. Second, project documentation provides a constant point of reference for others who need to know about work that has been completed.

Project documentation often takes the form of an engineering logbook or engineering notebook. The engineering notebook is usually a single bound book that contains records of all research, sketches, and designs, as well as records of tests completed. For the unit Challenge Projects and chapter Discovery Projects such as the reclamation design project in this chapter, this communication is done with the Engineering Blog on your Pre-Engineering Essentials website.

Patents

The patenting process establishes a legal record of the inventor of a new device or procedure. A patent enables an individual or a corporation to establish intellectual property rights. **Intellectual property** rights are the legal ownership of a work or invention that results from the use of creative thought, such as a manuscript or design. In the United States, the U.S. Patent and Trademark Office reviews patent applications for new and unique ideas. If the office awards a patent, the individual or corporation is given the exclusive right to control the production, distribution, and other rights of the patented product.

A **patent** is an agreement between the inventor of a device or procedure and the U.S. government. It allows the inventor to have the exclusive right to profit from a solution for a specified period of time. In exchange, the government receives full **disclosure,** or all of the information about the plans for the solution's development. At the end of the specified period, other people or companies can copy, manufacture, or sell the solution without giving the inventor credit or payment.

To secure a patent, an individual, partnership, or corporation must submit a written document along with drawings to the U.S. Patent and Trademark Office. They must show that their submission is a "new and useful process, machine, manufacture, or composition of matter, or any new and useful improvement thereof." They must also pay any applicable fees, depending upon the type of innovation or invention.

Witness and Disclosure

When attempting to secure a patent for design work, it is important to have witnesses for the work. Engineering notebooks often contain signature lines for "Witness" or "Disclosed to." Having signatures of witnesses can also ensure that other group members are aware of the work. This serves both a legal and a practical purpose for a project. If a team of people is working on a project, it ensures that team members will be aware of developments in the project.

✓ Reading Check Explain two reasons why it is important to document your work when creating new designs.

Fig. 3.2 Solution for Old Tires
Shredded tires are used to provide a cushioned surface to reduce injuries to children on playgrounds. *What might be some other uses for shredded tires?*

PROJECT CONNECTIONS

In the Discovery Project for this chapter, there is a problem paired with an opportunity. The problem is that there is too much material going into our landfills. The opportunity is to try to find useful things to do with certain items in the garbage. What is the item you intend to reuse? Why do you think it may be suitable to use for another purpose?

Engineering Problems and Opportunities

Engineering problems and opportunities come from a variety of sources. Professional engineers typically do not go looking for problems to solve. Instead, their companies and clients work with them to define the projects they are asked to solve.

When identifying a problem, it is important to specify the need or desire for a device. It is also important to describe the problem or opportunity in detail, so that as much as possible is understood about the project at its beginning. Solving the wrong problem may cost more than just time and money.

Sometimes an engineering goal is to solve a specific problem. Other times, it may be to improve an existing device or system. Regardless of the type of problem or opportunity, it is crucial to define the project as clearly as possible. This is often done through a design brief or a design statement.

For years, society has faced the problem of having too many discarded vehicle tires in landfills. This problem presented an opportunity for engineers. In response, several solutions developed. Today, shredded tires are used in road asphalt, as a playing surface for sports fields, and as a ground surface in children's playgrounds.

Identifying Stakeholders

Identifying stakeholders is part of the process of designing a solution to a problem. **Stakeholders** are any individual or group that has an interest in the project and can affect or be affected by its outcomes. This may include the project team, owner, or neighbors, among others. Stakeholders may also help define the problem or opportunity, even though they may not be aware of a solution.

Design Constraints

As mentioned in Chapter 1, a constraint is a restriction, control, or limitation. In the context of a design project, constraints that are clearly identified at the beginning of a project can help people organize their thoughts and ideas about how to solve a problem.

For professional engineers, design considerations are usually established in a planning and control document. This document is kept in a central place and provides one common document that can be used to find information about a project. This helps to ensure that each team member is aware of all aspects of a project.

Clearly defined constraints for a project are as important to its development as is a clear definition of the problem or opportunity. Clearly defined constraints are also important because they establish the criteria, or standards, by which ideas for solutions and prototypes will be measured. In other words, all ideas must be considered or tested in some way. If the criteria for a project are not written clearly, it is difficult to know if an idea or prototype has been successful.

Many design criteria and constraints revolve around eight universal resources:

- Time
- Energy
- Space or Area
- Tools
- People
- Materials
- Capital
- Information

PROJECT CONNECTIONS

List the stakeholders for your project.

---

*e*ssentials

Virtual Lab:
Design Constraints in Engineering Research and Design

It is crucial to understand how design constraints affect the engineering research and design process. Some components can have negative effects on a design. Engineers must constantly consider design constraints. Design constraints are limitations on the conditions under which a system is developed. They can also limit the requirements of the system. It is important to identify each design constraint, because they place limits on the entire design process.

View Go to your *e*ssentials ONLINE to view the *Virtual Lab: Design Constraints.*

Beginning with the resources on this page, what are some of the criteria and constraints that you have established for this chapter's Discovery Project?

STEM CONNECTION

Classify Data Collection Techniques In considering materials for a specific project, engineers may want to review the quality of the materials available. Therefore, it may be necessary to collect data regarding the quality of these materials. Engineers must be familiar with various types of data collection and descriptive statistical techniques. Simple, stratified, and systematic sampling techniques are three ways in which engineers may collect samples for their review of materials.

Personal Tutor

View
Go to your *essentials* ONLINE to view the *Personal Tutor: Classify Data Collection Techniques.*

✔ **Reading Check** **Discuss** three main things to consider when defining an engineering problem.

Time

As with any project, there are always deadlines that set a timeline for the project. For example, an engineer or team may define when initial research should conclude, when development of a first prototype should be completed, and so on.

Energy

The amount and type of energy that can be used for a project may also be limited. Some sources of energy may not be available because of environmental concerns or local regulations.

Space or Area

The physical size of a completed project may also be defined in project constraints. A device must often fit within a certain area or a certain range of measurements.

Tools

The tools available to use also have an effect on factors such as time required and construction methods available to complete the final product. For example, if certain construction equipment is not available in a certain geographic area, it may not be possible to construct a bridge or other structural project using the desired methods.

People

The number of people available to lead or assist with a project may be that project's most important factor. When working on a project, an engineer will find that there is always a limit to the number of people who can be assigned to it. Identifying the right people to work on a project also contributes to its success. People bring different skill sets to a situation, so correct personnel selection is highly important. Since salaries are a company's highest operating expense, this is another consideration. With these factors in mind, building the best possible team for a project is the first step toward success.

Materials

The types of materials that can be used for a project may also be limited based on their availability and cost. An engineer or team might only have access to certain locally available materials. This can limit the types of designs that may be considered.

Capital

The amount of money allocated to a project will dictate the quantity and quality of the other resources available to it. It is important to establish a project budget with as much detail as possible.

Information

As the quantity of written material available in the world has increased, so has the challenge to find the right information. Engineers need the skills to identify trustworthy information and should know when to question the reliability of a source. The more trustworthy and relevant the information collected for a project, the more smoothly the design process will go.

Other Design Factors

Appearance

A product's appearance is often an important factor in design, although how something works, or functions, can be more important than how it looks. An engineer designing a bridge for an historic part of a city must pay attention to the appearance of the surrounding neighborhood. However, computer engineers are seldom concerned with how the electronic parts of their products look, because they focus on function. In this case, esthetic decisions may be left to industrial designers.

Durability

A durable item is one that is designed to withstand unexpected stresses. For example, an outdoor light fixture must be designed to withstand harsh weather and maybe even an occasional bump by a passing vehicle. Light fixtures that are used only indoors can be less durable.

Fig. 3.3 Space Constraint
Fenway Park in Boston, MA, exhibits quirky characteristics that were necessary due to limited space. These characteristics include unusual field dimensions and a 37 ft. wall in left field. *What are some other factors that present space challenges to engineers?*

PROJECT CONNECTIONS

In addition to constraints that have already been determined, what other factors may be important in the design of your project?

Career Center

Landscape Architect When a piece of land and its associated structures are no longer being used, should we just abandon them? What about the effect on the community and the environment? Should ways to reuse or recycle old products be a part of the design process from the beginning? Watch the video on how an abandoned elevated railway bed was turned into a park.

Go to your *essentials* ONLINE to learn more about education, career paths, and the future of a landscape architect.

Flexibility and Simplicity

Some devices and products need to be designed to be adaptable, or flexible. This means they can be used in various situations. For instance, sport utility vehicles (SUVs) are designed to be family vehicles, as well as to tow, and to be used for offroad excursions.

Simplicity is also a desirable component for most designs. However, it often becomes a challenge to incorporate simplicity into a design that also needs to be flexible. In the case of the SUV, adding 4-wheel drive for offroad flexibility makes the design of the vehicle more complex.

Safety

The designer must strive to foresee any potential unsafe uses or circumstances when designing any product. The need for safety is especially important when designing something that may be used by a small child, such as a crib, or any toy with small parts. The safety of people and animals is always a top concern.

Ergonomics is the study of how people interface and interact with products, devices, and machines. Ergonomics relies upon anthropometric data and other factors that are used to determine how large or small an item can be and what shape it should be. Anthropometric data comes from statistical analysis of the sizes of humans and the specific distances between the different parts of the body. For example, in the design of a computer mouse, the engineer or designer should consider the average size and typical span of the human hand. Likewise, there is anthropometric data that is incorporated into the designs of furniture, vehicles, industrial equipment, and any other device that is operated by humans,

In addition to human factors, an engineer must also keep environmental factors in mind when designing devices and systems. The materials selected for a product, the tools used to build it, and the energy used to power it may all have undesired effects upon the earth's environment. An engineer must consider the entire product life cycle when making these design decisions.

SECTION 3.1   Check Your Understanding

After You Read   Perform the following tasks.

1. **Explain** why it is important to practice thorough project documentation.

2. **Identify** the eight (8) universal resources.

3. **Analyze** the purpose of a planning and control document and explain how is it used.

Research

When thinking of design, it is often helpful to remember the saying "don't reinvent the wheel." One goal of research is to find out if anyone has ever attempted to develop a solution to the problem you are trying to solve. When conducting research for a project, it is important to examine many sources. That may seem daunting, but there are often good pieces of knowledge within larger sources of information.

Both print and electronic resources should be used during the research stage. Books, magazines, government documents, standards documents, and trade journals may all contain relevant information. Even some historical documents contain important information. Many of these documents are now available in electronic form. Ultimately, the engineer or team must decide if a source of information is reliable and relevant, and how it may affect the solution.

Often an engineer will discover through research that all or part of the problem has been solved by an existing product. If existing technology completely solves the problem, the engineer might stop here. If only part of the problem has been solved, however, the engineer might use reverse engineering to see how the existing product works and to determine if all or part of that product could be useful in solving the current problem. **Reverse engineering** is the practice of analyzing a device, object, or system, often by taking it apart, to determine how it operates. Some questions that guide engineering research include:

- What has already been done to solve the problem?
- How do existing products fall short in terms of the constraints?

Human sources of information are another resource engineers use when researching for a project. Speaking to experts in the field may reveal new ideas for the project. Even talking about a project with colleagues who are distanced from it can reveal unforeseen factors.

Brainstorming and Idea Development

A set of rules is often established for brainstorming and idea development All initial ideas should be considered. The team should work in an environment that will allow ideas to flow. Ideas for a solution to a problem may come at any time, so it is important to document all suggestions using notes and/or a sketch.

Sketching

Effective engineers are able to communicate and document solutions. In the early stages of development this is often accomplished through detailed sketches and notes. Sketches and notes, although not always formal, tend to follow a standard drawing convention. Engineers use sketches to show what an object looks like from a front, top, right,

essentials

Visualization

2D and 3D Drawings The engineering design process has many steps, from the initial ideation stage that might involve sketching and simple drawings, to the production of a new or improved product that might require multiple technical drawings. Being able to make sketches and drawings, both 2D (two-dimensional) and 3D (three-dimensional), of your ideas lets you share them with others throughout this process.

Group Workspace

Sketch six views of an object using standard multiview orientation. After you have completed your sketches, describe which views are necessary to fully describe the object.

Go to your **essentials** ONLINE to learn more about developing your 2D and 3D drawings.

cross-sectional, or other view. Sketches are also used to show an object in a three-dimensional or pictorial view.

The engineering design process should not be thought of as always linear. At times it is cyclical instead. It is important to remember that a good idea may lead to more research, which may lead to other ideas and still more research. An engineer will typically go back to a source of information as an idea is developed further.

Alternative Solutions

It is important to consider more than one solution for a design problem. Performing initial development of more than one idea can have advantages. First, the initial idea does not always turn out to be the best. Second, if several ideas are explored, parts of various solutions can often be combined to form a single better one.

Choosing the Best Solution

Effective decision making and analysis are critical to the engineering design process. All **viable**, or practical, ideas must be analyzed for their expected performance. An engineer must effectively evaluate ideas and choose the best concept based upon the problem and constraints. This can be challenging when ideas have not yet become actual products.

Many methods can be used to determine the pros and cons of a design idea. Mathematical models, physical models, and analysis are used to determine if a design is the best or most viable.

Functional Analysis

An engineer must determine first if the design will work as expected. Knowing whether a design will work before it is constructed may be difficult, but this is a fundamental question for all design projects.

Other common questions engineers must answer while determining the best solution include:

- Can the product be manufactured or constructed easily?
- Is the solution safe? Might it damage a person or property?
- Is the product marketable (in the case of a product that will eventually be sold)?
- Does the product or device comply with applicable local, state, and federal regulations?

The Decision Matrix

A **decision matrix** is a mathematical tool intended to justify a solution. It is used to narrow options and identify alternative solutions. It can also help in quantifying the viability of a design more reliably than by depending on the instincts of the designer or design team.

A decision matrix is made by listing the criteria and constraints for a project in order of importance. Then each criterion is given a value, or weight, based on its importance. More important criteria receive more points. Next, the designer or team judges each possible solution and awards rating points based on expected performance. The rating is multiplied by the weight to determine the score. The solution with the highest number of points is likely to be the most viable in the next

PROJECT CONNECTIONS

After you have developed several ideas to solve your problem, you must justify one idea as better than the others. What methods might you use to justify your decision?

Reading Check Discuss why engineers often develop two or more possible solutions to an engineering problem in the early stages of development.

Sample Decision Matrix

Criteria	Weight	Alternatives					
		Option A		Option B		Option C	
		Rating	Score[1]	Rating	Score[1]	Rating	Score[1]
Time (Criterion C1)	1	3	3	3	3	3	3
Quality (Criterion C2)	2	2	4	1	2	2	4
Cost (Criterion C3)	3	1	3	3	9	2	6
Total	6	6	10	7	14	7	13

Fig. 3.4 Simplifying Complex Decisions A decision matrix is often used by engineers to help them make decisions about a development project. *If the time rating in option B were a 1 instead of a 3, what would be the total score of option B?*

stages of development. The sample decision matrix in **Figure 3.4** contains three primary project criteria, which are rated against 3 options for each. In the example, Option B is the preferred choice.

Tradeoffs

The engineer must also weigh tradeoffs in design. Tradeoffs are common in the advanced development and fine tuning of a product design. For example, a team of engineers developing a design for an aircraft is considering using a more powerful engine than originally considered. Although this engine would provide more thrust, it also could be larger and heavier, thereby affecting other parts of the design.

Engineers must weigh the impact of each design factor and criterion on the project. Along with the stakeholders, engineers must decide whether a device's efficiency or its appearance is more important. They may also determine whether a product would sell if it cost a little more, but used more expensive, better-quality materials.

Implementation

The implementation stage of engineering design typically begins with the creation of drawings and models. These models are followed by prototypes, and finally full-scale development.

Drawings and Models

After they determine which idea will be taken forward, engineers produce more detailed drawings of the solution, called working drawings. Drawings of this type are usually completed using computer-aided design (CAD) software. They provide enough visual information and written plans about a design for it to be built.

Depending on available time and the size of the product, scale models might also be produced. They help to determine spatial relationships among the parts of the design.

Prototyping

A **prototype** is the first working model of a design. Prototypes can be developed in various ways, depending upon the size of the solution. The important thing to remember is that a prototype is an actual working device rather than a model.

essentials

STEM CONNECTION

Compare Unit Rates Cost is very often a constraint in engineering projects. This constraint can sometimes be broken down into fixed costs and indirect costs. As an engineer considers the fixed cost of materials, it is sometimes necessary to consider purchasing a slightly more expensive material to save in labor costs (indirect cost). Unit rates are often used in comparing the fixed cost of materials.

Personal Tutor

View
Go to your **essentials** ONLINE to view the *Personal Tutor: Compare Unit Rates.*

PROJECT CONNECTIONS

Before constructing a model or prototype for your project, develop detailed drawings and plans for it.

PROJECT CONNECTIONS

As you develop a model or prototype of your solution, what process could you use to test the device?

Rapid Prototyping

Only commercially available since the early 1990s, rapid prototyping is a process that allows an engineer or team to speed up the processes of designing and prototyping. A rapid prototyping machine can work in conjunction with CAD software to produce a physical model or prototype of a part or series of parts of a device. One common rapid prototyping device is a 3D printer, which typically uses plastic or another substance to build a three-dimensional piece or part.

Full-Scale Development

A full-scale prototype is the first fully operational solution. The reason a prototype is produced is to create the product under real conditions with the actual materials intended.

Testing and Evaluation

When testing a prototype or initial solution, keep accurate records and document all tests and evaluations. As a project continues through development, all testing and evaluation is done with the original problem, criteria, and constraints in mind.

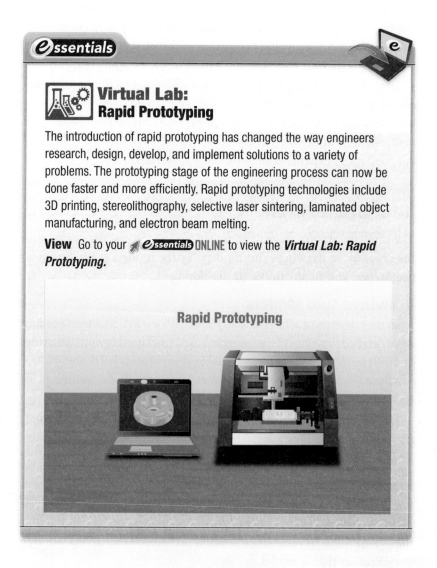

essentials

Virtual Lab: Rapid Prototyping

The introduction of rapid prototyping has changed the way engineers research, design, develop, and implement solutions to a variety of problems. The prototyping stage of the engineering process can now be done faster and more efficiently. Rapid prototyping technologies include 3D printing, stereolithography, selective laser sintering, laminated object manufacturing, and electron beam melting.

View Go to your *essentials* ONLINE to view the *Virtual Lab: Rapid Prototyping.*

Rapid Prototyping

A chart similar to a decision matrix can again be used effectively to determine the performance of a prototype. All design criteria should be listed in order of rank, and the device should be scored in each area of performance. This data can then be used to predict the success of future prototypes or future solutions.

Engineers may also be in charge of monitoring the implementation of a device or system after it has been developed. In some cases, testing can go on for the entire life cycle of a product. Testing is especially critical for designs for which a prototype cannot be built. For example, a bridge will undergo non-destructive testing throughout its lifetime.

Redesign and Next-Generation Prototyping

In some cases, a series of prototypes is developed prior to the first production runs of a device. This is done to ensure that the device functions as well as it can, and that the materials and production processes involved make the item profitable. This is especially true in business and for-profit settings.

Communicating Solutions

An engineer's responsibility is to communicate ideas throughout a project. This is required at various stages of development and implementation, not only at the theoretical stage of the project.

Reports In addition to team communications and the records kept in the engineering notebook, reports are often required and written throughout the development of a product. Documentation, research summaries, test results, and other major events in the engineering design process are reported in writing. Although reports may contain graphics and drawings, it is also important for an engineer to explain ideas and results in writing.

Presentations Engineers are often also responsible for communicating ideas, designs, and results through oral presentations. Visuals, drawings, multimedia, and animations may be used, but the engineer must also be comfortable and effective when presenting ideas to individuals and groups.

PROJECT CONNECTIONS

What are the most important aspects of your project? How can you communicate the main points of your project to an audience? What types of communication methods might you use?

Reading Check Explain the three main steps in the implementation stage of engineering design.

Check Your Understanding

After You Read Perform the following tasks.

1. **Describe** how using a decision matrix contributed to your chapter project.

2. **Discuss** the benefits of reverse engineering.

3. **Explain** the difference between prototyping and rapid prototyping.

Review and Assessment

Problem-Solving Process

Identify

A furniture company wants to create a line of low-cost, environmentally friendly furniture. Your department must design and create a coffee table for this line. The company has provided these design criteria:

- The design (i.e., coffee table) must fold flat.
- It must be made from cardboard.
- It must support a total weight of 40 lbs.

Set Up

1. Research the project. Ask: *"What types of connections can hold the table together?"* and *"What loads and forces will affect it?"*
2. Research coffee table sizes, styles, and structures.
3. Brainstorm ideas for the overall look, size, and assembly.
4. Use a decision matrix to choose the best solution.

Execute

5. Plan the table with your team. What resources will you need? Where can they be obtained? How will you minimize waste?
6. Keep sketching and recording ideas to improve your design.
7. Build mock-ups of the solution, using various construction methods. You may need to use different fastening methods.
8. Meet with your team after each session to discuss accomplishments and problems, and to set goals for the next session.

Evaluate

Develop a testing method that will test the structural integrity of the table as well as ease of assembly. Use a table to record test data. This information will be used to determine the most successful design.

Share

Share your work by creating a brief report with these items:

- Summary of any information that was gathered.
- Sketches that the group produced.
- Description of your testing process.
- Summary of your evaluation.

Discuss the relationship between your product and the eight universal resources. Explain how the chosen material will affect the environment. List both desirable and undesirable attributes of the design.

Critical Thinking

Key Concepts

1. **Identify** possible design constraints for an engineering project.

2. **Summarize** three main reasons engineers thoroughly document their work.

3. **Compare and contrast** flexibility and simplicity in engineering designs.

4. **Evaluate** the importance of an engineer's ability to illustrate ideas using sketches. Discuss how this skill contributes to the design process.

5. **Analyze** the benefits of creating prototypes for a design project and describe when rapid prototyping might be used over other methods.

Problem Solving   21st Century Skills

6. **Share** some of the tradeoffs engineers might encounter when designing a solution. Explain how criteria and constraints might affect engineering decisions.

7. **Discuss** with your classmates potential design problems or opportunities and define constraints for these hypothetical projects.

Activity Center

Go to the **Activity Center** to review chapter vocabulary and key concepts.

Engineer's Toolbox

Go to the **Engineer's Toolbox** to:
- Access Academic Activities
- Access the Competitive Event Prep Activity

---

essentials   DISCOVERY PROJECT

Designs for Reclamation

Commercial establishments such as restaurants, hotels, offices, and stores produce more waste than residential sources do. While much of that waste is recycled, many common items still end up in landfills. However, it may be possible to use the waste to address a problem or opportunity if new ways to recycle these materials can be developed.

Go to your *essentials* ONLINE to complete this chapter's Discovery Project.

Design and Modeling

ESSENTIAL QUESTION Why do engineers need to be able to sketch?

Being able to sketch, draw, and model designs is part of the foundation of good engineering. Engineers use various tools from both traditional and recent technologies to assist them in the design process. Tools such as computer-aided design (CAD) are now indispensible to the engineer.

The use of these skills and systems allows engineers to design and analyze their designs in detail before production. In addition, it is also important for the engineer to understand the processes of modeling, manufacturing, and prototyping.

*e*ssentials

DISCOVERY PROJECT

Designing a Sorting Device

 21st Century Skills Explain how sketching, drawing, and modeling show engineering creativity and innovation.

Single-stream recycling allows people to gather all of their recyclable materials into one collection container. The materials are then separated by sorting devices at another location. In this chapter's Discovery Project, you will create a device to sort plastic bottle caps, used nine-volt batteries, and metal washers.

 Group Workspace

During the video, watch and listen for material properties that are key to the sorting and reuse of recyclable materials. Describe some of the devices that are used in the video to sort the materials.

 Engineer's Toolbox

Go to the Engineer's Toolbox to:
- Access Note-Taking Activities
- Access Graphic Organizers
- Access Academic Standards met by this chapter

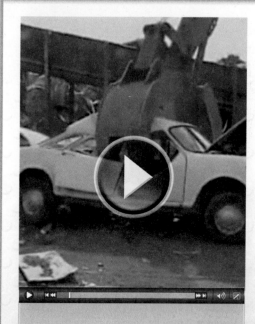

Go to your *e*ssentials ONLINE to view the Chapter 4 Discovery Project Launcher video to learn about sorting devices for recyclable materials.

READING GUIDE

Before You Read What methods do engineers use to create effective sketches and drawings? How are models created and used by engineers?

Main Idea
An engineer's design skills begin with the ability to sketch and draw. There are many ways to create theoretical and physical models.

Objectives
- **Identify** the sketching skills and techniques used by engineers.
- **List** the different types of lines in engineering drawings.
- **Discuss** the most common views, perspectives, and types of drawings of engineered objects.
- **Compare** the types of theoretical models and their uses.
- **Examine** the methods of generating three-dimensional models.
- **Analyze** the features and purpose of a prototype.

Vocabulary

Content Vocabulary
- computer-aided design (CAD)
- scale
- working drawing
- orthographic
- tolerances
- alloys
- isometric
- rendering
- optimize
- computer simulations
- mockup

Academic Vocabulary
- device
- drafting
- dimensions
- perspective
- parameters
- variables

Note-Taking Activity
Draw this table for each section. Write key terms and phrases under **Cues**. Write main ideas under **Note Taking**. Summarize the section under **Summary**.

Cues	Note Taking
•	•
•	•
Summary	

Graphic Organizers
Draw the graphic organizers. Use them to organize information as you read.

Go to your *essentials* ONLINE for downloadable graphic organizers.

Types of Models

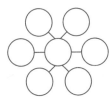

STANDARDS

ACADEMIC

Technology

ITEEA STL9.03 A prototype is a working model used to test a design concept by making actual observations and necessary adjustments.

ITEEA STL20.03 The design of structures includes a number of requirements.

Mathematics

NCTM Geometry Use visualization, spatial reasoning, and geometric modeling to solve problems.

Science

NSES E Students should develop abilities of technological design, understandings about science and technology.

ITEEA *International Technology and Engineering Educators Association*
NCTM *National Council of Teachers of Mathematics*
NSES *National Science Education Standards*

Reading Integrate and evaluate content presented in diverse formats and media, including visually and quantitatively, as well as in words.

Speaking and Listening Make strategic use of digital media and visual displays of data to express information and enhance understanding of presentations.

Sketching

The ability to sketch one's ideas is of critical importance, especially when designs are being documented for the purpose of patenting. Big, important ideas related to a project are often captured in a sketch before they are developed further and incorporated into the design of a product or process.

Within a sketch, notes about an idea can be crucial to the understanding of a device. The goal of the sketch is often twofold. First, the engineer is capturing the idea. Through the process of drawing, he or she begins to work out important details. Second, a complete and high-quality sketch can be used to communicate an idea to others. (See **Figure 4.1**.)

Sketching usually follows one or more of the drawing conventions covered later in this chapter—orthographic, isometric, cross-sectional, or others. The tools for sketching are simple. Pencil and paper can easily be used to capture and record an idea. Whether it is in an engineer's logbook or elsewhere, the purpose of a sketch is to document and communicate an idea.

Fig. 4.1 Sketches Engineers capture and refine their ideas using sketches. *How do sketches help an engineer work out the details of an idea?*

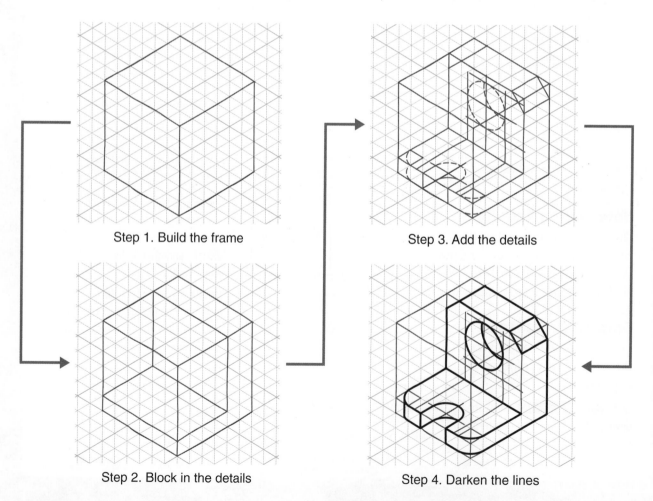

Step 1. Build the frame

Step 3. Add the details

Step 2. Block in the details

Step 4. Darken the lines

essentials

Virtual Lab: Computer-Aided Design (CAD)

The ability to use various tools to express visual representations of ideas and solutions is a valuable skill for engineers. Sketching, drawing, and using computer-aided design (CAD) software are just a few of the techniques engineers use daily. Computer-aided design allows people to share ideas and solutions. It also makes it possible to work out any potential design problems well before construction or production begins. Mastering the skill of using CAD helps engineers design solutions successfully.

View Go to your ✎ essentials ONLINE to view the *Virtual Lab: Computer-Aided Design (CAD)*.

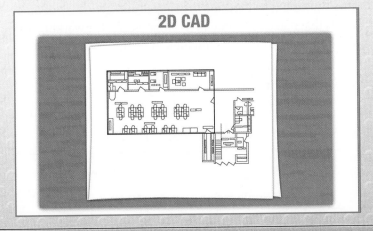

2D CAD

PROJECT CONNECTIONS

As you brainstorm ideas for your sorting mechanism, be sure to sketch important details about the size and function of the device. As you practice sketching your ideas, see if others can understand your ideas based solely on a sketch that you show to them.

Drawing Tools and Standards

Engineers often use traditional drawing tools to draft their designs. The process of traditional drafting involves a drawing table or surface with a straight edge, a T-square and triangles (or drafting machine) for drawing straight lines, compasses or templates for drawing circles and arcs, pencils and pens, and a good quality paper such as vellum.

Today, engineers and draftspersons often use computer software to draw the details of their designs. **Computer-aided design (CAD)** software can be used to develop designs in two or three dimensions. Use of this software allows for easy updates if changes need to be made in a design.

Regardless of the drawing tools used, certain conventions are common to engineering drawings. These consistent features and methods lead to better understanding and less confusion on the part of the people who need to interpret the drawings. There are even standard sizes of paper for engineering drawings. (See **Figure 4.2** on page 72.)

Lettering in engineering drawings is almost always in capital letters. In addition, many other standards, abbreviations, and symbols (most of which are unique to certain fields of engineering) may be included in an engineering drawing.

✓ **Reading Check** **Identify** an engineer's goal when creating a sketch.

Formal engineering drawings are always drawn or printed to scale. Scale means that the ratio of the object in reality is drawn or printed on paper in proportion to its actual size. (See **Figure 4.3**.) Full scale means that one inch (or other unit of measure) on paper is equal to one inch in reality. If an object is much larger or smaller than the paper on which it is being drawn, the object would be drawn or printed to a specific scale.

Working Drawings

A working drawing includes the complete plans for an engineered product. It is generally prepared before a prototype is produced or an item is first manufactured. Drafting is the process that is used to prepare working drawings of a product.

Again, formal conventions, or agreed-upon standards, are typically used to prepare engineering drawings. The overarching purpose of a working drawing is to describe the shapes and geometry of an object or objects that make up a system. In other words, the working drawing should look like the object would look in reality.

Fig. 4.2 Drawing Paper Sizes
This chart lists standard U.S. drawing paper sizes.

U.S. Customary Drawing Paper Sizes

A	B	C	D	E
8.5" × 11"	11" × 17"	17" × 22"	22" × 34"	34" × 44"

Fig. 4.3 Drawing Scales This chart shows common engineering drawing scales.

Engineering Drawing Scales

	Type of Scale	Enlarged scale	Size as	Reduced scales
Inch Scales	**Decimal Inch**	100:2	1:1	1:2
		4:1		1:3
		2:1		1:4
	Fractional Inch		1:1	1:2
				1:4
				3:4
	Civil Engineer's Scale		1:1	1:20
				1:30
				1:40
				1:50
				1:60
Foot Scales			1:1	$\frac{1}{8}$" = 1 foot
				$\frac{1}{4}$" = 1 foot
				1" = 1 foot
				3" = 1 foot
Metric Scale (Millimeters)		100:1	1:1	1:2
		50:1		1:5
		20:1		1:10
		10:1		1:20
		5:1		1:50
		2:1		1:100

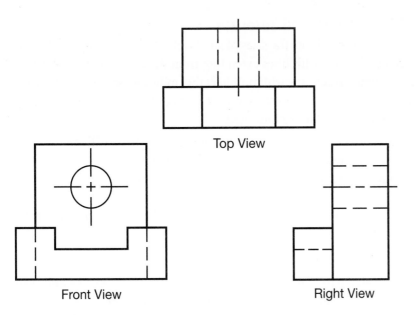

Top View

Front View Right View

Orthographic Projection

An **orthographic** projection, sometimes called a multi-view projection, is a type of drawing that depicts an object in a two-dimensional way. Generally, at least three aligned views of an object's front, top, and right sides are enough to show its geometry. (See **Figure 4.4**.) However, sometimes auxiliary, or extra, views of an object are needed to show all of its detail. In addition, a cross-section, or sectional view, may also add required detail. In some cases, the term "plan view" is used to describe the top view of a product, while the term "elevation" is used to describe a side view.

Line Styles and Types

Several different types of lines depict various aspects of a design. In general, the visible edge of an object is drawn with a solid dark line, referred to in drafting as a visible line. Hidden lines are evenly dashed lines that indicate spaces or voids in an object. Center lines are alternating long- and short-dashed lines that indicate the center of a symmetrical or round object. (See **Figure 4.5**.)

Fig. 4.5 Line Styles These different types of lines have different purposes in engineering drawings. *How are center lines represented?*

Hidden line	Center line	Symmetry line	Extension and dimension lines
Thin	Thin Alternate Line and Short Dashes	Center Line Thick Short Line	Thin Dimension Line Extension Line
Leaders	**Break lines**	**Cutting-plane line**	**Visible line**
Arrow Dot Thin	Long Break Thin Short Break Thick	Thick or	Thick
			Stitch line
			Thin or Small Dots
Section lines	**Viewing-plane line**	**Phantom lines**	**Chain line**
Thin Lines	Thick or	Thin	Thick

Dimensions and Tolerances

Dimensions indicate the sizes of an object and its various parts. This is generally done with lines extending from the object (extension lines) and a dimension line with numbers that indicate the distance between the extension lines. Arrows at both ends of the dimension line show what distance is being indicated.

Tolerances in an engineering drawing are indicated with a ± next to the dimension. Tolerance is how much an actual measurement can vary from the design dimension without affecting the product's performance. This is also known as an acceptable margin of error. Precision to the exact dimension is not always possible in the manufacturing of the object.

Materials and Finishes

The material from which an object is to be made should also be indicated clearly in an engineering drawing. This is very important information, as there are so many different types of materials available for the production of an object. There are thousands of different metal alloys (substances made up of more than one metal), many different types of plastics, and numerous other materials that could be specified for a design.

Engineering drawings also indicate finishes. Before production, engineers may specify paints, treatments, and manufacturing techniques that will be used to finish an object. These specifications need to be represented in the drawings of that object. In cases of a very complex drawing or series of drawings, a separate schedule may be used to specify materials and finishes. In this case, a letter, number, or symbol on the drawing would indicate the type of material or finish. The

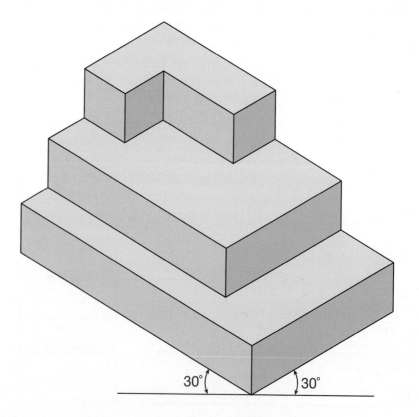

Fig. 4.6 Isometric Drawing An isometric drawing is one way to represent three dimensions of an object. *How many sides are visible in an isometric drawing?*

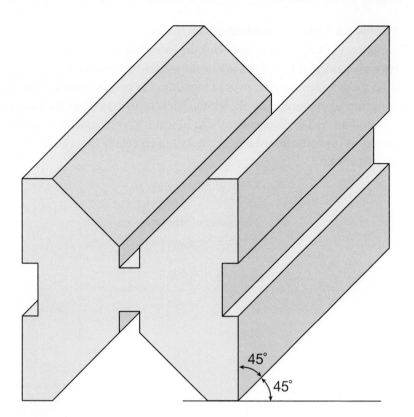

Fig. 4.7 Oblique Drawing Oblique drawings are another method of representing a three-dimensional object in two dimensions. *What are some objects that lend themselves to being drawn in this way?*

45°

45°

person manufacturing the item then refers to the appropriate schedule to find out what type of finish is needed.

Pictorial Drawings

Orthographic drawings are two-dimensional. For this reason, a pictorial drawing is sometimes used to show a more three-dimensional appearance of an object. Some of the various types of pictorial style drawings are isometric, oblique, and perspective drawings.

Isometric One of the most common types of pictorial drawings is an **isometric** drawing. In an isometric drawing, one corner of an object is drawn with two sides emerging from that corner at 30-degree angles from horizontal. In this way, the width and depth are shown equally and to the same scale as the height, making it an ideal projection for many engineering purposes. The top of the object is also visible. (See **Figure 4.6**.)

Oblique An oblique drawing shows a complete side of an object square with only one side drawn, usually to the right and at a 45-degree angle. The top of the object is also visible in this type of drawing. This projection is easier for many people to master than some other drawing projections used by engineers.

Oblique drawings, however, are not the most realistic looking three-dimensional drawings. This is because they utilize "forced depth" or "foreshortening"; that is, the front of the object in an oblique drawing is a standard two-dimensional drawing that faces the person viewing the image, while one side and the top of the object are drawn at an angle and with less depth (to simulate a three-dimensional view). In most oblique drawings, the side with the greatest detail or complexity is shown facing the viewer. (See **Figure 4.7**.)

essentials

e

STEM CONNECTION

Describe and Draw As engineers design, they often have to present various depictions of their model. One way to do this is to create an orthographic sketch of the item in question. These sketches will show three views of the item. Most often, these views depict the front, top, and right sides of the item. However, the engineer should produce the views that provide the most detailed information about the item.

Personal Tutor

To see examples of various views of an object, go to your *essentials* ONLINE to view the *Personal Tutor: Describe and Draw.*

After you have completed detailed working drawings for your project, create an exploded view diagram of how all of the component parts of your design should fit together. Use this diagram to help explain to the other students and your teacher how the component parts of your project will work together as a complete system.

Exploded View An exploded view, or assembly type, drawing is a variation of (and is often based on) the isometric or oblique style. This type of drawing is usually made to show how the component pieces of a device or system are meant to fit together. These types of drawings are common in consumer applications, such as instructions for how to assemble an item or disassemble the product in order to repair it. Exploded view drawings are also used in engineering, especially for presentations. (See **Figure 4.8**.)

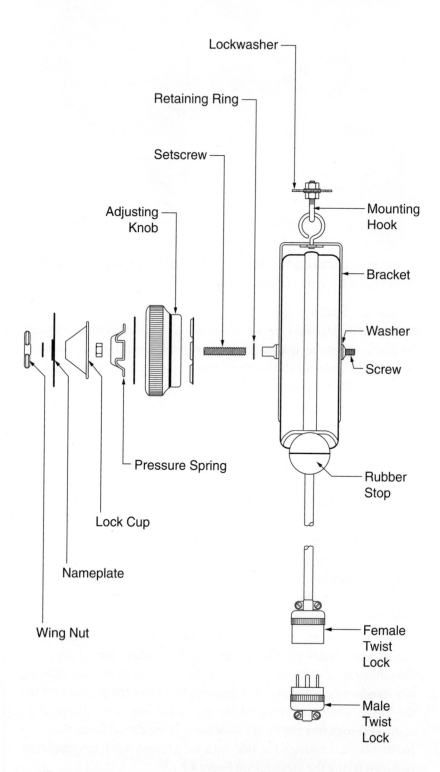

Fig. 4.8 Exploded View Drawing
Exploded view drawings show all of the components of an object. *Why are they used for assembly instructions?*

Perspective Though less common in the field of engineering, the perspective drawing is a type of pictorial drawing that shows an object in a realistic, three-dimensional fashion. A one-, two-, or three-point perspective drawing uses vanishing points to create a view of an object that is somewhat more realistic to the human eye. A **rendering** (visual depiction) may be used in engineering to display an object, device, or product in color and/or with other more realistic detail, such as materials and finishes. (See **Figure 4.9**.)

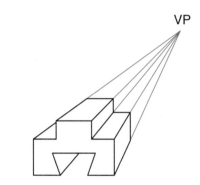

VP

(a) Parallel—One Vanishing Point

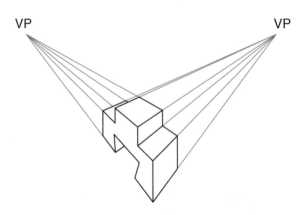

VP   VP

(b) Angular—Two Vanishing Points

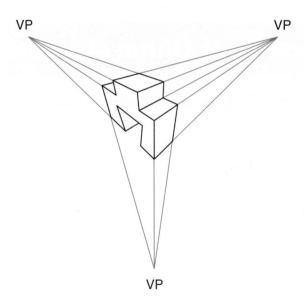

VP   VP

VP

(c) Oblique—Three Vanishing Points

Fig. 4.9 Perspective Drawing
There are several types of perspective drawings. *Which part of this figure shows one-point perspective?*

Patent Drawings

When applying for a patent for a device, certain types of drawings need to be included to substantiate the claims made on the patent application. Specific types and sizes of paper are required, as is the use of black ink. There are also special requirements for scale, shading, symbols, and other drawing conventions. The United States Patent and Trademark Office publishes guidelines and requirements for patent drawings in the United States. (See **Figure 4.10**.)

Fig. 4.10 Patent drawings must meet the unique guidelines of the United States Patent and Trademark Office. *What purpose do these standardized guidelines serve?*

SECTION 4.1

Check Your Understanding

After You Read Perform the following tasks.

1. **Identify** the elements that make up a useful engineering sketch.

2. **Discuss** why it is important to be able to render a three-dimensional design in a two-dimensional format.

3. **Explain** how an engineer's personal characteristics, such as creativity and resourcefulness, might impact his or her designs.

Theoretical Models

As computing technology has advanced, so has the use of mathematical, computer, and other theoretical models in engineering. CAD and other computer software applications have provided engineers with the tools needed to enhance and optimize their designs. This speeds up the process from design to manufacture.

Optimization

Models and simulations allow the engineer to **optimize** (make as effective as possible) his or her designs. Optimization can lead to savings in time and cost of a project in the long term. Even minor adjustments made to a design in an effort to optimize it or improve its performance can produce large savings. In bridge design, for instance, civil engineers seek to use the optimized types and amounts of materials to reduce the cost of materials and the amount of time needed to construct the bridge.

Virtual Lab: Modeling

Mathematical models and physical models are two different types of modeling procedures available to engineers. Mathematical models typically use computer software to generate a theoretical model. Engineers use these models to predict future trends, costs, and other factors. A physical model is a real world model, often built to scale. It allows the design to become something that can be observed, analyzed, touched, and used. Physical models are realistic, materials-based representations of ideas and solutions.

View Go to your *essentials* ONLINE to view the *Virtual Lab: Modeling.*

Mathematical Models

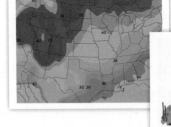

Fig. 4.11 Animation This screen shot is from a computer-generated animation of an auto accident. *What is another event that can be analyzed or predicted using this technology?*

PROJECT CONNECTIONS

Use "found" materials such as scrap paper and cardboard to create a mockup of the design that you have developed for your sorting mechanism project. After you have finished, make notes about needed or suggested changes to the design based on the spatial relationships in your mockup.

Computer Simulations

Computer simulations are types of mathematical analysis that are used in place of physical models and prototypes. They can speed up the process of design, since actual objects do not need to be fabricated. They can also reduce the cost of a project, as these analyses require a minimum of materials and personnel.

Simulations are often used in engineering, especially in the design of very complex systems. They are used to analyze the conductive, structural, electromagnetic, and other behaviors of objects and systems.

Simulations are especially important in the modeling and design of safety systems, since the conditions for an anticipated safety concern cannot always be matched in reality. For example, a building designed to withstand the effects of an earthquake or a fire must rely on simulated conditions for analysis of the design. The results of computer simulations are analyzed in great detail so that the design can be further optimized.

Today, many CAD software packages include tools that can be used for the analysis and optimization of a product while still in the design phase.

Animations Animations are one type of computer simulation used in engineering. The Finite Element Method (FEM) is a type of mathematical and computer analysis that is used in product design. For example, FEM can be used to predict how a car will deform in a crash. This method explores various material properties and can be used to optimize the weight, material, and cost of a product. Although FEM generally refers to the mathematics behind this type of analysis, its output can be used to generate an animation of the results. The use of animation for visualization has dramatically improved the efficiency of the design process in many industries. (See **Figure 4.11**.)

Mathematical Models

A mathematical model is a mathematical representation of all aspects of a system. This type of theoretical model can be used to predict such things as consumer behavior, population growth, and features of engineered products.

A mathematical model can be used for analysis or estimation. For example, if the amount of stress applied to concrete by a vehicle crossing over a bridge is known, a mathematical model can be used to estimate the lifespan of that bridge. Other factors, such as weather, make the analysis more complex, so a more sophisticated model is necessary to complete the analysis and optimize the design.

When using a computer simulation or a mathematical model for design purposes, engineers enter parameters and variables into formulas or software. They use simpler mathematical formulas to determine specific aspects of their designs. Strength of materials, applied mechanics, thermodynamics, electricity, and simple machines all have associated mathematical formulas that engineers utilize.

One mathematical model that is applied in engineering is Fourier analysis. This model is widely used in electronics and communications to help analyze and describe waveforms in electrical and optical signals. It is used to analyze and optimize signals in communications applications.

Physical Models

In addition to theoretical, computer, and mathematical models, physical models of a design can aid in analysis and optimization. Various types of physical models, such as mockups, form study models, rapid prototypes, and full-scale prototypes, are used when designing a product.

Mockups

A scale model that is used for the very early evaluation of a design is usually referred to as a **mockup**, which is a physical representation of a product. This is the most basic form of physical modeling used in most design processes. Engineers may use simple materials such as paper, cardboard, and even "found" materials to assemble the mockup quickly, This type of model can help show physical relationships between the various parts of a design.

The term mockup is now also used in some situations to refer to "digital mockups," which are actually computer simulations of objects in the design process (as described earlier in this section).

Reading Check **Identify** some strengths of theoretical models.

essentials

STEM CONNECTION

Determine the Scale

When physical models are used in the initial design of an item, the engineer must determine what scale is most appropriate for this model. Models are often created to save money and/or increase safety during the testing phase of the engineering design process. Engineers must identify the constraints for building and testing the model when they are determining the scale.

Personal Tutor

To see an example of determining the scale of a model, go to your **essentials** ONLINE and view the *Personal Tutor: Determine the Scale.*

Form Study Models

A form study model is a scale model of a design that is usually of better quality and materials than a mockup. The purpose of this type of model is to help the designer get a better sense of the look, feel, size, and proportions of his or her design. A form study model might not use the same materials as those that will be used in manufacturing. It would also not necessarily simulate the actual function of the product. (See **Figure 4.12**.)

Rapid Prototyping

Rapid prototyping is the development of models and prototypes by using a CAD system to develop the design, and a 3D printer to construct a three-dimensional physical model of the design. 3D solid modeling usually refers to a three-dimensional object within CAD software. However, it can also be used to describe a physical model made via rapid prototyping.

Three-dimensional printing, or 3DP, is an overarching term used to describe how a machine can build a physical model. This is done using additive layers of plaster, corn starch, resin, or other material. 3DP parts may be used as functional parts in a working model or prototype if they are made from the appropriate materials. They may also be used for the actual manufacturing of a product if only a few units of the item are needed. (See **Figure 4.13**.)

Fig. 4.12 Form Study Model
This scale model represents a larger object. *How does a form study model differ from a mockup?*

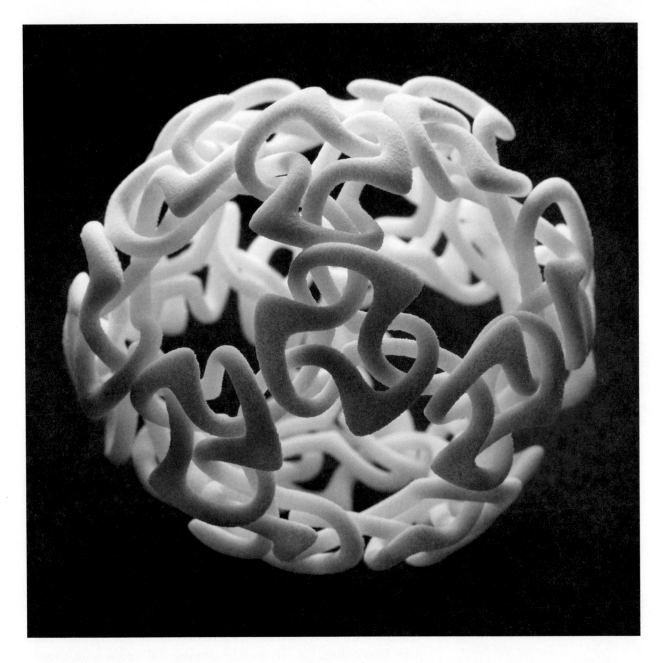

Fig. 4.13 Three-Dimensional Printing This object was created using three-dimensional printing. *What are some advantages of this type of printing for engineers?*

There are many different methods used in 3DP. The means and materials used for their outputted models vary a great deal. It should also be noted that the word rapid in the case of rapid prototyping is a relative term—many of these methods may need several hours or even days to build the object. Most of the processes are additive, meaning that material is added to build up the object physically.

Selective Laser Sintering Selective Laser Sintering (SLS) is an additive process that uses a laser to fuse a powdered substance together. The powdered substance in SLS may be a plastic such as nylon or polystyrene, a metal such as steel or other alloy, or a ceramic material such as glass or sand. The main advantage of SLS is its ability to produce strong, usable parts. One disadvantage is that it can take a very long time for the parts to cool down from the process.

Fused Deposition Modeling In the Fused Deposition Modeling (FDM) process, a plastic or metal filament from a spool is fed through

Fig. 4.14 Appearance Model This model shows the appearance of a planned bridge. *To what people or organizations might such a model be presented?*

a nozzle, which melts and deposits the material to build the part. This additive process most often uses plastic material such as ABS plastic resin or polycarbonate, but can also use some metals or even waxes. The main advantage of FDM is that it can be used to prototype quality plastic parts for special functional applications. A disadvantage is that the parts it produces may have a slightly bumpy appearance, depending on the way the part is constructed.

Stereolithography Stereolithography (SLA) uses a liquid resin and an ultraviolet laser to construct parts. Exposure to the UV laser "cures," or solidifies, a pattern traced on the resin material one layer at a time. After laser curing, the part must be cleaned of all excess resin, usually in a chemical bath. While SLA produces parts that are strong enough to be machined and used as patterns for other processes such as casting, the process has some limitations. The cost of its machines and resins make it expensive.

Laminated Object Manufacturing In Laminated Object Manufacturing (LOM), a plotter-type device uses a knife or a laser to cut cross-sections of thin paper, plastic, or metal. An adhesive is then used to glue the sections together to build up to the total thickness of the part. The LOM process can be done for a much lower cost than that of stereolithography, especially if it uses paper. However, a large amount of waste is produced. This process can also be used to develop larger parts, although those parts may have a lower degree of accuracy when compared to other 3DP processes.

Electron Beam Melting Similar to the SLS process, Electron Beam Melting (EBM) uses an electron beam to melt powdered material to

✓ **Reading Check** **Compare and contrast** a prototype and a model.

build up a part. This process is used only for metals and, in industry, is most often used to build high-quality titanium-alloy parts. The resulting parts are extremely dense and free of voids, and are therefore very strong. The equipment required for this process, however, is extremely expensive.

Appearance Models

Used primarily in fields such as industrial design and architecture, an appearance model can be used to study the intended color, finish, and other aspects of an engineered product. The main purposes of this type of model are promotion and demonstration; for that reason, it is usually a model of high quality and detail. For example, a civil engineer might create an appearance model so that the design can be presented to stakeholders in advance of construction. The intention is to provide a way for others to get an idea of how the product will eventually appear. (See **Figure 4.14**.)

Prototypes

The rapid prototyping methods discussed in this chapter are often used to produce simple models rather than prototypes. The definition of a prototype is the first full-scale working version of an item. However, if a model has at least some functionality, it may be called a prototype.

At the full-scale prototyping stage of design development, the engineer attempts to manufacture the first of a product using all of the intended materials and manufacturing processes that will be necessary in production. Again, for a device to be called a prototype, it must be a functional product.

A full-scale prototype is used to test the product's design against all the criteria and constraints that were set forth in a project. Sometimes several generations of prototypes may be developed as solutions to a design problem. Each prototype is systematically tested and evaluated. The results are used to inform the redesign and reimplementation of the next prototype and eventually the full-scale production of the product.

Essentials

Visualization

3D Modeling Three-dimensional modeling software is becoming more prevalent in the world of engineering design, thanks to faster computers and better software. 2D multiview drawings made using the techniques of orthographic projection can be automatically extracted from the 3D models and used to make production drawings. To create these 3D models, you need to be able to visualize what the object looks like from all sides and to break it down mentally into its basic components.

Group Workspace

Pay careful attention to the order of operations when sketching composite shapes. Describe how the order of operations affects the sketch of a composite shape.

Go to your **essentials** ONLINE to learn more about developing your 3D modeling.

Check Your Understanding

SECTION **4.2**

After You Read Perform the following tasks.

1. **Identify** which type of model is easiest to revise or update.

2. **Examine** how cost affects an engineer's choice of modeling method.

3. **Assess** how prototypes help engineers critique and adjust their designs.

Review and Assessment

Problem-Solving Process

Identify

In response to the development of smaller, more powerful personal computing devices, an established electronics company wants to develop a tablet computer that will appeal to high school and college students. Your team is to design a mockup of the product for the executive board's production approval. Below are the main design criteria.

- A 9.5″ screen.
- Several input ports, such as USB, FireWire, and memory card.
- Several output ports, such as VGA, HDMI, and mini-stereo.
- Ergonomic design.

Set Up

1. Research the project. Ask: *"What activities will the user be performing?"* and *"In what settings will the computer be used?"*
2. Investigate the features of existing tablet computers to help identify what innovations are needed.
3. Brainstorm potential solutions. Develop sketches of how you want the product to look. Identify possible materials and finishes.
4. Choose the best solution, using criteria and constraints as guides.

Execute

5. Determine modeling materials that can be used, as well as the best type of model to convey the fit and finish of the product.
6. Keep sketching and recording ideas to improve your design.
7. Prepare models of the solution, using a combination of drawings, renderings, and models to convey your overall design.
8. Meet with your team regularly to discuss product development. Outline important features and discuss potential drawbacks.

Evaluate

Present your drawings and model to a group of potential users. Ask them to critique the features, feel, and finish of your design.

Share

Create a multimedia presentation about the product. Include information about the problem that you solved as well as the criteria and constraints involved. Include the drawings, renderings, and models that you produced, as well as feedback from the potential user group.

Critical Thinking

Key Concepts

1. **Identify** the methods and processes that engineers use to create and model their designs.

2. **Summarize** the various standards and perspectives used in engineering sketches and drawings. Name the advantages of different perspectives.

3. **Compare and Contrast** the various methods of creating three-dimensional models. Consider different situations for which each method would be appropriate.

4. **Evaluate** the different types of theoretical models and the uses of each.

5. **Analyze** the advantages of prototypes and the situations in which they are more appropriate than models.

Listening

21st Century Skills

6. **Compare** ideas about how the sketching, design, modeling, and prototyping processes can help engineers make improvements to their designs.

7. **Collaborate** with your classmates to discuss how a design's constraints and its criteria can sometimes compete with one another. Allow each classmate to suggest at least one constraint that may be encountered.

Activity Center

Go to the **Activity Center** to review chapter vocabulary and key concepts.

Engineer's Toolbox

Go to the **Engineer's Toolbox** to:
- Access Academic Activities
- Access the Competitive Event Prep Activity

DISCOVERY PROJECT

Designing a Sorting Device

Waste-management companies must sort a wide variety of recycled materials before processing them for future reuse. In this project, you will design and build a device that will sort three types of objects (plastic bottle caps, used nine-volt batteries, and metal washers) for recycling. In the process, you will use the sketching, drawing, and modeling techniques used by engineers to create and refine ideas for new devices.

Go to your *essentials* ONLINE to collaborate with your team on this Discovery Project.

Systems and Systems Thinking

How do engineers think about systems?

Engineering uses technology to build the systems that meet our needs. Over time, engineered systems and the problems they seek to solve have become more complex. That is why it is important to understand systems concepts. A system is a collection of parts working together for a common goal. The parts of a system work with each other, and the way they interact determines how the system behaves. Often a system is actually a collection of systems working together. The systems that are part of larger systems are called subsystems.

e ssentials

DISCOVERY PROJECT

Go to your *e ssentials* ONLINE to view the Chapter 5 Discovery Project Launcher Video to learn about the challenges of improving an existing system.

Identify and Improve an Existing Safety or Security System

21st Century Skills — **Explain why it is important to gather information from those who use a system before trying to improve it.**

Systems are made of components and subsystems that work together. Improving systems that work with existing systems like the bridge project in the video presents added challenges. Your school is a system that has other systems within it. Identify a safety or security system within your school that can be improved. Select a system that applies to a classroom, lab, or the entire school. Create a physical or computer model of the improved system. Demonstrate how it is an improvement over the original system.

Group Workspace

Summarize some ideas about the importance of understanding the area over which this bridge spans.

Engineer's Toolbox

Go to the Engineer's Toolbox to
- Access Note-Taking Activities
- Access Graphic Organizers
- Access Academic Standards met by this chapter

READING GUIDE

Before You Read Engineering often involves creating systems or series of systems to solve problems. What are some engineered systems you encounter every day? Why are engineers encouraged to use systems thinking?

Objectives

- **Identify** natural, human-made, and engineered systems.
- **Explain** the difference between open- and closed-loop systems.
- **List** the common elements of the universal systems model.
- **Apply** the universal systems model to engineered systems.
- **Discuss** the elements of systems thinking.
- **Discuss** the challenges of developing new systems to work with existing systems.

Vocabulary

Content Vocabulary

- LED (light-emitting diode)
- reflector
- circuit
- current
- voltage
- universal systems model
- feedback
- open-loop system
- closed-loop system
- subsystem
- emissions
- propulsion

Academic Vocabulary

- interact
- elements
- input
- output
- diversity
- aids

Note-Taking Activity

Draw this table for each section. Write key terms and phrases under **Cues**. Write main ideas under **Note Taking**. Summarize the section under **Summary**.

Cues	Note Taking
•	•
•	•
Summary	

Graphic Organizers

Use graphic organizers to organize information as you read.

Go to your **essentials ONLINE** for downloadable graphic organizers.

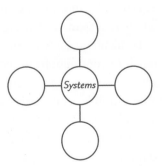

ACADEMIC

Technology

ITEEA STL2.3 The stability of a technological system is influenced by all of the components in the system, especially those in the feedback loop.

ITEEA STL2.10 Complex systems have many layers of controls and feedback loops to provide information.

Mathematics

NCTM Problem Solving Solve problems that arise in mathematics and in other contexts.

Science

NSES 1 Students should develop an understanding of science unifying concepts and processes; systems, order, and organization; evidence, models, and explanation; change, constancy, and measurement; evolution and equilibrium; and form and function.

ITEEA *International Technology and Engineering Educators Association*
NCTM *National Council of Teachers of Mathematics*
NSES *National Science Education Standards*

College & Career READINESS

Writing Arguments to support claims in an analysis of substantive topics or texts, using valid reasoning and relevant and sufficient evidence.

Systems

Structure

Systems can be large and complex, such as the air traffic control system that monitors and directs the flights of thousands of airliners around the globe. An automobile is a complex system that is assembled from thousands of parts that must interact with others. A washing machine is not complex, but it includes a number of systems and subsystems. Can you name some of them? An **LED** (light-emitting diode) flashlight is an example of a small system that uses an LED, which is a semiconductor that glows when electric current passes through it. Systems built into the flashlight include the LED, power source, switch, lens, a **reflector,** or curved metal or plastic that reflects light, and a **circuit,** or series of electronic components, to regulate **current** (flow of electricity)and **voltage** (rate at which electricity is drawn). Despite variations in size and complexity, however, all systems have common characteristics.

Interconnectivity

Every system has its own purpose. Think about your cell phone. Its primary function is to help you communicate with friends and family. A basic cell phone is made from electronic components and other parts that work together to allow it to send and receive calls and text messages. There are also more advanced phones that can be used for many other applications. Your cell phone is a system that is part of a larger system. The larger system includes the company that provides your service, towers, and access to satellite systems, as well as the larger national or international wireless network system.

All parts of a system must be present for the system to work properly. For example, if you remove the battery from your cell phone, it will not work until the battery is replaced. Similarly, the parts of system must be arranged in a specific way. Your cell phone may be designed so that there is only one way to install the battery, but that is not always true. Have you ever placed the batteries in an electronic device incorrectly? What did you do to get the device (the system) to work?

Systems have boundaries, but an element in one system is often also part of another system. Systems that seem to be separate can affect one another. Think about a city where a large percentage of the workers use mass transit to commute from the suburbs. If a strike shuts down the train system, thousands of additional people may choose to travel to work by automobile. The increased highway traffic may create congestion that will cause more people to arrive late for work and also be delayed in returning home at the end of the day. The mass transit system and highway system are not really separate. They are each a part of a greater transportation system. **Figure 5.1** shows a diagram of a typical system and its boundaries. Each loop represents a boundary.

PROJECT CONNECTIONS

Make a chart that identifies the expected, desirable, and undesirable outputs of the system you are working on. Also try to anticipate any unexpected and desirable outputs that may result from your plan.

✓ **Reading Check** **List** some of the elements of your local transportation system.

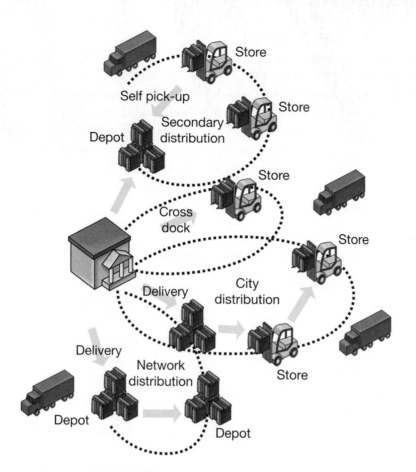

Fig. 5.1 Distribution System Note the boundaries indicated by dotted lines on this diagram of a system. *What are the boundaries of the system you are developing for your chapter Discovery Project?*

Kinds of Systems

Natural Systems

Some systems are natural. The solar system is a natural system composed of the sun, planets, natural satellites (moons), stars, asteroids, meteoroids, and comets arranged in a certain way. Other natural systems are biological. There are many different kinds of biological systems. For example, a coral reef is part of the marine ecosystem that includes the ocean and all the plant and animal life it contains. The human body is a complex biological system that is sustained by other systems, such as the circulatory system, respiratory system, digestive system, skeletal system, nervous system, and reproductive system. Each system in the human body is necessary and must work properly in order for us to be healthy.

Human-Made Systems

There are many kinds of human-made systems. Schools such as the one you attend are usually part of larger organizations referred to as school systems. School systems are made up of buildings, teachers, administrators, students, classroom supplies, buses, and much more. School systems use all those resources to achieve the goal of educating the school-aged residents of the community. Government systems exist at the local, state, and federal levels. They work together to provide services that the public needs. Within the government there are additional systems designed to meet the needs of specific groups such as senior citizens and children. Although these systems are not usually designed by engineers, they are similar to engineered systems.

essentials

STEM CONNECTION

Use Venn Diagrams

Graphic organizers such as Venn diagrams are used to display relationships between different things. Venn diagrams can be used to organize quantitative or qualitative information, showing similarities and differences within the diagram.

 Personal Tutor

View

Go to your *essentials* ONLINE to view the *Personal Tutor: Use Venn Diagrams.*

PROJECT CONNECTIONS

Identify some of the systems that help to ensure the safety of students and others at your school.

Reading Check **List** some of the systems that make up a traffic control system that would improve safety at an intersection near your school.

Engineered Systems

The task of designing engineered systems begins with identifying a need or opportunity. For example, suppose a growing community finds that there have been frequent collisions at certain intersections. What need is indicated and what kinds of systems might assist in meeting the need? Engineered systems deliver services such as traffic control, cable television, telephone, and the Internet. Engineered systems create the dozens of manufactured products that we use every day. A process such as a new way of reducing emissions from a coal-fired power plant is also an engineered system.

The Universal Systems Model

The **universal systems model** can be used to describe how any system works. It can be applied to all systems: large or small, simple or complex, and natural or human made. According to the universal systems model, all systems have a common set of elements: a need, input, process, output and **feedback**, or an evaluation of the results or output of a system or process. The elements are described below and illustrated in **Figure 5.2**.

- **Input** – What you want the system to do, and the resources that are put into the system
- **Process** – The action part of the system, where resources interact or are combined
- **Output** – The result of the system once the process has been completed
- **Feedback** – Information about the input, process, or output, which is used to adjust the system

Fig. 5.2: Universal Systems Model
The universal systems model can be used to analyze any system. *How can you apply the universal systems model to the work you are doing to develop your chapter Discovery Project?*

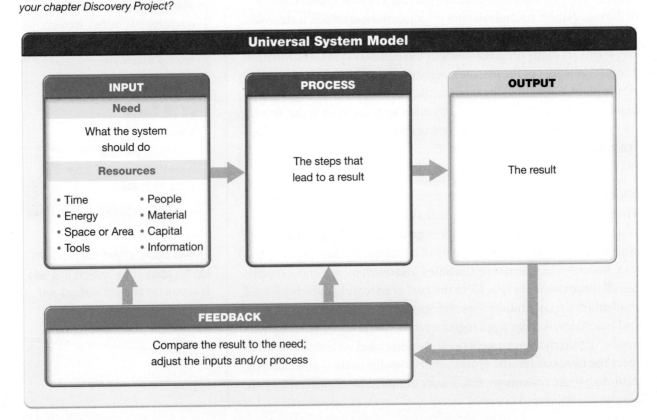

Universal System Model

INPUT	PROCESS	OUTPUT
Need		
What the system should do	The steps that lead to a result	The result
Resources		
• Time • People • Energy • Material • Space or Area • Capital • Tools • Information		

FEEDBACK
Compare the result to the need; adjust the inputs and/or process

Open- and Closed-Loop Systems

Some systems have no way of adjusting to changing conditions. For example, suppose you have a basic clothes dryer and want to dry a shirt that was just washed. You place the shirt in the dryer, select the high temperature setting, and set the timer for 60 minutes. After 60 minutes a bell signals the end of the cycle. You remove the shirt and notice that it is very hot and has shrunk until it is about the right size for your younger sister. The dryer did not know that the shirt was being over-dried. This kind of system is called an **open-loop system**. Open-loop systems do not respond to changing conditions. This can be a serious limitation.

A more advanced dryer will allow you to select how dry you want your clothes to be. A built-in sensor compares the moisture level of the clothing to the setting selected and turns the dryer off at the right time. This kind of system is called a **closed-loop system**. Closed-loop systems are able to adjust for changing conditions. Many engineered systems utilize sensors to monitor how the system is working and use that information to adjust the process through feedback, which compares the system output to the desired goal.

Fig. 5.3 Landfill Outputs This landfill produces both intended and unintended outputs. *Predict some intended and unintended outputs from your chapter Discovery Project.*

PROJECT CONNECTIONS

List three systems that are a part of your overall school and three that are specific to a lab. Determine whether they are open-loop or closed-loop systems.

Reading Check **Explain** how engineers use the universal systems model in their work on systems that involve energy.

Applying the Universal Systems Model

Below are examples of how the universal systems model can be applied to three different kinds of engineered systems. **Figure 5.4** is a systems diagram of a hotel reservation system.

Information System: Internet Hotel Reservation System

- **Input** – The goal is to keep the hotel fully occupied, and the input is travel requests from potential customers.
- **Process** – Data management
- **Output** – Reservations
- **Feedback** – Customers receive an emailed survey asking them to describe how they felt about their recent stay. An example of multiple system outputs is shown in **Figure 5.4**.

Manufacturing System: Automobile Assembly Plant

- **Input** – The goal is to produce automobiles.
- **Process** – To assemble parts and paint the vehicle
- **Output** – An automobile
- **Feedback** – The vehicle is inspected and tested before it is shipped to the dealer. Customers let the dealer know if they are happy with their purchase.

Energy System: Electrical Generating Plant

- **Input** – The goal is to generate the electricity needed by customers and the input is fuel, such as coal, gas, or nuclear energy.
- **Process** – To use fuel to produce steam to operate turbines to turn generators.
- **Output** – Electricity for homes and businesses
- **Feedback** – Control systems monitor demand and adjust the amount of electricity produced.

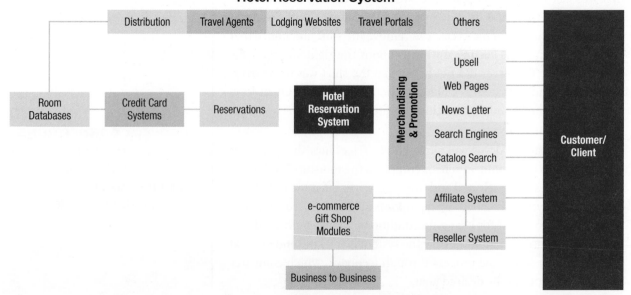

Hotel Reservation System

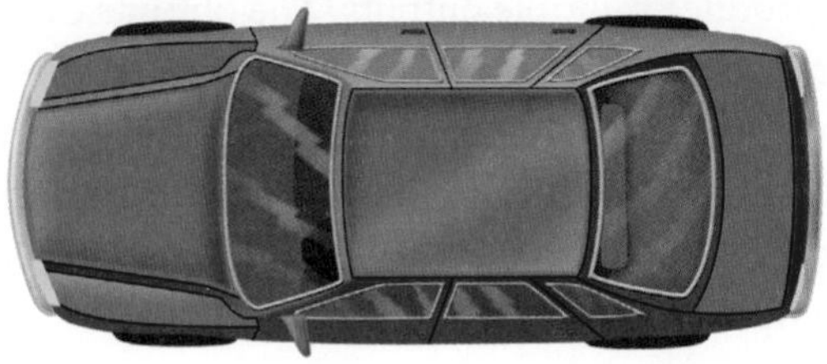

Internet access
GPS
Tire Pressure monitoring
Display systems
Rear-seat entertainment
DVD player
Park/reverse assist
Night vision and lane warning
Mobile phone
Audio system
Games console

Fig. 5.5 System of Systems This diagram shows a system of systems with each callout naming a system within the system of an automobile. *Identify a larger system of which the system you are building in your chapter Discovery Project could be a part. Where does your project fit into that larger system?*

Subsystems

A **subsystem** is a smaller system that is part of the larger system. Think back to the LED flashlight mentioned earlier in this chapter. Although it is a fairly simple product, it has several subsystems including:

- The battery as a power source
- The LED to provide the light
- A reflector to direct the light
- A lens to focus the light
- An on/off switch to control the overall system

Each of these components represents a necessary subsystem. In other words, if the battery is drained, the LED fails, the reflector is corroded, or the lens or switch is broken, the system will fail. If one of the subsystems is not working properly, the flashlight will not work as intended.

Complex systems are often systems of systems. Communication is an example of a system of systems that is important to daily life. The communication systems that we regularly use include:

- Telephones (wireless and land lines)
- Cable television
- Internet
- Radio
- Newspapers and magazines

Each of these is a system, and each is composed of subsystems. For example, publishing a newspaper or magazine requires subsystems to complete the tasks of writing, editing, printing, advertising, and distributing.

Each subsystem needs human and technical resources. **Figure 5.5** shows how an automobile includes many systems to result in the overall transportation experience. In addition to systems that ensure the vehicle's safe operation, such as the systems for steering, ignition, braking, etc., an automobile may also include additional convenience or comfort systems such as an audio system, GPS system, or video game system. Often, these systems will interact or communicate with each other. For instance, the lighting for an automobile dashboard display system will automatically turn on whenever the headlights are turned on.

essentials

Career Center

Environmental Engineer

Do social and cultural issues play a part in design and design standards? Should they? Do you think university studies should focus primarily on the technical aspects of design? If so, which standards should be pursued? The video discusses the "Living Building Challenge," its cost, implementation, relationship to green design standards, and ways of thinking about building design in terms of wants versus needs.

Go to your essentials ONLINE to learn more about the education, career paths, and future of an environmental engineer or urban planner.

System Outputs

Systems often produce multiple outputs. The outputs can be expected, unexpected, desirable, or undesirable. Automobiles provide a convenient means of transportation. That is an expected and desirable output. However, automobiles produce pollution, consume a finite supply of fuel, and are sometimes involved in collisions. These are all undesirable but expected outputs.

To address undesirable outputs, engineers for automotive companies continue to design systems that reduce **emissions** (gases discharged in the air) and increase passenger safety. Other outputs associated with automobiles are the creation of job opportunities for automobile repair technicians and work for replacement parts manufacturers. These outputs might be positive or negative, depending upon your perspective. For the auto repair technician this is a positive output, but for the automobile owner, this is more likely a negative output. Can you think of another unexpected and desirable output related to the automobile?

Currently about 50 percent of the electricity produced in the U.S. comes from coal-fired plants. The electricity produced is desirable, but other outputs such as emissions to the atmosphere and the need to dispose of the tons of ash they produce are undesirable. If a company located near the power plant gets government approval to make and sell a new concrete mix that uses large quantities of ash, and agrees to purchase a large percentage of the ash produced, that would be a desirable and unexpected output.

Figure 5.6 shows an electric power plant that uses biofuels rather than coal to generate electricity. Many electric utility companies are

Fig. 5.6 Power of Biofuels Electric utility companies are working to reduce emissions from their power plants by substituting biofuels for coal in their generators. *How can you reduce the negative impact of your chapter Discovery Project on the local environment?*

working to reduce emissions from their power plants by using biofuels in their generators.

Use of alternative energy sources is expanding beyond the use of biofuels. Wind turbines and photovoltaic arrays are used to create electricity without the pollution and ash created by coal-burning plants. Still there are undesirable outputs. For instance, an undesirable output of wind turbine power generation is noise pollution. Photovoltaic arrays are not perfect either, as large arrays in empty land would have an impact on the environment and ecosystems. Engineers working on these systems need to anticipate these outcomes, and consider them in the decision-making process for the project.

Reading Check **Outline** why engineers need to be aware of all potential system outputs when they are designing a new system.

*e*ssentials

Virtual Lab: Stability

Specific system components can influence a design's functionality and stability. To accomplish the goal of a system, all components must work together. Understanding and applying the concept of physical stability in potential solutions is an important factor in many designs.

View Go to your *e*ssentials ONLINE to view the *Virtual Lab: Stability.*

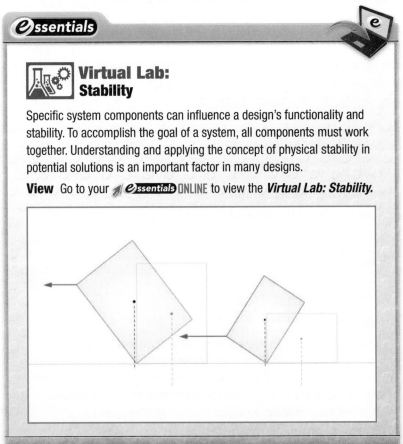

Check Your Understanding

After You Read Perform the following tasks.

1. **Identify** three types of systems.
2. **Describe** the universal systems model and explain how it can be used.
3. **Analyze** the outputs of the system that makes a lawnmower engine operate.

Systems Thinking and Applications

Systems Thinking

Systems thinking is a process used to solve complex problems. In traditional thinking we try to understand something by analyzing its parts. Systems thinking focuses on the system as a whole by studying relationships among its parts instead of the individual parts. The idea is to understand the system as whole. Systems thinking can be used to solve complex problems while considering long-term consequences of a system.

Elements of Systems Thinking

Key elements of the systems thinking process include

- Understanding the needs of stakeholders.
- Developing creative solutions.
- Considering how the system will perform in its life cycle.
- Considering how the subsystems will affect one other.
- Identifying tradeoffs—What are advantages and disadvantages?
- Managing risk—Planning to address what could go wrong.
- Assessing the impact of the overall system

Reading Check **Evaluate** how systems thinking helps engineers to solve complex problems.

essentials

Virtual Lab: Systems Thinking

Engineers consider the way a system will perform over its lifetime, its potential long- and short-term positive and negative effects, and how to manage challenges that may arise from the solution. They also consider the possibility that a solution may be worse than the original problem. Systems thinking allows engineers to solve complex problems.

View Go to your *essentials* ONLINE to view the *Virtual Lab: Systems Thinking.*

Systems Engineering

Systems engineering involves the application of systems knowledge and systems thinking. Most engineers working in the systems engineering field have a degree in one of the engineering disciplines described in Unit 2 of this book. Many systems engineers continue their studies at the graduate level. NASA employs systems engineers to lead various aspects of the space program. The Federal Aviation Administration is using systems engineers to plan the next generation of air traffic control systems. Mass-transit systems and aircraft manufacturers also employ large numbers of systems engineers.

Systems engineers need good communication and leadership skills to successfully coordinate the many activities required to build products such as a passenger airliner. Airliners require dozens of engineered systems including:

- **Structural** – the fuselage of the plane
- **Propulsion** – the engines that move the plane
- **Electronics** – to monitor and control all the major systems
- **Mechanical** – landing gear
- **Ergonomics** – to ensure that there is a good match between the systems and the pilots who operate them

Systems engineers working in the aviation industry do not need to be experts in all of these fields, but they do need to have the ability to understand how the aircraft works as a whole. They also need the ability to bring other engineers together to work as a team, to produce the best possible product. Systems engineering is a rapidly growing field with excellent career opportunities for people who enjoy developing creative solutions to complex problems. In **Figure 5.7**, systems engineers streamline the production of a new aircraft.

PROJECT CONNECTIONS

Select three elements of the systems-thinking process and describe how considering them will assist in the design of the safety system that your team is working on.

Fig. 5.7 Engineering Systems
Systems engineers streamline the production of a new aircraft. *List three ways in which systems engineering could help you to streamline the production of your chapter Discovery Project.*

Visualization

Graphing Data There is more to visualization in engineering than the geometric data represented through the sketches, 2D drawings, and 3D models we have discussed previously. Engineering also involves a lot of non-geometric technical data, and sometimes this information is more easily explained with the use of graphics than with just words and numbers.

Group Workspace

Create a flowchart describing how to complete steps in a task. Determine whether a scatter plot, single bar graph, or single-line graph best represents the data you have charted.

Go to your *e*ssentials ONLINE to learn more about developing your data graphs.

PROJECT CONNECTIONS

Think about the advantages and disadvantages of your school's current security or safety systems. Be prepared to explain how your system will improve the safety or security of your school or your classmates.

Reading Check **List** some common traits of effective systems engineers.

Systems Trends

As systems become increasingly complex and vital to our everyday lives, the need has developed to ensure the continued operation of these systems. Engineers who develop systems, therefore, must often build security into their designs. Engineers are also challenged to improve the efficiency and speed of their systems as they add to the functions and complexity.

Complexity

Systems will continue to become more complex. Digital electronics is one of the major technologies that has contributed to this growth in complexity. Around the year 2000, the typical automobile had one computer module. Today a similar vehicle has 30 computer modules that control the engine, steering, braking, navigation, and many other systems. Digital systems improve the operation of the vehicle, but add a level of complexity that makes diagnosing and correcting problems challenging. Today when a warning light indicates a problem with a system, the vehicle will likely require attention from a technician who will connect it to a computer system designed to diagnose the problem.

Importance

Many recently designed systems are now essential to daily life. Most of us would feel lost without our cell phones. In addition to millions of voice calls, millions of text messages are sent every day. An automobile Global Positioning system (GPS) helps keep drivers from getting lost. The U.S. Postal Service is delivering much less mail than it did in the past because email is used for a large percentage of today's business and personal communication. More and more people are getting their news from the Internet instead of from newspapers.

Security

Security is an increasingly important issue. Government agencies are developing new security systems to monitor communication among suspected terrorists. The Transportation Safety Administration is using new scanners for screening airline passengers. Businesses use security systems that limit building access and require staff to wear photo identification. Software to control computer system access is also important.

Speed

We expect systems to operate faster than ever before. Many of us would like everything to operate at Internet speed. We want to get the news on our computers or cell phones as it happens. Stores are increasing the use of self-service checkout systems to reduce waiting times. The automated toll collection systems used on some highways are another example of a time-saving system.

Connecting Old and New

Existing systems that have been around for a long time are sometimes referred to as legacy systems. Thousands of bridges in the U.S. are old and in need of repair or replacement. Many of these structures were built when the population was smaller, and fewer vehicles were on the road. Recall how the Chapter 5 Discovery Project video presents the challenges of adding new elements to an existing design. Sometimes old and new technologies need to be connected. Although modern trains use locomotives that can run at speeds of 100–150 miles per hour, they often run at half that speed due to limits of existing track systems.

The Workforce

Although the workforce contributing to the design and maintenance of systems is more diverse than ever before, more diversity is still needed. Having women and men from different nationalities and backgrounds working in technical fields can be beneficial because they often view things from different perspectives. This aids in the development of creative solutions to problems. Young people are good at adapting to rapid change, so there will be opportunities for them in systems-related projects. **Figure 5.8** shows the diversity in the engineering profession.

Reading Check Analyze how the existence of older systems presents unique challenges for engineers developing new systems.

STEM CONNECTION

Multi-Stage Tree Diagrams
All engineers are required to make informed decisions as they work through the engineering design process. Decision-making tools, such as multi-stage tree diagrams, are sometimes used to help display information and alternative solutions. These types of tools show the interrelationships among conditions that are defined within the problem.

Personal Tutor

View
Go to your *essentials* ONLINE to view the *Personal Tutor: Multi-Stage Tree Diagrams.*

Fig. 5.8 Diversity A team of engineers is working on its latest project. *How do you think your chapter Discovery Project might benefit from the diversity of a project team such as the one in the photo?*

Check Your Understanding

SECTION **5.2**

After You Read Perform the following tasks.

1. **Identify** six of the components of systems thinking.

2. **Evaluate** what may happen to the demand for systems engineers over the next twenty years.

3. **Analyze** how the role of a systems engineer is complicated by the need to incorporate legacy systems into their new designs.

Review and Assessment

Problem-Solving Process

Identify

Many Americans plant gardens to enjoy fresh produce. GardenGreenEarth.com, a site devoted to low-impact agriculture, has hired your engineering firm to develop a low-cost moisture sensor that gardeners can make at home. You must incorporate the following criteria:

- Visually output moisture level: Dry, OK, Wet
- Housing made of recycled materials
- Durable (will be left in ground during the entire growing season)

Set Up

1. Research the project. Ask: *"What physical characteristics must be monitored?"* and *"In what conditions must the sensor work?"*
2. Analyze commercial moisture sensors to understand how they work. Research suitable replacements for expensive electrical components that can be found in your home or hardware store.
3. Brainstorm various solutions. Create sketches of the overall look of the sensor. Identify possible recycled or repurposed materials. List systems that will be interconnected to form the product.
4. Use a decision matrix to choose the best solution. Be sure to use criteria and constraints as guides in judging the best idea.

Execute

5. Plan the solution with your team. What materials can be used? How will the components and housing be connected or fastened?
6. Keep sketching and recording ideas to improve your design.
7. Prepare prototypes of the solution, using various methods. Consider the environment in which the device will be working.
8. Meet with your team at the end of each session to discuss how the various systems interact. Plan your steps for the next session.

Evaluate

Test each design in a controlled setting. Calibrate the sensor to base readings on the same criteria. Record your findings in a table.

Share

Create an assembly guide that includes a bill of materials, tools, process description, and difficulty rating. Describe how the systems interact to create the final product, so the user can troubleshoot if necessary.

Critical Thinking

Key Concepts

1. **Identify** the three main kinds of systems.

2. **Summarize** the benefits of the universal systems model and explain how it works.

3. **Compare and contrast** the four types of system outputs, and how they may influence design decisions.

4. **Evaluate** the trash removal system in your town using elements of systems thinking. Remember to apply the key elements of the systems-thinking process.

5. **Analyze** the outputs of the systems in place to educate students in your school. What are some expected, unexpected, desirable, and undesirable outputs of that system?

Teamwork *21st Century Skills*

6. **Share** some of the systems you encountered in the completion of your chapter Discovery Project with your classmates. Create and deliver a presentation showing how these systems are interrelated.

7. **Collaborate** with team members to create a universal systems model for a complex system, such as a nationwide recharging system for electric vehicles.

Activity Center

Go to the **Activity Center** to review chapter vocabulary and key concepts.

Engineer's Toolbox

Go to the **Engineer's Toolbox** to:
- Access Academic Activities
- Access the Competitive Event Prep Activity

---

essentials — DISCOVERY PROJECT GOAL

Identify and Improve an Existing Safety or Security System

Identify a safety or security system within your school that needs to be improved. You may select a system that applies to a particular classroom, such as a technology or science lab, or a system that applies to your entire school. Create a physical model or computer model of the improved system. Demonstrate the system and explain how it is an improvement over the original system.

Go to your **essentials ONLINE** to collaborate with your team on this Discovery Project.

ESSENTIAL QUESTION **What do engineers need to know about materials in order to make things?**

When an engineer designs a product or structure, one of the first considerations must be the materials to use in the project. There are several ways to establish the physical, chemical, optical, and other characteristics of a material. These characteristics will help determine the ways in which that material can be incorporated into the design of a product. The materials that are used when making and building products and structures introduce their own constraints. Manufacturing and construction processes are continually updated to accommodate newly developed materials.

essentials

DISCOVERY PROJECT

Designing Wind Chimes for Production

 21st Century Skills **Explain how creativity is an important part of the process of choosing the materials for a project.**

Wind chimes are found throughout the world. For their mass production, engineers must optimize materials and fabrication methods. In this project, you will design and make ecologically responsible wind chimes, selecting appropriate reclaimed or reused materials for the device based on material properties. After you complete your prototype, you will present ideas on how the device could be mass produced.

 Group Workspace

During the video, note specific ways in which materials can be worked and machined. How might you work with the materials that will be used to make your wind chimes?

 Engineer's Toolbox

Go to the Engineer's Toolbox to:
- Access Note-Taking Activities
- Access Graphic Organizers
- Access Academic Standards met by this chapter

Go to your *essentials* ONLINE to view the Chapter 6 Discovery Project Launcher video to learn about machining.

READING GUIDE

Before You Read How does the development of new materials affect the techniques used to fabricate various objects and structures?

Main Idea

Materials are classified and grouped, based on several categories of material properties. These materials are used in both small- and large-scale fabrication.

Objectives

- **Identify** the characteristics used to classify and group both natural and synthetic materials.
- **Evaluate** how engineers choose materials for a project.
- **Explain** how the strength of a material can be established.
- **Compare and contrast** manufacturing and construction.
- **Analyze** how fabrication techniques affect the design process.

Vocabulary

Content Vocabulary

- synthetic
- composite
- corrosion
- tensile strength
- compressive strength
- strain
- deflection
- yield strength
- fatigue
- elasticity
- ductility
- malleability
- conductivity
- machinability
- castability
- fabrication
- molding
- forming
- rolling
- extrusion
- tempering

Academic Vocabulary

- bonds
- stress
- construction
- sustainable

Note-Taking Activity

Draw this table for each section. Write key terms and phrases under **Cues**. Write main ideas under **Note Taking**. Summarize the section under **Summary**.

Cues	Note Taking
•	•
•	•
Summary	

Graphic Organizers

Draw the graphic organizers. Use them to organize information as you read.

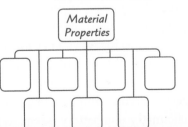

Go to your *e*ssentials ONLINE for downloadable graphic organizers.

STANDARDS

ACADEMIC

Technology

ITEEA STL19.02 Materials have different qualities and may be classified as natural, synthetic, or mixed.

ITEEA STL20.05 Structures can include prefabricated materials.

Mathematics

NCTM Problem Solving Apply and adapt a variety of appropriate strategies to solve problems.

Science

NSES F Develop understanding of personal and community health; population growth; natural resources; environmental quality; natural and human-induced hazards; science and technology in local, national, and global challenges.

ITEEA *International Technology and Engineering Educators Association*
NCTM *National Council of Teachers of Mathematics*
NSES *National Science Education Standards*

College & Career READINESS

Writing Produce clear and coherent writing in which the development, organization, and style are appropriate to task, purpose, and audience.

Speaking and Listening Integrate and evaluate information presented in diverse media and formats, including visually, quantitatively, and orally.

Materials

Understanding Types and Classification of Materials

Materials are classified into one of three major categories: natural, synthetic, or composite.

Wood from trees is an example of a natural material used in engineering. Most naturally occurring metals would also be considered natural for the purpose of this classification. Fibers from plants that are used in the engineering of textiles are also natural materials.

Synthetic materials are materials that are not found in nature. Two or more component parts are combined by design to form a new material. Metal alloys, synthetic fibers, polymers, and plastics are examples of materials that are designed and engineered. Most ceramic materials are considered synthetic.

Composite materials are made from at least two distinct materials, which remain separate and distinct in an application where they are combined. Common composite materials include fiberglass and carbon fiber.

We can classify materials in ways other than into these three major categories. Materials may also be grouped according to their unique characteristics and properties. For example, some materials are radioactive, hazardous, or flammable. An understanding of materials and all of the various means of classifying them is basic to any field of engineering.

Material Properties

The understanding of how materials are used in engineering begins with an understanding of their basic properties. Materials science, or materials engineering, starts with the study of existing materials in an effort to engineer new ones. As humans began to understand the elements in the periodic table, they started applying that knowledge to technological problems. An understanding of the various types of bonds, crystalline structures, density, and other characteristics of materials allows engineers to apply that knowledge in the creation and application of new products.

Chemical Properties

Knowing the engineering uses of materials begins with understanding how objects behave on a molecular or atomic level. Elements bond together in specific ways. They form two specific types of bonds, ionic or covalent, each of which builds a certain molecular structure. In addition, elements and materials are either acids or bases. These properties become apparent in certain types of engineering, such as in the chemistry of a battery (see p. 47). Certain chemical reactions are also used for technological purposes.

 **Reading Check** Contrast synthetic and composite materials.

PROJECT CONNECTIONS

Are the materials you are likely to use in your project natural, synthetic, or composite?

Engineers must be aware of a material's reactivity and how that may cause the corrosion of a material such as iron. **Corrosion** is a process of disintegration in which a chemical reaction causes metals to wear away. One common example of corrosion is the oxidation, or rusting, that can occur in some metals. Corrosion such as rusting can be uniform, or it can be localized in a number of ways such as pitting (corrosion in the form of cavities). An engineer's focus may include the prevention of corrosion with surface treatments, including coating and anodizing.

Strength of Materials

To learn about the strength of materials, we evaluate the ability of those materials to withstand stress. Stress is a measure of the amount of force exerted in a certain area when a defined load or force is applied. Materials deform molecularly under stress. By testing that stress, we are able to define a material as having certain types of strength or the ability to withstand a certain amount of stress.

Tensile Strength Ultimate **tensile strength** (sometimes referred to as ultimate strength) is the maximum stress that a material can withstand when subjected to tension (the stretching or "pulling apart" of an object). When under tensile stress, the atoms in a material are forced, or pulled, apart. Steel, for instance, is a material that has a relatively high tensile strength, hence its use in a large number of applications.

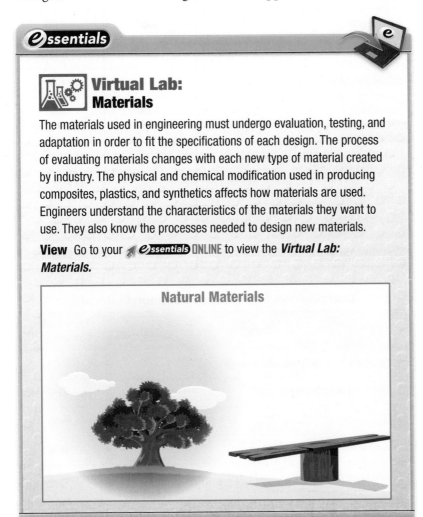

essentials

Virtual Lab: Materials

The materials used in engineering must undergo evaluation, testing, and adaptation in order to fit the specifications of each design. The process of evaluating materials changes with each new type of material created by industry. The physical and chemical modification used in producing composites, plastics, and synthetics affects how materials are used. Engineers understand the characteristics of the materials they want to use. They also know the processes needed to design new materials.

View Go to your *essentials* ONLINE to view the *Virtual Lab: Materials.*

Natural Materials

PROJECT CONNECTIONS

What are the tensile and compressive strengths of each of the materials you will use in your design?

Compressive Strength Compressive strength is a material's ability to withstand compression ("pushing together"). It is a measure of the maximum stress that a material can withstand under compression. Concrete is an example of a material that has a very high compressive strength. Steel also has a high compressive strength.

Shear Strength In shear, atoms in a material are forced to slide past one another. Reinforcing concrete with steel is intended in part to combat shear.

Deformation Deformation, or strain, is the change in a material's size or shape when stress is applied. In structural engineering, large components of a structure are under weight loads that cause deformation. There are many material properties and concepts related to deformation, the most important of which are described in this section.

Fig. 6.1 Tensile and Compressive Strengths
This chart shows the tensile and compressive strengths (represented as pounds per square inch, or psi) of several common materials. *How are these strengths important when choosing the materials for a project?*

Tensile Strengths of Common Materials

Material	Yield Strength (psi)	Ultimate Strength (psi)
Portland Cement	—	132
Pine (northern white, perpendicular to grain)	—	260
Concrete (glass fiber reinforced)	—	100
Polypropylene	3300	3390
Acrylonitrile Butadiene Styrene (ABS, molded)	2900	400
Rubber (natural vulcanized)	—	4060
Nylon (46)	6530	13000
Cast Iron	9500	17100
Aluminum (1000 series)	23900	29700
Copper (wrought)	7110	31200
Titanium	20300	31900
Steel (Astm A36 bar)	36300	58000

Compressive Strengths of Common Materials

Material	Compressive Strength (psi)
Pine (northern white, perpendicular to grain)	310
Pine (northern white, parallel to grain)	2370
Brick	3050
Concrete (glass fiber reinforced)	7200
Portland Cement	8400
Steel (ASTM A36 bar)	22000

Green reSource

Reconstruction In developing nations, homes built with local materials are often unable to survive natural disasters such as earthquakes and floods. International projects have introduced safer building practices when rebuilding damaged homes in these regions.

Go to your *essentials* ONLINE to learn more about Quake Resistant Homes: Re-Engineering Traditional Methods.

Group Workspace

One of the challenges of rebuilding in impoverished areas is the need for quality construction materials. Explain how sand is useful in home building. Determine if straw is useful in home building as well.

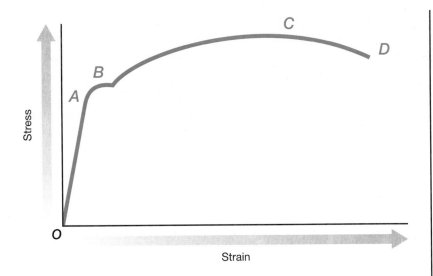

Deflection is a measure of how much a structural element bends under stress. In construction, the deflection of beams is an important calculation made by engineers; building codes specify the maximum amount of deflection allowed.

Yield strength is the point at which a material begins to deform permanently. Before this point is reached, the material will return to its original condition as soon as the stress that created the deformation has been removed. (See **Figure 6.2**.)

Fatigue, which results from repeated stress being applied, can also cause a material to fail. Fatigue is related to the impact strength of a material. The amount of stress that a given material can withstand before failing is that material's fatigue life.

Elasticity is the tendency of a material to return to its original shape after a stress is removed. Hooke's Law of Elasticity is a related concept that is used to approximate the properties of mechanical springs. Hooke's law describes the proportional relationship between a force applied to a spring and the amount that the spring stretches when that force is applied.

Ductility is the limit of how much a material can be deformed without fracturing. Metals generally have higher levels of ductility than other materials, allowing them to be machined and formed using methods that would not work as effectively with brittle materials such as plastics.

Malleability, a concept similar to ductility, refers to a material's ability to be deformed, but this time under compression.

Electromagnetic Properties

We can also classify materials according to their electromagnetic properties, such as conductivity. All materials are classified as a conductor, an insulator, or a semiconductor. Materials also have other distinct properties that are related to a material's ability to store electric and magnetic energy. Electromagnetic properties are explored in greater detail in Chapter 8.

PROJECT CONNECTIONS
How might fatigue affect the sound of a wind chime over a period of time?

PROJECT CONNECTIONS
Will changes in temperature change the sound of your wind chimes?

Thermal Properties

A material's ability to conduct heat is referred to as its thermal **conductivity**. Aluminum, copper, and gold each have a very high thermal conductivity. Conversely, fiberglass has a relatively low thermal conductivity, making it appropriate for use as insulation. (See **Figure 6.3**.)

Materials expand when temperature changes. A material's coefficient of thermal expansion is the value that is used to describe this change in volume. This is important in various engineering applications. For example, engineers who design vehicle tires or bridges need to pay close attention to the coefficient of thermal expansion.

A material's flammability refers to how easily it will burn or ignite. This concept is important in building materials and in engineering applications that involve certain liquids or gases.

Materials also have specific melting and boiling points at specific temperatures and pressures. These values must also be considered for many applications.

Fig. 6.3 Thermal Conductivity
This chart lists the thermal conductivity of several common materials. *What is a common use for materials with low thermal conductivity?*

Material	Thermal Conductivity–k–(W/mK)
Cotton	0.03
Styrofoam	0.033
Fiberglass	0.04
Paper	0.05
Asbestos mill board	0.14
Gasoline	0.15
Sand, dry	0.15–0.25
Hardwoods	0.16
PVC	0.19
Water	0.58
Asphalt	0.75
Glass	1.05
Porcelain	1.5
Carbon	1.7
Cement, mortar	1.73
Stainless Steel	16
Lead	35
Tin	67
Iron	80
Nickel	91
Brass	109
Aluminum	250
Gold	310
Copper	401
Silver	429

1 W/(mK) = 1 W/(m°C) = 0.85984 kcal/(hr m°C) = 0.5779 Btu/(ft hr°F)

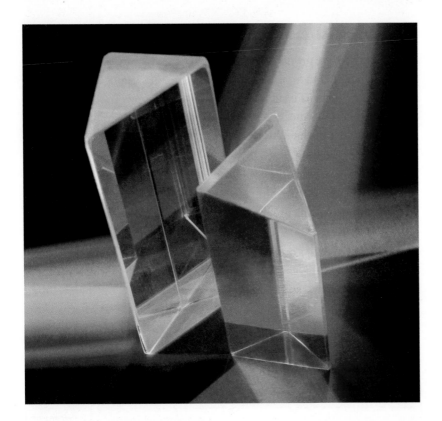

Optical Properties

Materials also have specific optical properties. Optical properties relate to how materials interact with light waves. Those optical properties are reflection, refraction, diffraction, dispersion, polarization, luminosity, color, and absorption. (See **Figure 6.4**.)

Reflectivity is the degree to which a light wave will "bounce back" from the surface of a material. Conversely, absorption is a material's tendency to absorb light waves. Refraction is the "bending" of a light wave when it encounters a material. Dispersion is how a light wave separates into colors when it encounters a material. Polarization produces light with waves that vibrate in a single plane. The polarization of light when passing through a material has many applications in photography and optics.

A material's color is also an optical property and a key factor in engineering. The term *luminosity* relates to the brightness of a material.

A material's optical properties are also important in telecommunications applications. Optical fiber is increasingly being used to transmit signals.

Acoustical Properties

The acoustical properties of a material have to do with how a sound wave behaves when it encounters that material. It may be desirable to have sound pass through a material, but in noise-control and soundproofing applications sound should be well absorbed by the material. Good sound-absorbing materials are usually very porous. Acoustical properties are also the basis of technologies such as sonar and ultrasound medical diagnostic tools.

eSsentials

Career Center

Materials Engineer Have you ever paid much attention to the roof on a building? Does it have any uses other than protection from weather? Many structures also have mechanical systems such as air conditioning units on the roof. Some homes have solar panels or other equipment on their roofs. What is the covering on a typical roof? Tar? Asphalt shingles? Tiles? Watch the video about a roof at the California Academy of Sciences. This is definitely not an ordinary roof!

Go to your eSsentials ONLINE to learn more about the education, career paths, and future of a materials engineer.

Manufacturing Properties

Materials also have properties that are related to manufacturing processes rather than to their actual scientific properties. For example, the **machinability** of a material is its ability to be worked, or machined, to a surface finish or at certain speeds. Degrees of machinability are based largely on the hardness of the material. (See **Figure 6.5**.)

Castability refers to how easily a material such as a molten metal or a ceramic is poured into a mold, or form, and solidified. Plastics and metals also have specific temperatures at which they can be extruded. Casting and extruding are discussed in more detail in the next section, but the basis for each process lies in the properties of the material.

As new materials are researched and developed, engineers gain more options for the various applications at their disposal. For example, in recent years some structural elements have been developed using plastics in place of metals. This is based on the strength of the plastics, as well as their other properties.

Machinability Table–Part 6 (Other Materials)

Material	MR	Material	MR
Aluminum-bronze (9.5% Al)	0.60	Leaded commercial bronze	2.40
aluminum silicon-bronze	1.80	Leaded copper	2.40
Architectural Bronze	2.70	Low leaded brass	1.80
Chromium-copper	0.60	Manganese bronze	0.90
Commercial bronze (90% Cu)	0.60	Naval brass	0.90
Cupro-nickel	0.60	Nickel	2.00
Deoxidized Copper	0.60	Nickel-silver (20% Ni)	0.60
Forging brass	2.40	Phosphor-bronze (10% Tin)	0.60
High-leaded brass	2.70	Zinc	2.00

Fig. 6.5 Machinability
This chart shows the machinability of some common metals. The higher the rating, the easier the material is to machine. The lower the rating, the more difficult the material is to machine. *How does a material's machinability help to determine its usefulness in product manufacturing?*

SECTION 6.1 Check Your Understanding

After You Read Perform the following tasks.

1. **Discuss** how the optical properties of a material help determine its usefulness to engineers.
2. **Identify** what methods are used to determine a material's various types of strength.
3. **Analyze** how the classification of materials aids the design process.

Introduction to Fabrication

Fabrication is the manufacturing or construction of various products. Fabrication of products of all sizes is generally referred to as *manufacturing*. The term *construction* tends to cover larger-scale on-site fabrication. The process of selecting materials for manufacturing and construction is done systematically. Final decisions about which materials to use in the fabrication of various products are dependent on a range of factors, including desired properties, ability to be manufactured, and cost.

Manufacturing

Manufacturing is the process of converting materials into usable finished products. The manufacturing process begins with obtaining raw materials. As described in Section 6.1, some materials come from natural sources, whereas other materials are synthetic. A material's properties are the primary reason why an engineer would select it for use in manufacturing a particular product or for a specific application.

Many methods and processes are used to manufacture engineered products. These processes are grouped into seven techniques: casting, molding, forming, separating, joining, treating, and finishing.

Casting

In casting, metals and ceramics are cast into various shapes using patterns. A mold is created and a soft or liquid material is poured or forced into the mold. Usually the mold is made from another material, such as wood, metal, or wax. Another common type of casting is the sand casting of metals. In sand casting, a pattern is placed into a special sand and then removed from it, leaving a space or void in the sand for a liquid material to fill. Molten metal is then poured into the void and left to cool to a solid form. When it is cool enough, the sand is removed from the casting, leaving the desired metal piece. This type of process is also applied to ceramics. Fixtures such as ceramic sinks, toilets, and tubs are manufactured in a similar manner. (See **Figure 6.6**.)

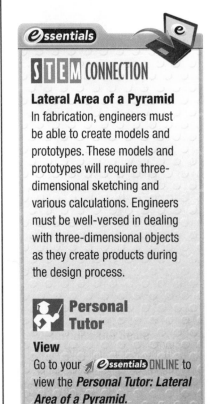

Fig. 6.6 Casting This bell is being produced from molten iron using casting. *Why is sand ideal for use in casting?*

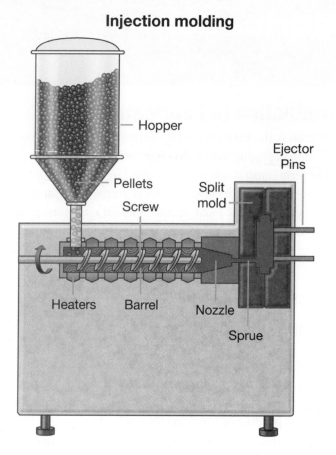

Injection molding

Hopper

Ejector Pins

Pellets

Split mold

Screw

Heaters   Barrel   Nozzle

Sprue

Fig. 6.7 Injection Molding Plastic toys can be quickly manufactured using the injection molding process. *Why is injection used for mass producing many consumer items?*

Molding

Molding is similar in many ways to casting. This term is generally used for the manufacture of some plastic products. In molding, material is heated and then injected, blown, or pressed into a mold.

Injection molding is one of the most common types of molding used in product manufacturing. It is ideal for the production of large numbers of simple plastic objects with minimal labor costs and waste of materials. In a typical injection molding process, small bits of plastic are fed into a machine, heated, and then injected into a metal mold using air pressure. The plastic takes the shape of the cavity in the mold.

Forming

Many different types of manufacturing processes are referred to as **forming**. These include forging, rolling, extruding, pressing, bending, shearing, compressing, drawing, and stamping. Forming can be applied to natural materials, metals, and plastics. In most (though not all) forming processes, the material is heated to make it more workable.

Common compression processes are forging, drawing, stamping, bending, and rolling. In forging, metal is usually heated to a high temperature to make it more malleable. It is then placed between two dies and compressed. The metal is shaped by the dies. Finally, it is hammered or pressed into its desired shape. Wrenches, hammer heads, and other tools are made of forged iron or steel. Drawing is a stretching process. For example, wire is made by pulling, or drawing, a metal such as copper through a series of dies until the desired diameter is achieved.

Stamping is widely used in the automobile industry to produce sheet metal parts for components such as fenders. Flat sheet metal is placed between dies that come together to shape the metal. Sheet metal, tubing, and many plastics can be shaped by bending.

In **rolling**, a malleable material is drawn through rollers that press it and make it thinner. Sheet metal is usually manufactured using a process that involves rolling. Rolling is also used in the manufacturing of commercial products such as aluminum foil. (See **Figure 6.9**.)

Extrusion is a common forming process applied to metals and plastics. In this process, a malleable material blank is pressed through a die and forced into the desired shape. This process is used to manufacture pipe and other structural materials. (See **Figure 6.10**.)

Separating

Separating processes are applied to virtually all materials. How the processes are performed depends upon the properties of the material. Cutting and sawing, pulverizing, turning, drilling, shaping, and planing are separating processes used in manufacturing.

The most common separating processes involve cutting, by which the material is physically separated into pieces. Natural materials such as wood are sawed, or milled, into desired shapes. Some materials such as metal and diamond might be cut by a laser.

Turning is a process in which the material rotates. When a stationary tool encounters the rotating material, it removes some of that material to form a desired shape. (See **Figure 6.11**.)

PROJECT CONNECTIONS

What is the best tool to use to cut your wind chime pipes to the proper length?

Fig. 6.8 Forging The forging process has been used for centuries to create metal products. *How are hard metals such as steel or iron prepared for forging?*

Fig. 6.9 Rolling This sheet metal mill shows the metal-forming process of rolling. *How is rolling related to stamping?*

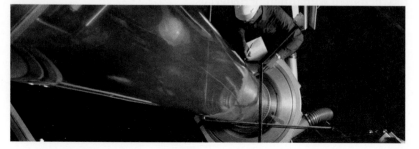

Fig. 6.10 Extrusion Pipes made of metal or plastic are commonly made using extrusion. *Why is this process especially useful when working with brittle materials?*

Fig. 6.11 Turning A lathe is a device used to rotate an item being machined by turning. *What makes this process unique among separating methods?*

Other separating processes include oxyacetylene cutting, water-jet cutting, and laser cutting. Oxyacetylene cutting combines oxygen and acetylene gases to produce high-temperature flames for heavy-duty cutting. Water can be used for cutting when it is forced through a nozzle at high speed. High-intensity laser beams are used to cut wood, metal, paper, and plastics. Shearing is a way of separating materials without losing any material. Cutting fabric with scissors is an example of shearing. Separating processes involving the removal of material are known as chip removal. Sawing and drilling are common chip removal processes. Many machine shop tools such as milling machines, lathes, grinders, and sanders shape materials using chip removal.

Joining

As with separating, many different processes are categorized as joining. These include fastening, adhesive bonding, thermal joining, brazing, and soldering.

The most common types of joining processes are those that involve fastening materials together using other products. Nailing, screwing, bolting, riveting, stitching, and stapling are all examples of fastening processes. Since each of these offers certain advantages and disadvantages in the design and engineering of products, the engineer must consider tradeoffs. For example, nails might offer faster application but might create a less durable connection in certain types of applications or when used with different materials.

Although most mechanical fasteners are made of metal, they can also be made of other materials such as plastic. Mechanical fasteners can be used to join dissimilar materials, and materials that are joined in this way are easy to disassemble. However, using fasteners usually requires drilling a hole, and that can weaken the material.

Another way to join materials is by using adhesives or glues. There are thousands of different kinds of adhesives, which can be used to join similar and dissimilar materials. For example, hot glue is a way to fasten together the pieces of a physical prototype. Similar hot-melt adhesives in bulk form are used in packaging. Many adhesives are strong and weather-resistant and can be applied using automated systems.

Thermal joining processes, which use heat, can be a good way of joining materials that have similar melting points. Metals and plastics are commonly joined using thermal processes. Common thermal joining processes include welding, brazing, and soldering. In welding, the materials to be joined are melted. A filler material with a similar melting temperature is used to help connect the molten material. Heat from a flame, electric arc, laser, or ultrasound is used to melt the metal or plastic and the filler material. After cooling, a strong joint results. Brazing and soldering differ from welding because they use a filler material of lower melting temperature than the materials to be joined.

Treating and Finishing

Materials can be treated during the manufacturing processes. This means that some method is used to change the materials' properties. Ceramics may be baked, or "fired," at a high temperature to increase their strength. Another common example is a process called **tempering**, in which a metal such as steel is hardened. In tempering, steel is brought to a high temperature and then quenched (cooled very quickly in a bath of water or other liquid).

PROJECT CONNECTIONS

Decide how to fasten together the parts of your wind chime.

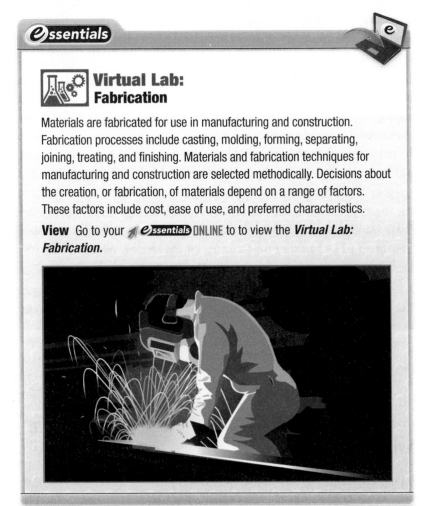

*e*ssentials

Virtual Lab: Fabrication

Materials are fabricated for use in manufacturing and construction. Fabrication processes include casting, molding, forming, separating, joining, treating, and finishing. Materials and fabrication techniques for manufacturing and construction are selected methodically. Decisions about the creation, or fabrication, of materials depend on a range of factors. These factors include cost, ease of use, and preferred characteristics.

View Go to your *e*ssentials ONLINE to to view the *Virtual Lab: Fabrication.*

Fig. 6.12 Tempered Glass
Automobile windows are commonly made of tempered glass. *What are the benefits of using tempered glass in various environments?*

A familiar application of the tempering process is the creation of safety glass. Thermal and chemical treatments may be used in this process. This increases the strength of the glass, and also changes how the glass behaves when broken. The new molecular structure causes the glass to break or shatter into smaller and less dangerous pieces. Glass doors, side and rear vehicle windows, and glass for roofs are usually made of tempered glass. (See **Figure 6.12**.)

Chemical conditioning techniques use chemicals to change the properties of materials. Vulcanization, for example, makes tires heat resistant and more durable. Many plastics are also conditioned by chemical processes.

Mechanical conditioning occurs when metals are forced into shape. The process of forging wrenches and similar products increases their strength and durability by changing the internal structure of the materials used.

Reading Check **Evaluate** what factors go into an engineer's choice of joining method when designing a given product.

Blasting, sanding, buffing, polishing, chemical and electrochemical plating, coating, and grinding are some of the methods that are used in the fine machining or finishing of products. Sand blasting is typical in the manufacture of metal products. In sand blasting, air pressure forces silica (sand) or another "shot" material against the surface of an object to bring it to a smoother finish or to remove undesired material.

Plating and coating are very common in the manufacture of products. In metal plating, an object is typically dipped into molten material. Coating, on the other hand, is usually painted or sprayed onto an object.

PROJECT CONNECTIONS

What types of finishing processes will you use for your chimes? Would these processes work well in mass production?

Construction

Whereas manufacturing usually refers to making products in one place that will be sent to another place, *construction* generally refers to large-scale applications in which fabrication techniques are carried out at the site where the product will remain. Some of the processes described above, including casting, separating, joining, and finishing, are used in construction. (See **Figure 6.13**.)

Metals

Steel and other ferrous alloys are common in large-scale applications such as bridges and buildings. Copper, tin, and aluminum are also used, but are often cost-prohibitive.

Steel offers several advantages as a construction material. It has good tensile and compressive strength. It is relatively flexible, and can last a long time in most applications. A major disadvantage is corrosion, or rusting. Surface treatments, coatings, and other methods are used to combat corrosion. Steel is sometimes galvanized with a layer of non-corrosive zinc. Cathodic protection uses an electrical current to keep steel from corroding.

Concrete

Concrete is prepared from a mix of cement, coarse aggregate such as rock or stone, a fine aggregate such as sand, and water. It is the most used human-made material in the world. Concrete can be pumped or cast into a form, or even sprayed in some construction applications.

Concrete is typically used as a mortar for brick or block, and in compressive applications such as beams, columns, and foundations. It is also used for floors, roofs, pavement, and even as a coating.

As a material, concrete has high compressive strength. Its lower tensile strength can usually be overcome with reinforcement with steel mesh or rods, known as rebar. Another advantage is its durability. It reaches its ultimate strength in about 30 days, and then lasts for a very long time, usually at least 100 years. It is fire-resistant, and relatively low-maintenance and energy-efficient. It is environmentally sustainable and is considered especially environmentally sound if made with recycled aggregates and additives.

Concrete also has its disadvantages. One is its limited workability once it has cured. Concrete is strong, but is also very heavy and cannot be used to cover very large areas because of its thermal expansion and contraction. Some combinations of its materials can also be problematic in terms of the length of time involved for the concrete to set, or cure, and the strength and workability of the end product. Concrete gives off heat during curing, and it tends to retain heat once cured. It is also sometimes difficult to repair and maintain.

Visualization

Assembly Drawings
Engineering drawings of an assembled product can be very complicated. To show all of the details, a type of drawing called a section view is used. Section views are drawn as if someone has removed part of the object to reveal its internal features.

Go to your *essentials* ONLINE to learn more about developing your assembly drawings.

Group Workspace

View an assembly drawing. List materials visible in the section view. Determine whether or not the various patterns make it easier to identify individual parts.

Fig. 6.13 Construction
Construction involves fabricating a project's components at that project's site. *Which parts of the manufacturing process might be the easiest to perform on site? Which might be the most difficult?*

Fig. 6.14 Concrete The foundation of a building is created by pouring a concrete form. *Why is concrete an ideal material for this purpose?*

Other Construction Materials

For thousands of years, humans have used natural materials such as wood, mud and clay, stone, and fabrics to fabricate buildings, bridges, and other structures. Modern developments in material science and engineering have produced alternatives to those materials for use in large-scale fabrication.

Plastics have been used in construction for decades. For example, they have been used to replace heavy and expensive metal materials for piping in buildings. New developments in plastics now allow their use as structural members also.

Glass became a more widely used material in large structures after the development of advanced steel alloys in the twentieth century. Frames made of these steel alloys made it possible to use larger pieces of glass as windows and as exterior covering. Glass offers advantages for lighting and good weather protection, but it allows heat to pass through easily. Engineers have developed structures such as multi-pane and insulated windows that make glass more appealing as a construction material. In addition, glass blocks can be used to construct walls.

Fig. 6.15 Fiberglass This bathtub enclosure is made of fiberglass. *What other features of a home may be created with composite materials?*

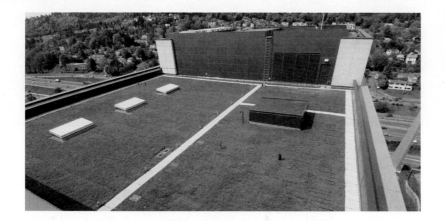

Composite materials such as fiberglass, fiber-reinforced concrete, and engineered wood products (including plywood, laminated beams, and oriented strand board) offer engineers additional options for designs and methods of large-scale fabrication.

Green Building Materials

In recent years, there has been a growing demand for sustainable materials in construction. Fast-growing woods such as bamboo are used in a variety of ways in the construction of buildings. In large cities, living roofs, which incorporate plant life into the roof of a building's design, can help combat what is called the "urban heat island" effect. This effect refers to the tendency of asphalt, concrete, and other roofing products to retain too much heat. Living, or "green," roofs can reduce a building's heating and cooling costs, remove carbon dioxide from the air, and in some cases even be used as gardening space. (See **Figure 6.16**.)

Organic architecture stresses the use of more locally available materials. Using such materials helps reduce the cost and environmental effects of transporting construction materials. In addition, recycled materials such as glass and crushed used concrete are often used as aggregates for new concrete.

Technology is even being developed to incorporate clean energy technologies directly into building materials themselves. For example, photovoltaic material and thermal solar energy catchers can be built directly into roofing materials.

Reading Check **Evaluate** what materials and construction techniques have changed the construction process in recent years.

Check Your Understanding

SECTION **6.2**

After You Read Perform the following tasks.

1. **List** which materials lend themselves to the process of casting or joining.

2. **Explain** how manufacturing differs from construction.

3. **Analyze** the advantages that new construction materials have over those that have been used for centuries.

Review and Assessment

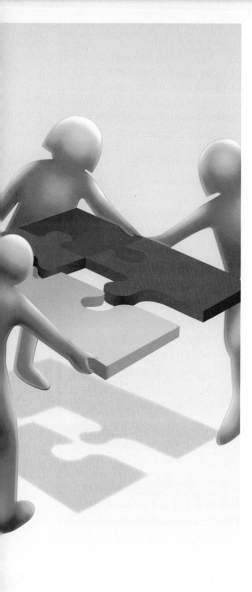

Problem-Solving Process

Identify

You have been hired by GreenCo Alpha, a green building material company, to design a new energy-efficient insulation that is made from recycled materials. The insulation must be made of recycled materials, and must have an efficiency rating similar to that of fiberglass.

Set Up

1. Gather background information about the properties of insulation, how insulation works, and the types currently being used. List some common characteristics of various types of insulation.

2. Brainstorm potential solutions. Decide what materials will be used and how they will be processed into the final form.

3. Choose the best solution. Consider manufacturing techniques and applications. Use a decision matrix to help make your choice.

Execute

4. Plan the fabrication. What resources do you need? What procedures will be used to produce the finished product?

5. Keep sketching and recording ideas. They may be used to improve your design and the overall quality of the material.

6. Build prototypes of the solution, using various ways to carry out the production. You may need to wrap the insulation in some sort of covering to make installation easier.

7. At each session's end, ask the team: *How is the project progressing? Do design or production methods require modification?*

Evaluate

Develop a method that will test the insulation properties of your product. Compare your product to existing insulation. Record the testing data in a table. Use this information to analyze the most successful design.

Share

Create a promotional brochure, pamphlet, or video for the new product. Describe the key characteristics of the product, how it works, its green attributes, and its advantages over other types of insulation. Describe the testing of the product and how it performed compared to standard fiberglass batt insulation. Finally, include installation instructions, specifying any equipment needed and noting any safety concerns.

Critical Thinking

Key Concepts

1. **Identify** the methods that engineers use to classify different types of materials.

2. **Summarize** the ways used by engineers to identify the strength of a material.

3. **Compare and Contrast** several of the different types of fabrication techniques that are used in manufacturing and construction.

4. **Analyze** which materials and processes are ideal for the creation of sustainable homes and buildings.

5. **Examine** the constraints that various types of materials introduce into the design process.

Information Literacy

6. **Share** ideas about how engineers choose materials for their designs.

7. **Collaborate** with classmates to discuss how fabrication processes are changing to meet new needs and challenges in the construction industry.

Activity Center

Go to the **Activity Center** to review chapter vocabulary and key concepts.

Engineer's Toolbox

Go to the **Engineer's Toolbox** to:
- Access Academic Activities
- Access the Competitive Event Prep Activity

DISCOVERY PROJECT

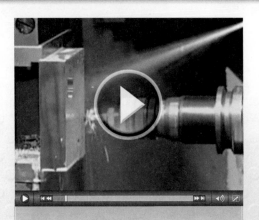

Designing Wind Chimes for Production

Wind chimes are found throughout the world. While craftspeople and artisans produce some of them, the mass production of wind chimes requires engineering to optimize materials and fabrication methods. In this project, you will design and make an ecologically responsible wind chime, selecting appropriate reclaimed or reused materials for the device based on material properties. After you complete your prototype, you will present ideas on how the device could be mass produced.

Go to your *essentials* ONLINE to collaborate with your team on this Discovery Project.

Review

College & Career
READINESS

Critical Thinking

Key Concepts

1. **List** the great engineering achievements of the twentieth century.

2. **Summarize** the connections among science, technology, mathematics, and engineering.

3. **Define** the common design process steps.

4. **Review** the sketching skills and techniques used by engineers.

5. **Explain** the various methods of generating three-dimensional models.

6. **Name** the elements of systems thinking.

7. **Analyze** the characteristics used to classify and group both natural and synthetic materials.

8. **Evaluate** how engineers choose the right materials for a project.

Communication
21st Century Skills

9. **Share** your ideas about some of the natural, human-made, and engineered systems that you encounter each day.

10. **Discuss** the ways in which the materials and fabrication techniques chosen for a project can affect the design process.

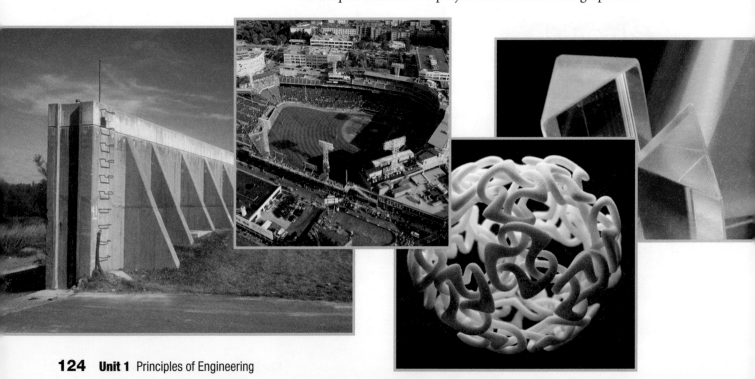

Design and Build a Wind-Powered Generator

Project Process

IDENTIFY

1. Research important related concepts, including basic turbine electrical generation and power, voltage and current, and basic circuitry.

2. Summarize the main challenges.

3. Outline this unit's key concepts.

SET UP

4. Choose materials, including found materials, to use in your design.

5. Research and develop alternative ideas and solutions for designing and building a wind-powered generator.

6. Use a decision matrix to choose the best solution for further development.

EXECUTE

7. Create a detailed drawing of the generator that you intend to build.

8. Construct and test your first prototype and record the results.

9. Using the results, redesign your solution.

10. Construct and test your second prototype and record the results. Compare the power output and efficiencies of each prototype.

SHARE

11. Present your prototype to the class.

EVALUATE

 Group Workspace

12. Write about this project. Discuss the most difficult challenges you met and how you overcame them.

Project Evaluation Chart

 Go to the **Engineer's Toolbox** to access the Project Evaluation Chart.

Go to your *essentials* ONLINE for Challenge Project details.

Types of Engineering

Engineers employ many disciplines and skills in designing solutions to problems. Civil engineers plan and build bridges, roads, and dams. Electrical and mechanical engineers design power plants and transportation systems. Manufacturing engineers streamline production systems. Rarely, however, do projects involve only a single engineering discipline. For instance, a biomedical engineer may need to work with chemical engineers to develop a polymer that is compatible with the system they are developing. A mechanical engineer may be brought in to a civil bridge project, to design a device to move materials into position over a challenging ravine. But, whether they interact, collaborate, or work in independent teams, all engineers develop ways to solve problems or improve systems.

As you complete this unit project, do the following:

- **Identify** the main design goals for building an earthquake-resistant house.

- **Discuss** the main challenges in building an earthquake-resistant house.

- **List** the key steps needed to design and build an earthquake-resistant house.

- **Develop** possible ideas and solutions for your earthquake-resistant house.

- **Share** your ideas for an earthquake-resistant house.

Building an Earthquake-Resistant House

KEY QUESTION What are the main criteria for designing and building an earthquake-resistant house?

Buildings that resist earthquakes can save lives here in the United States and also in developing countries, where building practices may be less advanced. Engineers face the challenge of developing earthquake-resistance strategies for buildings, including schools and homes. They must consider the concepts of many engineering disciplines, such as structural and geological, when designing and building a house. In this unit's Challenge Project, you will create a model that illustrates how to design and build an earthquake-resistant house.

Remember that as you work through the Unit 2 Chapter Discovery Projects, you will gain knowledge and skills that will help you complete the Unit 2 Challenge Project.

In Partnership With

Engineering News-Record

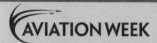
AVIATION WEEK

ACCESS Science
Inspiring Science Discovery

GreenSource

Designing and building structures and processes that protect lives and resources is a primary responsibility of engineers of all types.

Go to your *essentials* ONLINE to view the interview with architect Christopher Haas, who helped design the deYoung Museum in San Francisco. Learn about the structural-engineering steps taken to limit damage during seismic events. Then answer the question in the Engineer's Blog. See page 249 for a description of the steps you will follow to complete this unit project.

Group Workspace

What are some strategies that engineers and architects might apply to create buildings that can withstand seismic movement?

ENR
Engineering News-Record

Go to your *essentials* ONLINE for Challenge Project details.

Civil Engineering

ESSENTIAL QUESTION **How does civil engineering have an impact on our quality of life today?**

What do water towers, football stadiums, and airports have in common? They are all examples of civil engineering projects. Civil engineers benefit the public by working on projects to design, plan, and build the infrastructure of our country. Infrastructure refers to the structures, systems, and services that support daily life. These include large buildings, roads, bridges, tunnels, canals, water supply systems, and waste disposal systems. In this chapter, you will learn about the training and knowledge needed by civil engineers. You will also learn about the major technical areas and projects worked on by today's civil engineers, in areas such as construction engineering, environmental engineering, transportation engineering, and more.

*e*ssentials

DISCOVERY PROJECT

Design and Build a Model Lock System

21st Century Skills **Examine why critical thinking and systems thinking are important to the field of civil engineering.**

In this chapter's Discovery Project, you will learn where locks are used, why they are needed, and how they work. You will construct a working model of a lock system to move a toy boat from one level of water to another. Modeling supplies, including plastic containers, motors, syringes, tubing, and fasteners, will be needed. See page 147 for a brief description of this project.

 Group Workspace

Discuss why it is important for engineers to consider structures and forces when creating a lock system.

 Engineer's Toolbox

Go to your *e*ssentials ONLINE to view the video to learn about the operation of the Panama Canal.

Go to the Engineer's Toolbox to
- Access Note-Taking Activities
- Access Graphic Organizers
- Access Academic Standards met by this chapter

READING GUIDE

Before You Read How do you think the field of civil engineering has changed and developed since the time when the Egyptian pyramids were built?

Main Idea

Civil engineering is a wide-ranging field with a foundation in physical science concepts. Modern society depends on numerous infrastructures designed and constructed by civil engineers.

Objectives

- **Summarize** the history of civil engineering.
- **Evaluate** how different materials affect a building's structure.
- **Identify** the major branches of civil engineering.
- **Compare and contrast** structural engineering and geotechnical engineering.
- **Analyze** how a structure's environment influences its design.

Vocabulary

Content Vocabulary

- project management
- dead load
- live loads
- static loads
- dynamic loads
- aggregate
- I-beam
- municipal
- contaminants
- particulate

Academic Vocabulary

- license
- components
- techniques
- incentive
- primary
- investigations
- foundations

Note-Taking Activity

Draw this table for each section. Write key terms and phrases under **Cues**. Write main ideas under **Note Taking**. Summarize the section under **Summary**.

Cues	Note Taking
•	•
•	•
Summary	

Graphic Organizer

Use graphic organizers to write and organize information as you read.

Go to your  **ONLINE** for downloadable graphic organizers.

Major Branches of Civil Engineering

ACADEMIC

Technology

ITEEA STL18 Students will develop an understanding of and be able to select and use transportation technologies.

ITEEA STL20.02 Structures are constructed using a variety of processes and procedures.

Mathematics

NCTM Problem Solving Solve problems that arise in mathematics and in other contexts.

Science

NSES F Students should develop understanding of personal and community health; population growth; natural resources; environmental quality; natural and human-induced hazards; science and technology in local, national, and global challenges.

ITEEA *International Technology and Engineering Educators Association*
NCTM *National Council of Teachers of Mathematics*
NSES *National Science Education Standards*

College & Career READINESS

Reading Delineate and evaluate the argument and specific claims in a text, including the validity of the reasoning as well as the relevance and sufficiency of the evidence.

Reading Present information, findings, and supporting evidence such that listeners can follow the line of reasoning and the organization, development, and style are appropriate to task, purpose, and audience.

What Is Civil Engineering?

History of Civil Engineering

Civil engineering is one of the oldest and broadest engineering professions. Its roots go back to ancient times, when people first began to design shelters and construct roads. The first large public structures were the Egyptian pyramids, built around 2500 B.C. Later the Romans constructed civil structures such as roads, aqueducts, and dams throughout their empire. During the early 1800s, colleges in the United States and Europe established formal programs to prepare civil engineers. At about the same time, civil engineers formed organizations in an effort to share technical knowledge and gain recognition for the profession.

Today civil engineering is one of the largest disciplines within the field of engineering. Its achievements have had a worldwide impact. The American Society of Civil Engineers (ASCE) honored the accomplishments of civil engineers of the past century with its list of the Seven Wonders of the Modern World: the Channel Tunnel, CN Tower, Empire State Building, Golden Gate Bridge, Itaipu Dam, Netherlands North Sea Protection Works, and Panama Canal. (See **Figure 7.1**.)

Education

Civil engineering majors earn a four-year Bachelor of Engineering or Bachelor of Science degree. Students interested in pursuing a degree in civil engineering should make sure that the programs they are considering are accredited by ABET, Inc., a nonprofit agency that evaluates the quality of college engineering programs. Students majoring in civil engineering take courses in mathematics, physics, computer-aided design (CAD), and **project management** (planning and organizing). Generally they also have an opportunity to choose several courses in a specialty area of particular interest. In addition to completing the required course work, engineering graduates need to pass the national Fundamentals of Engineering (FE) exam, which may be taken during the senior year.

Licensure and Credentials

Obtaining a Bachelor's degree with a major in civil engineering and passing the Fundamentals of Engineering exam satisfies the basic requirements needed to apply for entry-level positions. Further education can be obtained by taking continuing education courses and pursuing a Master's degree. After several years of experience, some civil engineers prepare to become licensed as Professional Engineers (P.E.). The P.E. license is an important credential, similar to the licenses granted to other professionals such as attorneys and physicians. An advantage of holding the P.E. license is that it allows the engineer to submit plans for major public projects.

Green reSource

Building Levees Levees prevent streams and rivers from overflowing their banks. Wetlands and marshes provide natural buffers against flooding, but in their absence, artificial levees are constructed.

Go to your *essentials* ONLINE to view Growing Levee Defenses: Corps Offers Hands-On Training.

Group Workspace

The US Army Corps of Engineers builds and maintains levees. If a levee fails, the results can be disastrous. Identify and discuss a time when human-made levees failed to hold back floodwaters.

PROJECT CONNECTIONS

The American Society of Civil Engineers has published a list of the seven wonders of the modern world. Select two projects from that list and describe why you think they represent great civil engineering achievements.

Reading Check **List** some basic human needs that led to the development of civil engineering.

Fig. 7.1 Modern Wonders Civil engineers have participated in the construction of major landmarks throughout history, including the Seven Wonders of the Modern World: the (1) Channel Tunnel, (2) CN Tower, (3) Empire State Building, (4) Golden Gate Bridge, (5) Itaipu Dam, (6) Netherlands North Sea Protection Works, and (7) Panama Canal. *Name some other well-known structures that are great achievements of civil engineering.*

In addition to passing the national civil engineering P.E. exam, becoming a Professional Engineer requires the completion of several years of work with a progressive increase in professional responsibilities. P.E. candidates must also submit personal and professional references. Some states administer additional tests and have other requirements.

The P.E. exam requires engineers to demonstrate their technical knowledge and their knowledge of engineering ethics. Ethics for civil engineers and for engineers in general requires that engineers protect the public by "knowing and doing what is right." Engineering societies such as the American Society of Civil Engineers publish guidelines for professional conduct. The National Society of Professional Engineers publishes a Code of Ethics, which can be found in the appendix of this book.

Reading Check Identify what fields of study are part of a Bachelor's of Science (BS) degree in engineering.

Fig. 7.2 Loads Engineers need to consider the loads that will affect the structures they are designing. *What static and dynamic loads are shown in this picture?*

Key Technical Concepts

Engineers who work on civil engineering projects must be familiar with a number of technical concepts. Of particular importance to civil engineers, especially those working on large structures or systems, are the principles of forces and of the materials that must withstand those forces.

Structures and Forces

All structures are subject to forces. The type and intensity of those forces play a major role in the design of civil structures. The common loads and forces that affect structures are described below.

- **Dead load** refers to the weight of a structure, including the building materials used for its construction as well as the permanent equipment that is part of that structure. In the case of a train bridge, the dead load is the weight of the bridge itself.
- **Live loads** are loads that are not part of the structure itself. These can be static or dynamic, as defined below:
- **Static loads** are at rest at a given point in time. If a train has come to a stop on a bridge, it is a static load. The total weight of equipment permanently located on the second floor of a factory is another example of a static load.
- **Dynamic loads** change over time. A train passing over a bridge is a dynamic load. As a snowstorm increases the amount of snow on that bridge, the load created by that snow is a dynamic load, as it is growing in weight.

In practice, these loads combine to form the total load that must be considered during the design of a structure. During the design process, civil engineers use computers and specialized software to analyze the forces that will be applied to components and to the overall structure they are designing. (See **Figure 7.2**.)

Materials

In Chapter 6 you learned about some of the important characteristics of materials and found out what makes them suitable for particular applications. Concrete and steel are two of the most important materials used in the construction of civil engineering projects. Most modern civil projects are constructed from a combination of concrete and steel. Concrete is recognized as being the first human-made building material. The Romans used it in many of their projects as early as 500 B.C. Concrete is very strong in compression but weak in tension. To increase its tensile strength, it is often reinforced with steel mesh or rods called rebar.

Concrete Concrete is a composite made from a mixture of an **aggregate** (such as gravel), cement, sand, and water. There are many different kinds of concrete. The exact proportion of each of the ingredients determines the qualities of the concrete as it is being handled and after it has cured. Most concrete mixes reach about 95% of their final strength after three months. Preparing the correct mixture is important because incorrect mixtures can lead to structural failures. One way of testing a concrete mix is to perform a slump test. For slump testing, several samples from the same load are poured into cone-shaped forms. After the forms are removed, the heights of the samples are compared to determine the consistency of the mixture. (See **Figure 7.3**.)

ⓔssentials

STEM CONNECTION

Angle of Elevation

Civil engineers often use right-triangle geometry when designing structures. Geometry and trigonometry are two of the core subjects required for success in this field. Civil engineers often combine these math subjects with the use of physics as they work through design problems.

Personal Tutor

View

Go to your *ⓔssentials* ONLINE to view the *Personal Tutor: Angle of Elevation.*

Fig. 7.3 Slump Test Slump tests are one way of determining the quality of a concrete mix. *What does this slump test tell you about the concrete mix?*

essentials

**Virtual Lab:
Civil Engineering Overview**

Civil engineering allows humans to create buildings and other structures for specific purposes, such as protecting us against the effects of bad weather.

View Go to your **essentials** ONLINE to view the *Virtual Lab: Civil Engineering Overview.*

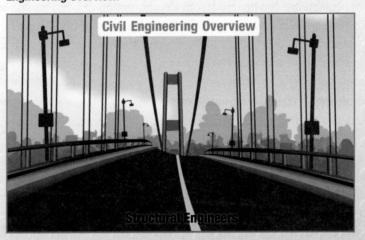

Civil Engineering Overview

Structural Engineers

PROJECT CONNECTIONS

Identify the major materials used to build of the locks of the Panama Canal. What were some of the factors that led to the selection of these materials?

Reading Check **Determine** why it is important for civil engineers to understand the characteristics of materials.

Steel Steel is an alloy that is made by melting iron and then adding carbon and other elements to give it the qualities desired. Generally steel has great tensile strength. The exact properties of a particular type of steel depend on the types and proportions of the elements added. Although the I-beam is the most familiar shape, structural steel can be made into many other shapes. Most civil structures are supported by a steel skeleton of beams and columns. In some structures, such as bridges, the steel structural members are visible. Combining steel and concrete helps to increase fire resistance, which is of particular importance in skyscrapers, apartment buildings, and other structures occupied by large numbers of people.

SECTION 7.1

Check Your Understanding

After You Read Perform the following tasks.

1. **Identify** some accomplishments of civil engineers in ancient and modern times.

2. **Compare and contrast** static loads and dynamic loads.

3. **Analyze** how loads and materials act as constraints upon an engineering design.

Civil Engineering Projects and Applications

One of the advantages of a civil engineering career is that there are many different areas that one might choose as a specialty. There are great opportunities for people who enjoy working outdoors, as well as a variety of positions for people who prefer to do most of their work in an office. A civil engineer working for a firm that specializes in building bridges, for instance, will find that every project presents new challenges because every site is different. This helps to keep the work interesting. This section of the chapter describes some of the major branches of civil engineering and a few of the projects that might be undertaken in those branches.

Construction Engineering

Construction engineering is an important civil engineering activity that ensures that large construction projects, such as houses, large buildings, highways, and bridges, are completed satisfactorily. Construction engineers make sure that structures are built according to plan, using the specified techniques and proper materials. They establish project schedules and prepare cost estimates.

As construction projects progress, construction engineers are responsible for seeing that they are completed on time and within budget. When projects take longer than anticipated, costs increase and profits decrease. (Sometimes firms receive an incentive, or financial bonus, for the early completion of a project. On the other hand, they may suffer a financial penalty if the project is not completed on time.)

Construction engineers supervise the people who are working on the project, so management skills are important for this type of position. They are involved with maintaining the safety of the project site and the workers on that site.

Construction engineers are also in charge of quality assurance. Quality assurance involves monitoring the construction to ensure that the project is being built according to established standards. For this reason, it is important for the construction engineer to have a strong understanding of the entire project as well as its day-to-day progress.

Environmental Engineering

Environmental engineers develop solutions to environmental problems. The goal of environmental engineering is to protect the public by planning, building, and operating systems that control water, land, and air. Because our society is more concerned about protecting the environment than ever before, the demand for environmental engineers is increasing.

---

essentials e

STEM CONNECTION

Simple Interest
Construction engineers are concerned not only with the design of structures, but also with the budgetary requirements of the design. As such, they need to be familiar with general business and finance concepts in order to be able to meet the budgetary constraints of their projects.

Personal Tutor

View
Go to your *essentials* ONLINE to view the *Personal Tutor: Simple Interest.*

✓ **Reading Check** Outline
why it is important for construction engineers to have good project-management skills.

Environmental engineers may work at government agencies to enforce environmental rules and regulations. Private companies also employ environmental engineers to develop systems that prevent or control pollution related to their production activities.

One area of engineering in which large numbers of environmental engineers work is that of water resource management. This includes drinking water treatment and the distribution and treatment of wastewater. Environmental engineers are also involved with systems that clean up contaminated sites and manage solid waste. (See **Figure 7.4**.)

Water Resource Management

Water is one of our most important resources. We need it to sustain life and the lifestyle to which we are accustomed. It is estimated that nearly a billion people in the world do not have access to clean water, and that more than two million children die each year from diseases caused by unclean drinking water. In Africa, the average person uses less than five gallons of water per day. The typical American, on the other hand, uses about 100 gallons each day. Water shortages in the U.S. and elsewhere are becoming increasingly common.

Fig. 7.4 Contaminated Land
Contaminated sites require the expertise of environmental engineers to be redeveloped. *What threats could arise from the improper cleanup of contaminated land?*

Civil engineers who specialize in water resource management work on a range of projects such as dams, canals, tunnels, levees, storage tanks, and **municipal** (city or town) water systems. They are concerned about both the quantity and quality of water. Sources of water include groundwater, lakes, reservoirs, rivers, and oceans. In some areas, there is interest in using water from oceans for drinking purposes. Desalination plants, which remove salt from ocean water, are located near the source. In most other cases, tunnels and pipelines are constructed to bring water from the source to a treatment plant. Sometimes the source and treatment plants are hundreds of miles apart.

The exact procedure for water purification varies according to the quality of the water and each community's needs, but in most cases it is similar to the following process. Pipes or tunnels bring the water from the source to the treatment plant. Screens are used to remove debris. Chlorine and chemicals may be added to adjust the pH of the water. The water is clarified by adding chemicals that cause suspended particles to join and form larger clumps. Then it is sent to a tank to allow the clumps to settle to the bottom of the tank. After it is filtered to remove the remaining particles, the water is disinfected and readied for distribution. Pumping stations and/or water towers are used to produce the pressure needed to distribute the water through mains to individual homes and businesses.

PROJECT CONNECTIONS

Each time a ship travels through the Panama Canal, more than 50 million gallons of fresh water flow into the ocean. Why should environmental engineers be concerned about this? What are some possible solutions?

Wastewater Treatment

Wastewater treatment plants collect sewage from homes, businesses, and industry, and remove **contaminants** (impure substances) so that the water can be put back into the environment safely. In most communities, a system of pipes and pump stations collects sewage and transports it to a municipal treatment plant. The three-stage process that is usually used to treat the sewage is similar to the water purification procedure described above, but with additional stages included.

During the first stage, referred to as primary treatment, the sewage is held in a large tank. Screens are used to remove materials such as twigs and leaves. Materials that float are skimmed off the top and those that settle to the bottom are removed. The heavy material, called sludge, is removed from the bottom of the tank and treated separately. The remaining liquid then moves to secondary treatment, during which biological processes remove the organic contaminants from human waste, food waste, soaps, and detergents. The third stage, called tertiary treatment, involves additional filtering and disinfection (most commonly chlorination, as it is effective and inexpensive). After disinfection, the treated wastewater is safely discharged into either the ground or an ocean, river, or lake.

Air Pollution Management

Some civil engineers work on improving air quality at manufacturing facilities and power plants. Their goal is to bring emissions, which can include **particulate** (tiny) matter and carbon dioxide, down to an acceptable level. Most of the electricity generated in the U.S. today comes from fossil fuel plants that use fuels such as coal, oil, and natural gas. The gases produced by burning these fuels contain carbon dioxide.

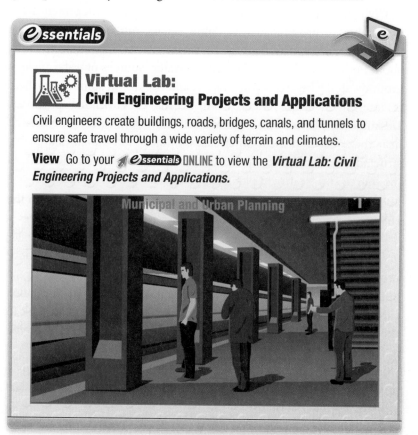

essentials

Virtual Lab: Civil Engineering Projects and Applications

Civil engineers create buildings, roads, bridges, canals, and tunnels to ensure safe travel through a wide variety of terrain and climates.

View Go to your **essentials** ONLINE to view the *Virtual Lab: Civil Engineering Projects and Applications.*

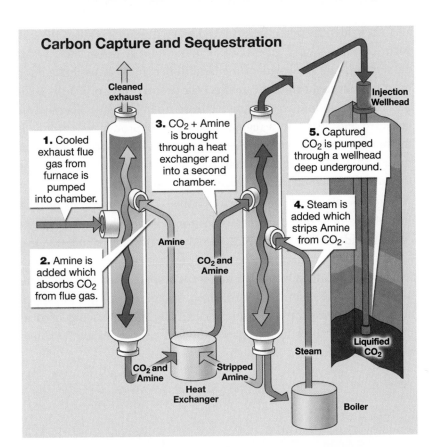

Carbon Capture and Sequestration

Cleaned exhaust

1. Cooled exhaust flue gas from furnace is pumped into chamber.

2. Amine is added which absorbs CO_2 from flue gas.

3. CO_2 + Amine is brought through a heat exchanger and into a second chamber.

4. Steam is added which strips Amine from CO_2.

5. Captured CO_2 is pumped through a wellhead deep underground.

Injection Wellhead

Amine

CO_2 and Amine

CO_2 and Amine

Stripped Amine

Heat Exchanger

Steam

Boiler

Liquified CO_2

Fig. 7.6 Emission Control
Environmental engineers can improve the way we interact with nature. *How do you think this device will affect the environment?*

Scientists concerned about climate change recommend that the quantity of carbon dioxide discharged into the atmosphere should be greatly reduced. Carbon dioxide "scrubbers" are being used to remove carbon dioxide before it is discharged at many plants. In addition, new technologies such as carbon capture and storage show great promise for reducing carbon emissions. Unfortunately, these systems are currently very expensive. As a result, only a few small-scale projects are currently in operation. (See **Figure 7.6**.)

Solid Waste Management

Solid waste management involves systems used to collect and process waste materials. One such system is incineration, the burning of trash at high temperatures. At some plants, the heat generated during this process can be used to heat nearby buildings or provide power production. Another method of managing solid waste is recycling. Many communities have programs that collect and sort materials such as aluminum cans, plastics, cardboard, and newspapers for processing and reuse. Effective recycling programs can greatly reduce the amount of trash going to landfills.

Municipalities use landfills as a safe location for storing solid waste such as the trash collected from homes and businesses. Some landfills are designed for storing hazardous waste from nearby industries. Although landfills are the least expensive way to handle solid waste, many of the existing facilities are full or nearly full. Finding a suitable location for a new landfill can be challenging because most people do not want to live near one. Noisy truck traffic in and out of the landfill site is another concern.

To help identify potential landfill sites, civil engineers study the soil, rock formations, and groundwater conditions at those sites. Water passing through the layers of the landfill becomes contaminated and must be collected before it can affect the groundwater or nearby lakes and streams. Liquid waste samples from operating landfills must be collected and tested on a regular basis. One byproduct of landfills is methane gas, which can be collected for use as fuel. Currently this gas from landfills is used in more than 100 locations in the U.S. and Europe for purposes such as heating greenhouses and generating electricity.

After locating and preparing a suitable site, a waterproof liner of clay, plastic, or a composite material is put in place. The liner functions as the foundation for the landfill. Contaminated water is collected in a leachate system so that it can be treated at a wastewater treatment facility. As trash is added to the landfill, it is compacted and covered with soil. Eventually, when the landfill has reached capacity, it is capped and covered with topsoil. Some former landfills are being used as recreational facilities such as parks and golf courses. **Figure 7.7** shows a typical landfill.

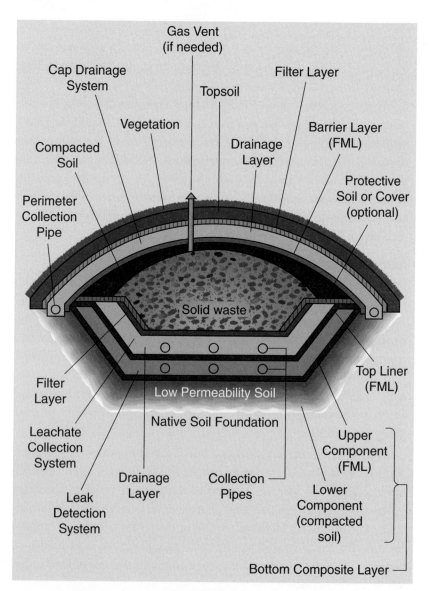

Fig. 7.7 Landfill This drawing shows the cross-section of a typical landfill. *How could a civil engineer change a landfill into something more appealing?*

Geotechnical Engineering

Geotechnical engineers investigate the soil and rock on and below a site that is being considered for a large structure. These investigations help determine if a particular site is appropriate for the proposed structure. Projects that require the work of geotechnical engineers include large buildings, tunnels, walls, dams and levees, bridges, and other structures that require certain soil conditions and characteristics.

Soil is one of the oldest construction materials. It is also one of the most complex, because there are so many types and variations of soil. Soil is a unique material because it has solid, liquid, and gas components. The solid component of soil can include particles of sand, clay, gravel, and other materials. Most often, water is the liquid component of soil, and air is the gas component. An engineering approach to studying soil began in the late 1700s, when the knowledge of mechanics was first applied to soil.

Geotechnical engineers must have an in-depth understanding of geology. In soil mechanics, engineers study the behavior of soil by evaluating the kinds of particles that make up the soil, the size of the particles, the percentage of liquid and gas in the soil, and how the soil behaves when subjected to a variety of laboratory tests. Boring and other soil sampling techniques are used to gather information about the soil beneath the surface. Samples from the borings can be evaluated onsite or in a laboratory. Test results will indicate whether or not the soil is suitable as is, or if steps such as adding, removing, or compacting the soil are necessary.

Foundations are important because they bear the weight of a structure and transmit the load to the earth. Geotechnical engineers design each foundation to support the load of a proposed structure. To do so, they consider the characteristics of the soil and rock at the site. Other factors such as the climate, stability of the ground, and slope of the land must also be considered.

Shallow foundations are suitable for most residential structures. Large structures, on the other hand, because they are heavy and must support large loads, require deep foundations. Some of these larger foundations include reinforcement from columns, tubes, and other devices. The Leaning Tower of Pisa in Italy is a well-known example of a structure with foundation problems. **Figure 7.8** shows one kind of deep foundation.

Structural Engineering

Structural engineering is a specialty area of civil engineering. Structural engineers make sure that buildings and other large structures are strong enough to resist the forces that act upon them. They identify the forces that act on a structure and determine how those forces will impact the structure. Some structural engineers specialize in earthquake engineering, which is particularly important for structures located in regions prone to earthquakes.

Fig. 7.8 Foundation The type of foundation needed is determined by the type of structure it will support. *What type of foundation is needed for a large skyscraper?*

Reading Check **Examine** how environmental engineers must balance the needs of society with those of the environment.

Reading Check Discuss why architects need the contributions of structural engineers when designing a building.

PROJECT CONNECTIONS

Sketch a map that shows the routes that a ship traveling from San Francisco to New York had to take before and after construction of the Panama Canal. How many miles of travel are saved by using the canal?

Structural engineers and architects often work together on projects. When they do, the architect focuses on designing a building that is functional and aesthetically pleasing, while the structural engineer makes sure that the building is structurally safe. For example, during the process of designing a new skyscraper, an architect may want to design a building that is attractive, functional, and unlike any nearby structure. A structural engineer working on the same building will make sure that the architect's design accommodates all the necessary systems—elevators, heating, air conditioning, electricity, communication, and others. Many factors are considered, such as how the building will react to high winds or fire. In addition to their work on buildings, structural engineers also contribute to the design of ships, oil rigs, dams, airliners, and one-of-a-kind structures such as the International Space Station. (See **Figure 7.9**.)

Transportation Engineering

Transportation is an essential part of daily life. Transportation engineers apply engineering principles to transportation problems as they design, build, operate, and maintain systems that efficiently move people and goods. Three major areas of transportation engineering are traffic engineering, rail system engineering, and air transportation systems engineering. Engineers who specialize in one of these three areas often work with engineers from the other two specialties. For example, the task of making a busy airport more efficient may require engineers from each of these areas to work together in designing new access highways and rail links.

Fig. 7.9 Extraterrestrial Engineering Structural engineering is not limited to buildings. *What contributions do you think structural engineers made to the International Space Station?*

Highway and Traffic Engineering

Highway engineering is the process of designing and building safe highways and roads. Highway engineers are concerned with the physical aspects of roads, including curves, the slope of the road, and whether there are obstructions that will limit the view of drivers. Other decisions that highway engineers make include deciding whether the pavement should be asphalt or concrete, determining if banking is required for curves, and deciding whether or not safety barriers such as guard rails are needed. Highway engineers usually work for government agencies (such as state departments of transportation) or for firms that build highways. They often collaborate with traffic engineers. (See **Figure 7.10**.)

Traffic engineers contribute to the design of new highways. They also work on transportation problems related to the use of existing highways, roads, and local streets. One of their major activities is to collect and analyze data on traffic volume and speed, accidents, and road conditions. When the data indicates a need for improvement, traffic control devices may become part of the solution. Traffic control devices include signs, signals, and roadway markings placed on or near roadways. Traffic engineers also help set speed limits. A commonly accepted goal is to set speed limits so that 85% of drivers drive at that speed. This allows police to focus on the 15% of drivers who do not observe the speed limits.

Rail System Engineering

Rail transportation is an efficient and reliable way to move freight, especially bulk goods that need to be transported over great distances. In communities surrounding major cities, passenger rail systems are a convenient way for people to get to and from work. Long-distance passenger train systems have been more successful in Europe than in the U.S., where such rail service is more limited. Civil engineers who work on railway projects design and build major components of the rail system infrastructure, including bridges, tunnels, tracks, and vehicle crossings. They also design and build stations and maintenance facilities. Railway systems employ engineers from other disciplines that specialize in areas

such as control systems, fare-collection systems, and locomotive and passenger coach design. All of these engineers need to work as a team to help the system accomplish its mission. (See **Figure 7.11**.)

Airport Engineering

Designing new airports and upgrading existing airports is a complex engineering activity that requires the expertise of engineers from the various civil engineering specialty areas mentioned in this chapter. The Federal Aviation Administration (FAA) sets the standards that guide airport design in the U.S.

Locating a site for a new airport or finding the space to expand an existing airport is one of the first steps. Many factors must be considered. Is there sufficient population to warrant the construction? Is the necessary land available? Are the existing highways sufficient, or will new highways be needed? Other concerns include noise and the availability of utilities.

The airfield itself is made up of runways, taxiways, and access roads, all of which need to be located and constructed with safety in mind. Runways are made from special mixes of concrete and asphalt designed to support the heavy loads created by airplanes during takeoff and landing. It is also important that the runways last a long time, since major repairs would be costly and disruptive.

Airport terminals include ticket counters, baggage handling systems, security systems and staff, aircraft gates, and support services that sell food and many other items. Other features include offices for the individual airline companies, fuel storage depots, maintenance facilities for the aircraft, and a fire station that must be strategically located to handle emergencies. Airports are constantly being upgraded, so there are excellent career opportunities for engineers of many specialties, whether they are interested in working for firms that design airports or at the airport itself on a permanent basis. (See **Figure 7.12**.)

Fig. 7.11 Railroad Maintenance
Civil engineers guide the construction and maintenance of railroad systems. *What maintenance issues are unique to railroads?*

Fig. 7.12 Airport Upgrade Airport renovation is an important civil engineering task. *Why do airports require periodic upgrades or expansions?*

Municipal and Urban Planning

Municipal and urban planners are involved in all aspects of life in towns and cities. Civil engineers and professionals from many other disciplines work together to improve the residents' quality of life. Civil engineers specializing in municipal planning are usually employed by local, state, or national government, or work for firms that specialize in this area. Their specific contributions include maintaining the infrastructure and anticipating how future growth will impact the need for new highways and systems such as water supply, sewer systems, and mass transit. The degree to which an area is planned varies widely among towns, cities, and regions. Other factors such as economic growth and political circumstances are constraints faced by municipal planners.

✓ **Reading Check** **Compare** some general activities common to engineers working with rail, traffic, and air transportation systems.

SECTION **7.2**

Check Your Understanding

After You Read Perform the following tasks.

1. **Identify** how civil engineers are involved in each method of travel.
2. **Summarize** how engineers help assure that we are provided with clean air and water each day.
3. **Analyze** the ways in which civil engineers can affect how communities, towns, and cities grow.

Review and Assessment

Problem-Solving Process

Identify

Modular construction relies on techniques and materials developed by civil engineers. One technique is the use of a roof truss for light commercial and industrial applications. Roof trusses allow architects to design and build long spans without support columns, resulting in open work areas and spacious storage facilities. You must design a truss that:

- has a 6-in-12 slope.
- spans a distance of 20 ft.
- can be built using single laminations.

Use the following criteria for your model:

- Build to a scale of 1 ft : 1 in.
- Use bass or balsa wood for the chords and webs.
- Use index cards for gussets.

Set Up

1. Research the project. Ask: *"What types of connections can best distribute the load?"* and *"What designs are the most effective?"*
2. Gather information about the various styles and types of engineered roof trusses and how the stress can be dissipated.
3. Brainstorm potential solutions. Develop ideas for the overall style and placement of structural components.
4. Using a decision matrix, choose the best solution.

Execute

5. Plan the building of the solution with your team. What resources will you need? How will you construct the model?
6. Keep sketching and recording ideas to improve the design.
7. Build mock-ups of the solution, using various methods.
8. At the end of each session, discuss the day's progress with your team. Keep a log of any problems, discoveries, or changes.

Evaluate

Test the prototypes. Develop a method that will test the structural integrity of the truss. Record test results and find the most successful design.

Share

Share your sketches and test results in a report. Discuss how the structural components and gussets handle the stress of the static load.

Critical Thinking

Key Concepts

1. **Identify** the major branches of civil engineering and the types of projects involved in each.

2. **Summarize** the history of civil engineering.

3. **Compare and Contrast** structural engineering and geotechnical engineering.

4. **Evaluate** the ways in which different materials affect the structure of a building.

5. **Analyze** how the environment influences the design of a structure.

Leadership 21st Century Skills

6. **Share** with your project team what you have learned about structures and forces, and how that information connects to your Discovery Project.

7. **Report** what you have learned about the construction, environmental, and transportation branches of civil engineering. How can information about these branches be applied to your Discovery Project?

Activity Center

Go to the **Activity Center** to review chapter vocabulary and key concepts.

Engineer's Toolbox

Go to the **Engineer's Toolbox** to:
- Access Academic Activities
- Access the Competitive Event Prep Activity

essentials

DISCOVERY PROJECT

Design and Build a Model Lock System

In this chapter's Discovery Project, you will design and build a model lock system. Your team's model lock system should be able to move a toy boat from one level of water to another.

Go to your *essentials* ONLINE to view the video to learn about the operation of the Panama Canal. Then collaborate with your team on this Discovery Project.

Electrical and Electronics Engineering

ESSENTIAL QUESTION **What is the main difference between a career in electrical engineering and a career in electronics engineering?**

Electrical engineers design and develop power generation and transmission systems. These systems supply the power that operates devices throughout the developed world. Electronics engineers design and develop electronic devices ranging from sensors that turn devices on and off to the mobile telephones and other devices that have become an integral part of our everyday lives.

*e*ssentials

DISCOVERY PROJECT

Design and Build a Survival Flashlight

21st Century Skills
Why are communication skills vital to the smooth execution of a project plan?

Energy of one form or another is required to create electrical energy. In disaster situations, human energy is sometimes the only resource available to create electrical energy. In this chapter's Discovery Project, you will design and construct a survival flashlight that is human-powered and can be used in emergency situations. See page 167 for a brief description of this project.

 Engineer's Blog

During the video, watch and listen for important facts about electric power generation. Write down some ideas about how to generate electrical energy.

 Engineer's Toolbox

Go to the Engineer's Toolbox to
- Access Note-Taking Activities
- Access Graphic Organizers
- Access Academic Standards met by this chapter

ENR.com

ENR
Engineering News-Record

Go to your *essentials* ONLINE to learn how an electric generator works. In your own words, write a description of the basics of how a device of this type creates electrical power.

READING GUIDE

Before You Read What is the primary focus of electrical engineering? What are some of the main challenges that electronics engineers will face?

Objectives

- **Discuss** specialty and licensure options of electrical engineers.
- **Identify** at least four measurements (and their units of measure) that are critical to electrical and electronics engineers.
- **Explain** Ohm's Law.
- **Describe** several ways energy is used to create electricity.
- **Compare** Direct Current and Alternating Current.
- **Analyze** the effect of digital electronics and integrated circuits

Main Idea

Electrical and electronics engineers supply electrical power and the devices that use electrical power to enhance the ease of modern life.

Vocabulary

Content Vocabulary

- electromagnetic force (EMF)
- conductors
- capacitor
- conductance
- electrochemical cell
- hydroelectric
- photovoltaic
- transformer
- schematic diagram
- resistor
- diode
- transistor
- analog
- digital

Academic Vocabulary

- principles
- distribution
- visible
- integrated

Note-Taking Activity

Draw this table for each section. Write key terms and phrases under **Cues.** Write main ideas under **Note Taking.** Summarize the section under **Summary.**

Cues	Note Taking
•	•
•	•
Summary	

Graphic Organizers

Use graphic organizers to organize information as you read.

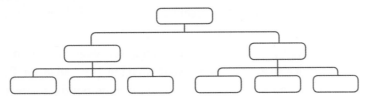

Go to your **essentials** ONLINE for downloadable graphic organizers.

ACADEMIC

Technology

ITEEA STL16.01 Energy cannot be created nor destroyed; however, it can be converted from one form to another.

ITEEA STL16.05 Power systems must have a source of energy, a process, and loads.

Mathematics

NCTM Algebra Use mathematical models to represent and understand quantitative relationships.

Science

NSES A Students should develop abilities necessary to do scientific inquiry, understandings about scientific inquiry.

ITEEA *International Technology and Engineering Educators Association*
NCTM *National Council of Teachers of Mathematics*
NSES *National Science Education Standards*

College & Career READINESS

Reading Determine central ideas or themes of a text and analyze their development; summarize the key supporting details and ideas.

Speaking and Listening Make strategic use of digital media and visual displays of data to express information and enhance understanding of presentations.

Electrical Engineering Overview

What Is Electrical Engineering?

Electrical engineering involves the study of electricity, mainly for power transmission and similar applications. It also includes subfields or specialties such as electronics engineering. Electrical engineers work with various devices including those used in power generation, systems used for power transmission, and systems used in broad scale communications.

The profession of electrical engineering grew from the development of communications systems such as the telegraph in the mid-1800s. Later that century, when electricity became a source of power, the profession developed further. This was aided by inventions by Alexander Graham Bell and Thomas Alva Edison. As the devices that used electrical power became more sophisticated, so did the profession of electrical engineering.

Reading Check **List** two major systems that electrical engineers build and maintain.

What is Electronics Engineering?

Electronics engineering is a specialty of electrical engineering. While electrical engineering primarily involves the transmission of electrical power, electronics engineering includes the transmission of information or signals. Electronics engineers and those who work in the subfields of electronics engineering design and implement the devices powered by electricity in our everyday lives. Everything from handheld smart phones to state-of-the-art televisions involves an electronics engineer at some point in its design.

Education

Electrical and electronics engineers in the United States have a four- or five-year undergraduate degree. The undergraduate degree requires specialized study in physics, mathematics, project management, and various other courses unique to electricity and electronic devices and designs. Many electrical and electronics engineers choose to engage in advanced study at the postgraduate level.

Licensure and Credentials

Many electrical and electronics engineers earn a license as a Professional Engineer (P.E.). Although this licensure is not required to be a practicing engineer, in most states and localities a P.E. is needed for someone to be responsible for a document, a set of plans, or a report.

The P.E. license is granted by a state. This license can then be endorsed by states other than the issuing state, making it possible for P.E.s to move around and work in different states throughout their careers. An electrical and electronics P.E. candidate must take a Fundamentals of Engineering exam and an exam in the desired field of specialty. The

National Council of Examiners for Engineering and Surveying (NCEES) develops and standardizes these national tests, but individual states set their own passing scores and some also set more specific requirements for licensure.

Key Technical Concepts

Electrical and electronics engineers must master knowledge of the forces and effects of electromagnetism. They must understand concepts including electrical current, charge, capacitance, induction, potential, power, and resistance as well as all of their associated units of measure. These engineers must also know the electrical properties of various materials and have the ability to use mathematical formulas related to electricity and other physics concepts.

Charge

Electrical charge is the relationship between protons and electrons. **Electromagnetic force (EMF)**, or the attractive or capacitive force which acts between charged particles, is the basis for all electrical interactions between particles of matter. Electrical charge is either positive or negative and is measured in coulombs.

Current

Electric current is the rate of flow of an electrical charge caused by electrons moving within a conductor. The unit of measure of electric current is the ampere. Effective **conductors**, such as copper or aluminum, contain mobile, or free, electrons, which means that electrons can move easily through the material. Current is measured using a device called an ammeter.

There are two types of flow of electric current: alternating current (AC) and direct current (DC). To put it most simply, the main way in which AC and DC differ is in the way the electrons flow. In DC, the electrons flow in a single direction, and in AC the electrons flow in alternating directions. DC is generally used in portable devices such as mobile telephones, and laptop or tablet computers. This is because DC is the type of current that can be acquired from an electrochemical reaction, such as in a battery. AC is generally safer to transfer over longer distances. It can travel much farther than DC, so it is the preferred form of current to transfer power to homes and other places using "the electrical grid."

Potential

Electric potential is sometimes referred to as voltage since it is measured in volts. Simply stated, voltage between two points is the electrical force that would drive an electric current between those two points. The greater the electric potential, or voltage, the greater the current can be. A standard AA cell is rated at 1.5 volts. Comparing that to a standard 9-volt battery, one would say that the 9-volt battery has more potential to provide energy than the one AA cell. Voltage is measured using a device called a voltmeter.

Fig. 8.1 Operation of a Capacitor

In a capacitor there is a pair of conductors separated by an insulator. *Why is it important to be able to store an electrical charge in a circuit?*

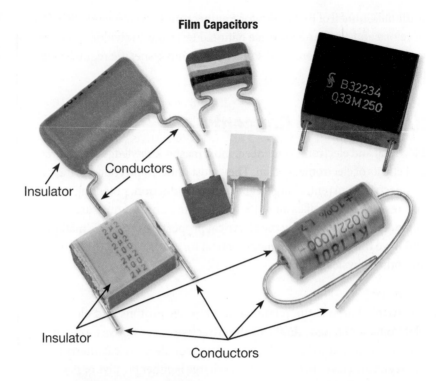

Film Capacitors

Insulator

Conductors

Insulator

Conductors

Ceramic Capacitor

Electrolytic Capacitor

Capacitance

A **capacitor** is an electrical device capable of storing an electrical charge. Its ability to store the charge is called capacitance. Capacitance is also a measure of the amount of energy stored for a given electrical potential. In a capacitor there is a pair of conductors separated by an insulator.

When there is a difference in voltage between the two conductors, energy is stored in an electrical field in the insulator. The more energy that can be stored, the greater the object's capacitance is. The unit of measure of capacitance is the farad, and it is measured using a multimeter.

Power

Electric power is the rate at which electrical energy is transferred. Electric power is determined by the potential and current in an electrical circuit. The watt is the unit of electrical power. More energy is transferred to a 60-watt light than is transferred to a 15-watt light, even though they

PROJECT CONNECTIONS

How much power will your survival flashlight require? What will be the source of the power, and how long will it take to produce?

may be on the same electrical circuit. According to Joule's law, electric power can be determined using the equation $P = VI$, where P is the electric power, V is the potential difference, and I is the electric current.

Resistance and Conductance

Electrical resistance is the opposition to the passage of an electric current in an object or material. Resistance is reciprocal to electrical **conductance,** meaning that they describe the same thing, but are expressed in a different way, using different units of measure. Resistance is measured in ohms, and conductance is measured in siemens. Resistance is measured using an ohmmeter. To convert from resistance in ohms to conductance in siemens, use the formula $R = \frac{1}{G}$ where G is the conductance measured in siemens, and R is the resistance measured in ohms. As these values are reciprocal, you would use a similar formula to convert conductance to resistance. To convert from conductance in siemens to resistance in ohms use the equation $G = \frac{1}{R}$.

Material Properties

In addition to the concepts related to electrical phenomena described above, an electrical engineer is also concerned with the various electrical properties of materials. The primary electrical property of a material is whether, at normal temperatures, it is a conductor, an insulator, or a semiconductor.

Pure silver, copper, gold, and aluminum have the highest conductivity of all the elements listed in the periodic table. Cost and availability can be a major factor in deciding what conducting material to use. In the past, a lot of electrical wire was made from aluminum. In more recent years, nearly all wire has been made from copper or copper alloys.

The purity, density, and temperature of a material make its electrical properties vary a great deal. Early in the twentieth century it was discovered that some materials displayed superconductivity, meaning that the material's resistivity at a very low temperature was zero, making it a perfect conductor for electricity. This means that in ideal conditions, once set in motion electrical current will flow forever in a superconductor.

Insulators are materials that do not conduct electricity well. Often, insulators are used to protect us from materials that are being used to conduct electricity. Plastic and rubber are commonly used as insulators. An example of an insulator application is in the plastic casing around electrical wire.

A semiconductor's conductivity falls in between that of a conductor and that of an insulator. Silicon is the most widely known and most widely used semiconductor in electrical applications. A semiconductor is a substance that sometimes acts as a conductor and sometimes as a resistor of electricity. Semiconductor technology has enabled electronic devices to become smaller and smaller. Advances due to the use of silicon chips are the basis for Moore's Law. In 1965 Gordon Moore predicted that the number of transistors that could be placed on an integrated circuit would double approximately every two years.

PROJECT CONNECTIONS

What types of materials will be used for the body of your device?

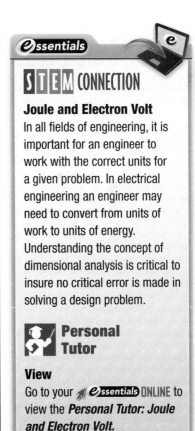

*e*ssentials

STEM CONNECTION

Joule and Electron Volt

In all fields of engineering, it is important for an engineer to work with the correct units for a given problem. In electrical engineering an engineer may need to convert from units of work to units of energy. Understanding the concept of dimensional analysis is critical to insure no critical error is made in solving a design problem.

Personal Tutor

View
Go to your *e*ssentials ONLINE to view the *Personal Tutor: Joule and Electron Volt.*

There are so many metal alloys and compound materials that it is difficult to determine the exact number. All of them have different electrical properties, allowing them to be selected for optimal use in engineering applications.

Laws of Physics

There are many laws, theorems, and formulas of physics that are applied in electrical engineering. For instance, Coulomb's law, Ampere's law, Gauss's law, Faraday's law, and Ohm's law all describe electrical relationships and phenomena. There are hundreds of mathematical equations that engineers use for the purposes of optimization and to perform simple calculations in the development of devices and systems.

Ohm's Law

Perhaps the most widely known law in the field of electricity, Ohm's law is named after the physicist who created it, Georg Simon Ohm. Ohm's Law defines the relationship among electrical potential (voltage), rate of flow (current), and resistance in an electric circuit. Ohm's law is the basis for simple to sophisticated circuit analysis, and is often employed by electrical and electronics engineers in their work.

The relationship among voltage, current, and resistance is always proportional. If two values of the three are known, then a simple calculation can determine the third. There are three common algebraic representations of this phenomenon. The formula that you choose to

Virtual Lab: Electrical Engineering

Electrical and electronics engineering processes allow people to generate, transmit, and store power. Power storage allows us to create and operate devices and manipulate the environment. Electrical engineers create a wide range of systems and devices used in communications and in power generation and transmission.

View Go to your *essentials* ONLINE to view the *Virtual Lab: Electrical Engineering.*

Electrical Engineering

express Ohm's Law should be based on which two of the three variables you know, and which one you are trying to discover:

$$current(I) = \frac{voltage(V)}{resistance(R)} \text{ or } I = \frac{V}{R}$$

$$voltage(V) = current(R) \times resistance(R) \text{ or } V = IR$$

$$resistance(R) = \frac{current(I)}{voltage(V)} \text{ or } R = \frac{I}{V}$$

If the voltage in a circuit is increased, the current will increase proportionally. If resistance is increased, then current will decrease proportionally. Voltage is expressed in volts, current is expressed in amperes, and resistance is expressed in ohms.

For example, if you build a simple series circuit using an incandescent light bulb that has a resistance of 2 ohms and a power source that provides 1.5 volts, then the current in the circuit would be 0.75 amps. If you increase the voltage in the same circuit to 3.0 volts, then the current would also increase to 1.5 amps. If you take the same circuit with 3.0 volts and instead used a light bulb with an increased resistance of 4 ohms, then the current would decrease to 0.75 amps.

Electrochemistry

Electricity can be generated in several ways. In what most people know as a battery (more formally known as an **electrochemical cell**), voltage is produced by a chemical reaction. In an electrochemical cell, voltage is produced using two electrodes and an electrolyte. In one well-known experiment, voltage is produced using a piece of steel and a piece of copper as electrodes, and a lemon or its acidic juice as the electrolyte. While this creates a very small amount of power, it does demonstrate the basic reaction in many battery types.

Scientists and engineers have developed more advanced substances and battery chemistries to create chemical reactions for various applications. Nickel, zinc, lithium, mercury, silver, and cadmium can be used with various electrolytes to create electrochemical cells. All of these offer advantages and disadvantages.

PROJECT CONNECTIONS
Determine if your device will need to store electrical energy and if so, how it may be stored. Will you be able to use a rechargeable battery or a capacitor to store power for later?

✓ **Reading Check** **Describe** the relationship among electrical potential (voltage), rate of flow (current), and resistance in an electric circuit, according to Ohm's Law.

Check Your Understanding

SECTION **8.1**

After You Read Perform the following tasks.

1. **Describe** why capacitors are used in circuits.

2. **Explain** how an electrochemical cell creates energy.

3. **Contrast** three of the material properties of which electrical engineers must be aware, and discuss why this knowledge is vital.

Electrical and Electronics Engineering Applications

PROJECT CONNECTIONS

The generator for your survival flashlight will need to be human-powered. What type of generator will you use? Can you reclaim one from another device? Can you build your own? Can you use a motor to act as a generator?

Types of Projects

Electrical and electronics engineers are employed in many industries, including telecommunications, energy and power, and computer hardware development. Electrical and electronics engineers may also be employed in more interdisciplinary industries such as aerospace, manufacturing, and transportation. An electrical or electronics engineer may also work to develop systems that are used in robotics, for life support, or even in entertainment devices such as amusement park rides.

Power Generation

The process of generating electricity is creating electricity from other forms of energy. This can be accomplished in various ways, many of which are based on the same primary principles, or generally applicable theorems or laws.

Electric Generators

An electric generator converts mechanical energy to electrical energy. Examples of electric generators include turbines and engines, both of which derive electricity from rotary motion. The magnetic fields that result from coils of wire moving around another wire create a steady flow of electrons. The first turbines used to generate electricity were human-powered. Following simple human-powered models, the same concept was applied to water physically moving a water wheel to create the needed rotary movement. Water is still used today as a source of power in **hydroelectric** power generation, or power generated from the movement of water. Today, steam engines and nuclear fission are also used to create the mechanical movement, but the basic principle (mechanical movement) of how the electricity is generated remains the same.

Fig. 8.2 Electric Generators
These hydroelectric generators inside a dam are used to supply energy to the electric grid. *What are some other ways in which electricity can be produced for the electrical grid?*

Gas-Powered Generators

An internal combustion engine can be used to generate electricity using gasoline or diesel fuel as a source of energy. Generally used for smaller scale applications, the rotary motion that comes from the reciprocating engine is used to generate electricity. This type of technology is often used for backup or emergency situations.

Fossil Fuel and Nuclear-Powered Generators

Fossil fuels such as coal, oil, and natural gas are also used to generate electricity. Burning these fuels creates heat, which is used to make steam. The pressure from the steam turns a turbine, which provides the rotary motion needed to generate electricity. Nuclear fission reactions produce heat, which is used in the same way as fossil fuels to create steam, which also is then used to generate electricity.

Other Sources of Electrical Power

As people have identified needs for alternative ways to generate electricity, engineers have developed new technologies. Some applications use biomass and geothermal energy sources to produce electricity. Tidal water movement is also used to generate power. New technology has optimized wind turbine efficiency. Finally, panel arrays called **photovoltaic** arrays use solar radiation to produce electricity.

Power Distribution and Transmission

Many electrical engineers are in charge of designing and maintaining power distribution and transition systems. Generally, electrical power is produced at a central plant or station using a generator or other means described above, and then the electricity is stepped up in voltage using a **transformer**. The transformer is used in this way because transferring the electricity at a higher voltage is more practical and economical. The power is transferred to high voltage transmission lines, then to a substation where the voltage is stepped down, again using a transformer. From the substation it then goes to a series of utility poles above ground or lines below ground, which bring the power to the customer.

Fig. 8.3 Parts of the Electrical Distribution System
Transformers (a), utility poles (b), high voltage power lines (c), and other components combine to form the electrical grid that supplies power to our homes and workplaces. *What is the function of transformers within the electrical grid?*

Reading Check **Discuss** how engineers use the universal systems model in their work on systems that involve energy.

Reading Check Describe how power is distributed and transmitted through the electrical grid.

Visualization

Electrical Drawings Electrical and electronics drawings are a little different than mechanical, architectural, or civil engineering drawings. The diagrams are not always drawn to a particular scale and often do not look like the finished product. Being able to visualize is very important here. The symbols on these drawings can help in making a mental picture of the finished product.

Group Workspace

Visualize the components of the electrical system in your home.

Go to your *essentials* ONLINE to learn more about developing electrical drawing visualization and interpretation.

"The Electrical Grid"

The interconnected system used in power generating applications for commercial and residential use is commonly referred to as "the electrical grid." Electrical engineers are challenged to develop systems and devices that work using the AC power commonly available from the grid. These applications and devices are sometimes referred to as on-grid applications.

Electrical engineers may also be involved in the design, maintenance and implementation of off-the-grid systems and devices. Sometimes it is not economically feasible to supply power to a place that is far from the closest available power lines on the grid. Also, some companies, institutions, and individuals have chosen to generate their own power for consumption. This is known as off-grid power.

Control

In addition to power generation and delivery, electrical engineering projects come from the need for electrical and mechanical control systems. Circuits and devices such as digital signal processors and microcontrollers are often used in the design of control systems.

Control systems are designed with a systems model in mind. Various inputs, controls, and outputs can be used or monitored, with or without sensors, and this approach can be implemented in the design of control systems for electronic devices. Take a commercially available dishwashing machine, for example. An engineer may design this device to go through a series of cycles from start to finish without any feedback from sensors. In more sophisticated models, sensors designed to monitor temperature, water consumption, and other things involved in washing the dishes may be incorporated into a system that provides feedback to a central control unit, or computer, which will then adjust certain aspects of the system as needed.

Circuitry

At the heart of all electrical and electronics applications is the design of the circuitry inherent in the devices. There are two main types of circuits, series and parallel. An understanding of how these circuits work is critical in the design of electrical and electronic systems.

In a simple DC series circuit, a power source and other electrical components are arranged in a closed loop (See **Figure 8.4**). For example, a 9V battery and two light bulbs connected together in one loop form

Fig. 8.4 Series Circuit This figure includes a schematic diagram that represents electrical components in a typical series circuit. *How could these components be arranged to form the circuit in your chapter Discovery Project?*

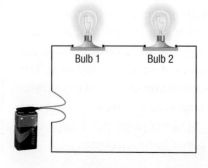
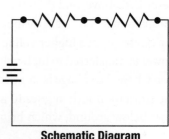

Schematic Diagram

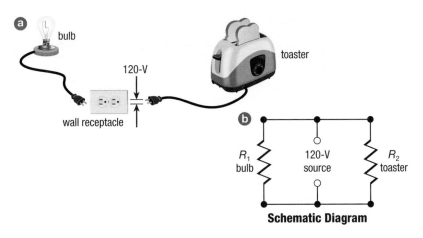

a bulb

120-V

wall receptacle

toaster

b

R_1
bulb

120-V
source

R_2
toaster

Schematic Diagram

a series circuit. In this scenario, the second light bulb would collect less power than the first due to the voltage drops that occur in a series circuit, and therefore be less bright in theory. The second light bulb would collect a decreasing part of the original nine volts. In this case, each would collect 4.5 volts. If one of the light bulbs is removed, the circuit is broken and the other light bulb will not function.

In a simple DC parallel circuit, a power source and other components are arranged in a step-like pattern. If the same 9V battery and two light bulbs were used, the voltage to each bulb would be the original nine volts. As a result, the bulbs will shine more brightly than in the series circuit. If one of the lights is removed, the other will remain lit, since there is no break in the connectivity to the second bulb. In **Figure 8.5** is an illustration of an AC parallel circuit. Because this is a parallel circuit, the energy supplied to the toaster and light bulb are unaffected by the other device.

Schematic Diagrams

In designing electrical systems, plan drawings are generally done using a **schematic diagram** of the electrical components instead of drawing what they would look like physically. A sample of a schematic drawing is shown in **Figure 8.5(b)**. There are standard symbols for electrical components in a schematic diagram. Solid lines are drawn to show that devices should be connected together and how they should be arranged in the circuit. There are standard symbols for electrical and electronic components that are used in schematics such as those for power sources, resistors, transformers, loads, and other components. See **Table 8.1** on page 160 for a listing of common electronic components and their schematic symbols.

Electronics

The term "electronic" is generally used to describe small scale electrical applications, yet the basic principles remain the same as for applications referred to as "electrical". On a small scale, electricity and the flow of electrons is managed and, in some cases, behaves differently than in large-scale power transmission or communications applications. Electronics engineers design devices, along with some of the applications for which

Reading Check **Determine** how knowledge of circuits and components contributes to the ability of an electrical engineer to provide the most efficient application for a project.

PROJECT CONNECTIONS
Draw a schematic diagram of the electronics that will be incorporated in your device. Use standard symbols in your diagram and show all of the connections.

Reading Check **Explain** how engineers use schematic diagrams to create their designs.

Type	Schematic Symbol	Notes	Type	Schematic Symbol	Notes
Fixed Resistor	*R*	Limits current and reduces voltage	Iron-Core Transformer	*T* Primary / Secondary	Steps up or steps down ac voltages
Variable Resistor	*R*	Has three external connections Varies voltage	Light-Emitting Diode (LED)	Anode / Cathode	Produces visible or infrared light
Fixed Capacitor	*C*	Stores electric charge Blocks dc, passes ac	Semiconductor Diode	Anode / Cathode *D*	Passes current in only one direction
Electrolytic Capacitor	*C*	Has large capacitance. Must be connected with proper polarity. Fixed values only	Zener Diode	Anode / Cathode *D*	Regular voltage
Variable Capacitor	*C*	Used for tuning radios, TVs, and other electronic communications equipment	Bipolar Transistor	Collector Base Emitter	Used for amplification and switching
Air Inductor	*L*	Induces voltage when current changes Passes dc, limits ac			
Iron Core Inductor	*L*	Used for low frequencies	Metal Oxide Semiconductor Field-Effect Transistor (MOSFET), Transistor	Drain Gate Source	Used for switching
Variable Inductor	*L*	Used for tuning radios, TVs, and other electronic communications equipment			

Table 8.1 Typical Schematic Symbols

PROJECT CONNECTIONS

Does your project require a resistor or resistors to control the flow of electricity to the light source?

they may be used. In general, electronics engineers understand the purpose and use of each of the following devices.

Resistors

Most any material has a resistance to electron flow. A **resistor** in an electronic circuit can be used to optimize the flow of current and control the voltage applied in a circuit. Resistors are commonly made from carbon, and sometimes from other ceramics and metals. Resistors are rated in ohms and they have numbers (see **Figure 8.6**) or color bands to code their ratings. For a resistor with the number code 272, the first two digits indicate the value, and the third digit indicates the power of 10 by which the first two digits are multiplied. Applying this information, the value of this resistor is 2,700Ω, or 2.7 kΩ ($27 \times 10^2 = 2700$).

Diodes

A **diode** is a device that is normally used to allow electric current to flow in one direction, but will block current from flowing in the other direction. Diodes can also be used to regulate voltage or even convert AC to DC. Most diodes are made from semiconductor materials such as silicon or germanium. Diodes are rated based on the voltage and current they allow to pass through. Note that if a diode is overloaded, it might explode.

Light-Emitting Diodes (LEDs)

LEDs are used as indicator lights in electronic devices. Some types of LEDs are also used as light sources and in applications such as traffic lights and televisions. They are made from combinations of semiconductor materials, such as gallium, zinc, and aluminum nitrides and phosphides, to create infrared, ultraviolet (UV), and visible-spectrum light. When a voltage is applied, the LED emits energy in the form of photons.

Transistors

Perhaps the most important electrical device developed in the twentieth century, a **transistor** is a semiconductor device that can be used to switch or amplify electronic signals in a circuit. Transistors are made from materials including germanium, silicon, and silicon carbide, and come in many different types. They generally have three connections or "legs" which would be labeled in a schematic as the base, the collector, and the emitter. Transistors are usually labeled based on their type.

The use of transistors in computing applications is the main reason they are one of the most important inventions of the twentieth century. Transistors are incorporated into very small integrated circuits. Today's computer processors contain hundreds of millions of transistors.

Capacitors

A capacitor is used to store energy in a circuit. They may also be used to block the flow of DC and to filter out interference in electrical signals. Most capacitors are made from ceramic or metal-oxide film, but the principal of capacitance can also be demonstrated with glass, plastic, and even air or paper. Metal-oxide film capacitors are known as electrolytic capacitors and potentially have a higher capacitance than other types. Capacitors are rated in farads based on their capacitance.

Larger capacitors can store a high voltage and can be harmful when discharged. Devices that contain large capacitors should not be opened or worked on by an untrained person.

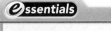

STEM CONNECTION

Resistance and Current in a Parallel Circuit Electrical and electronics engineers often work with circuitry. It is important for them to be able to solve basic problems relating to circuits in parallel as well as to circuits connected in series.

Personal Tutor

View

Go to your *essentials* ONLINE to view the **Personal Tutor: Resistance and Current in a Parallel Circuit.**

PROJECT CONNECTIONS

Is it possible to use a small DC motor to act as a generator in your device?

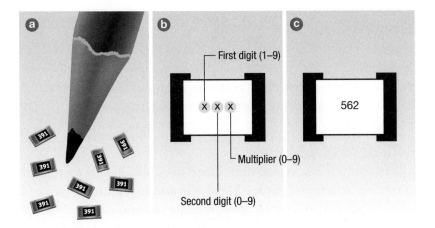

Fig. 8.6 Resistor Codes The first image (a) shows the relative size of surface-mount resistors, Resistors are coded to show the amount of resistance they provide (b). *Use calculations to determine the rating of the resistor in (c).*

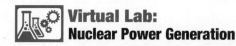

Virtual Lab: Nuclear Power Generation

An electrical engineer designs, develops, and implements some of the most critical and enjoyable elements in modern life. Digital cameras, phones, and energy and power systems are all created by electrical engineers. Electrical and electronics engineering applications comprise numerous power generation systems, including nuclear power.

View Go to your *essentials* ONLINE to view the *Virtual Lab: Nuclear Power Generation.*

Nuclear Power Plant Personnel

Inductors

An inductor is a coil of wire that is used to store energy in a magnetic field. Induction can be used to charge devices such as powered toothbrushes where there are no metal contacts with the charger device. Because inductance varies when metals are present near or inside an inductor, it can also be used as a sensor in metal detection devices. Inductors are rated in units of henries.

Sensors

There are many different types of electrical and electronic sensors that can be used inside devices. An electronic temperature sensor is called a thermistor. Electronic hygrometers can be used to sense humidity. Photoresistors can be used as light sensors. Many types of sensors can be used to provide feedback in a control system and/or to simply measure levels.

Actuators and Motors

An actuator is a mechanical device used to create physical movement in a system. A common motor is a type of an actuator that, when powered by electricity, creates rotary motion. A motor can be used with different types of gears to create and change rotary, linear, reciprocating, or oscillating movement in a system. Electrical and electronic actuators have many applications in engineering.

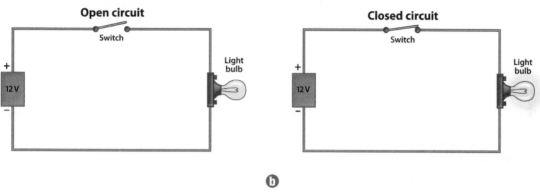

Fig. 8.7 Typical Switches
(a) Various switching devices are used in electrical circuits. (b) Switches shown in a circuit diagram. *Which of these switches in (a) would you select for use in your chapter Discovery Project?*

Rotary Switch **Toggle Switch** **Dual In-line Package (DIP) Switch**

a

Open circuit — Switch — + 12 V − Light bulb

Closed circuit — Switch — + 12 V − Light bulb

b

An electric motor works in a way that is similar but more or less opposite to an electric generator. A combination of magnets and coils of wire convert electrical voltage to mechanical movement. There are many types of motors available for various applications. Servos and stepper motors are types of motors that are widely used in computer output devices such as printers and in some robotics applications.

Switches and Relays

An electrical switch at the basic level is used to either break/complete, or open/close, or turn on/turn off a circuit. Switches come in many shapes and sizes as shown in **Figure 8.7**. It is important for an electrical engineer to understand the purpose and applications of many basic types. A toggle switch is an example of a simple switch that turns a device on or off. A rotary switch is used on devices which have two or more different "states" or modes of operation, such as to select from possible settings on a clothes washer, or to select air output settings in a car's climate control system. The Dual In-line Package (DIP) switch is used in some remote controls to prevent interference when the remote control is used to operate more than one device.

A relay is a type of switch that is electrically operated rather than mechanically operated. Relays have many applications in the transportation industry and other fields. Relays were integral components of early telegraph machines and telephone exchanges, and have had many applications in the rail industry.

PROJECT CONNECTIONS

If your device will be designed to store power for a short time, you will probably need to incorporate a switch into its operation. What type of switch would be best for this application?

Fig. 8.8 Printed Circuit Boards
The use of printed circuit boards enables efficient production of electronic devices, increasing reliability and decreasing size. *Name some devices you use every day that you think might include printed circuit boards in their design.*

Component side

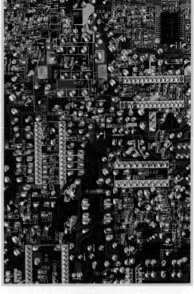

Solder side

Greening the Construction Fleet Hybrid cars are a common sight on today's roadways. Fuel-efficient construction vehicles are becoming more common as well.

 Group Workspace

The engine in a construction vehicle is very different than the engine in a passenger car. Outline what engineers should consider when designing an industrial engine.

Go to your *essentials* ONLINE to learn about the Big Electric Cat Bulldozer.

Printed Circuit Boards

Many electrical and electronics engineers design printed circuit boards (PCBs) for use in their design applications. A printed circuit board enables engineers to replace bulky wiring with circuits that are smaller in scale.

On a printed circuit board, components with leads and surface mount components are mounted to one side. The leads extending through the board are then soldered on the side opposite the components. (See **Figure 8.8**.)

Analog vs. Digital Electronics

In the early years of using electricity to provide energy to do work, all electrical signals were **analog**. This meant that the electrical signals in circuits could be continuously variable. Modern electronics has moved to a **digital** domain, or one in which electrical signals are commonly transferred at two different levels, to indicate low and high. In logic and computing devices, these lows and highs can be translated into a series of ones and zeroes, also known as binary code.

With digital electronics have come many new devices such as integrated circuits (see **Figure 8.9**) and microprocessors. In an integrated circuit (IC) chip, several small-scale electronic devices such as resistors and transistors can be put together in a small space. This helps to save space and optimize the size of devices. Microprocessors are also built by putting very small-scale devices on a small chip, which is commonly called a "microchip."

The design of these small-scale devices has led to the use of the term "microelectronics," which is specialty field in electrical engineering. The design and development of semiconductors, integrated circuits, and microprocessors are all included in the category of microelectronics.

Fig. 8.9 Integrated Circuits
The development of the integrated circuit enabled electronic circuitry to become even smaller, thus ushering in the era of powerful portable devices. *What newly available devices can you think of that are as small as they are because they have integrated circuits in their design?*

Telecommunications

One of the largest industries to employ electrical and electronics engineers is telecommunications. Although the industry is increasing its use of light and fiber-optic cables, communications systems are largely based in electronics. Whether communications happen over the airwaves such as in radio or microwave transmissions, or over lines of copper, coaxial, or optical fiber, there are electrical and electronic devices at both ends of the system that use electricity to code, transmit, and decode the communications signals.

Some telecommunications devices include those used in broadcast and cable television, internet service, telephone lines and mobile devices.

Reading Check **List** three ways in which communication signals are currently transmitted.

Check Your Understanding

SECTION **8.2**

After You Read Perform the following tasks.

1. **Identify** four common sources of power used in electrical generators.

2. **Evaluate** why is it necessary to transmit electricity at a high voltage.

3. **Analyze** how the application of digital electronics helps to expand the electronics industry.

Review and Assessment

Problem-Solving Process

Identify

GlobalSolar, a small electronics firm, is developing a solar charging backpack to allow mobile devices to be used in remote areas. They have hired your team to design and prototype this device. Your prototype should meet the following requirements:

- Provides 5 VDC (Volts of Direct Current) of stable power.
- Connects via a mini USB A plug.
- Charges while device is in a backpack/bag.

Set Up

1. Collect information. Ask: *"What are the required components?"* and *"What conditions will the device need to work in?"*
2. Gather information. Analyze commercial and DIY solar chargers. Research circuits that allow a device to charge while plugged in.
3. Brainstorm solutions. Develop charging circuit drawings and product sketches. Develop a bill of materials for each design.
4. Choose a solution. Consider criteria, constraints, and durability for each prototype. Use a decision matrix to make your selection.

Execute

5. Plan the project with your team. Can some components be recycled products? How will the solar panel be fastened?
6. Keep sketching and recording ideas. They may be used to improve your design and the overall quality of the device.
7. Prepare solution prototypes, using various wire routing and mounting methods. Take operating environment into account.
8. Meet with your team after each session. Discuss your progress. List what went well and what did not. Plan your next session.

Evaluate

Test each design. Ask volunteers to use the backpacks. Have them fill out a questionnaire about their experience. Next, examine the product to see what what should be redesigned. Record your findings.

Share

Share your work by creating a step-by-step assembly guide for the product. Create a table listing materials, tools, and assembly steps. Use photographs to show the placement and connection of the components.

Critical Thinking

Key Concepts

1. **Identify** key technical concepts of electrical and electronics engineering.

2. **Summarize** the field of electrical engineering

3. **Compare and Contrast** the primary focus of electrical engineers with that of electronics engineers.

4. **Evaluate** four ways in which electricity is generated. Then discuss instances when each method might be preferred over the others.

5. **Analyze** the difference between the work of electrical engineers working on power generation and distribution, and of electronics engineers developing circuitry. What are some advantages and disadvantages of each type of work?

Teamwork

6. **Share** with your project team what you have learned about power generation and distribution, and how it connects to your Discovery Project.

7. **Discuss** the role of electronics engineers in the development of circuitry. Describe how the careful creation of schematic diagrams aids them in their work.

essentials

Activity Center

Go to the **Activity Center** to review chapter vocabulary and key concepts.

Engineer's Toolbox

Go to the **Engineer's Toolbox** to:
- Access Academic Activities
- Access the Competitive Event Prep Activity

DISCOVERY PROJECT

Design and Build a Survival Flashlight

Energy of one form or another is required to create electrical energy. In disaster situations, human energy is sometimes the only resource available to create electrical energy. In this chapter's Discovery Project, you will design and construct a survival flashlight that is human-powered and can be used in emergency situations.

Go to your *essentials* ONLINE to view the video to learn about power generation. Then complete the Discovery Project.

Mechanical Engineering

ESSENTIAL QUESTION	**Are today's engineering principles new?**

Mechanical engineering is a wide-ranging field based upon mechanics, which is a branch of physics that involves motion and movement. It includes the study of statics and dynamics, thermodynamics, hydraulics and pneumatics, and simple machines and complex mechanisms. The foundation of mechanics is the understanding of Newton's laws of motion: inertia, momentum, and action and reaction. Engineers who specialize in mechanical engineering focus on energy, mechanical, and manufacturing systems. Their work may involve products and systems as varied as home heating systems, jet engines, power plants, and bicycle gears.

essentials

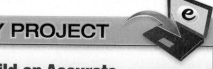

DISCOVERY PROJECT

Go to your **essentials** ONLINE to view the video to learn about building and testing a trebuchet.

Design and Build an Accurate Launcher Prototype

 21st Century Skills

Discuss why teamwork is an important part of designing, building, and testing a mechanism.

Why must engineers consider the concepts of applied mechanics when designing launcher mechanisms? In this chapter's Discovery Project, you will create a launcher prototype. See page 183 for a brief description of this project.

 **Group Workspace**

How can the principles of mechanics be applied to the creation of launchers like the trebuchet?

 **Engineer's Toolbox**

Go to the Engineer's Toolbox to:
- Access Note-Taking Activities
- Access Graphic Organizers
- Access Academic Standards met by this chapter

READING GUIDE

Before You Read What kinds of products do mechanical engineers develop? How do mechanical engineers use simple machines?

Objectives

- **Summarize** Newton's three laws of motion.
- **Evaluate** the laws of thermodynamics.
- **Compare and contrast** hydraulics and pneumatics.
- **Discuss** simple machines.
- **Identify** five different types of motion.
- **Analyze** the purpose of basic mechanisms.

Main Idea

Mechanical engineering involves applying the principles of physics to the design of machines and systems. Mechanical engineers combine simple machines to create more complex machines.

Vocabulary

Content Vocabulary

- mechanics
- inertia
- momentum
- statics
- dynamics
- thermodynamics
- turbine
- hydraulics
- mechanical advantage
- pneumatics
- simple machine
- mechanism

Academic Vocabulary

- transmission
- alternative
- nuclear
- complex
- transfer
- vehicle

Note-Taking Activity

Draw this table for each section. Write key terms and phrases under **Cues**. Write main ideas under **Note Taking**. Summarize the section under **Summary**.

Cues	Note Taking
•	•
•	•
Summary	

Graphic Organizers

Use graphic organizers to write and organize information as you read.

Go to your 🚀 **essentials ONLINE** for downloadable graphic organizers.

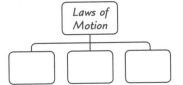

ACADEMIC

Technology

ITEEA STL4.02 Making decisions about the use of technology involves weighing the trade-offs between the positive and negative effects.

ITEEA STL16.01 Energy cannot be created nor destroyed; however, it can be converted from one form to another.

Mathematics

NCTM Measurement Apply appropriate techniques, tools, and formulas to determine measurements.

Science

NSES B Develop an understanding of the structure of atoms, structure and properties of matter, chemical reactions, motions and forces, conservation of energy and increase in disorder, and interactions of energy and matter.

ITEEA *International Technology and Engineering Educators Association*
NCTM *National Council of Teachers of Mathematics*
NSES *National Science Education Standards*

Reading Determine central ideas or themes of a text and analyze their development; summarize the key supporting details and ideas.

Mechanical Principles and Systems

What Is Mechanical Engineering?

Mechanical engineering is the second largest and perhaps broadest engineering discipline. Mechanical engineers specialize in the design and development of systems of all types. They use systems for many applications, such as tools, machinery, and other devices. In addition, some mechanical engineers specialize in fields related to energy and power generation and transmission. Others specialize in systems that work by using fluids.

Mechanical engineering, like other engineering fields, relies heavily on applied principles of physics in the design of systems. Think of mechanical engineering whenever you see a system that is designed to move anything, from very small to very large, over any distance. Basically, almost anything that moves either itself or other things was probably developed by a mechanical engineer. (See **Figure 9.1**.)

The work of mechanical engineers focuses on three systems:

- Energy systems
- Mechanical systems
- Manufacturing systems

Energy systems involve the production of energy and its transfer from one form to another. Mechanical systems are used in motor vehicles, all kinds of machines, and medical devices. Engineers design and develop the manufacturing systems that help convert raw materials into finished products.

Fig. 9.1 Engineering Products
Mechanical engineers design and develop systems and products as varied as wind turbines and robots. *What principles do mechanical engineers apply?*

Alternative Energy

Concern about reducing the use of imported oil and the environmental impact of fossil fuels has led to increased interest in alternative energy systems. Mechanical engineers are contributing to a wide variety of projects, including the development of wind turbines, systems that generate power from ocean tides, and the design of a new kind of service station that will exchange batteries for totally electric vehicles.

Heating and Cooling

A significant number of mechanical engineers work in Heating, Ventilation, and Air Conditioning (HVAC) or related fields. They apply principles of thermodynamics to move air, or to heat or cool large and small spaces. Mechanical engineers may design refrigeration devices or climate control systems for large buildings.

Manufacturing

More than one-third of all engineering jobs are found in the manufacturing industry. Mechanical engineers design and implement machinery for automated production, and robotic assembly systems. They design any of the myriad of other machinery used in the context of manufacturing.

Medical Systems

Mechanical engineers also work with medical professionals in research, development, and application, as robotic surgery and new medical diagnostic devices are developed.

Applied Mechanics

Some mechanical engineers specialize in the more scientific field of applied mechanics, studying objects, forces, and motion for application in various technologies.

Mechanics is a branch of physics that is dedicated to the study of motion and movement. Mechanical engineers rely on these principles as they design various devices. Because mechanical engineers must work with very intricate systems that have many moving parts, they must be able to understand and optimize movements and interaction between the parts. In applied mechanics, the following terms describe interactions between bodies:

Space	Force	Momentum
Mass	Energy	Time

Mechanical engineers need to understand how big things are, how much mass things have, how much force is being applied, how much energy things have, how much momentum things have, and how long interactions take, so that they can optimize mechanical systems.

Green reSource

Wind Power Electrical engineers solve problems related to electrical energy produced by wind-powered turbines. But mechanical engineers are behind the inner workings and moveable parts of these high-tech devices.

Go to your  ONLINE to learn more about how green technology powers the 547 Art Center in Greensburg, Kansas.

Group Workspace

Consider the many parts that comprise a wind-powered turbine. Identify ways engineers might improve or optimize this mechanism.

Reading Check **List** three systems that are the main focus for mechanical engineers.

PROJECT CONNECTIONS

How will you apply concepts of applied mechanics to design your launcher?

Newton's Laws of Motion

Sir Isaac Newton's three laws of motion, which explain the relationship between the forces acting on a body and the motion of that body, are at the heart of applied mechanics. At a basic level, these laws describe inertia, momentum, and action and reaction. These forces are important for the day-to-day activities in mechanical engineering. In 1687, Newton published a book to describe his understanding of the motion of physical objects and his three laws of motion.

Inertia The first law, the law of **inertia**, states that a body tends to stay at rest or in uniform motion unless acted upon by an outside force. The net force acting on an object is equal to the sum of all forces acting on the object. If that sum is zero (0), the object's state of motion does not change.

Momentum The second law deals with momentum. **Momentum** is the product of mass and velocity. The second law is often expressed this way: $F = ma$. The net force on an object (*F*) is equal to the mass of the object (*m*) multiplied by its velocity (*a*). Change in motion is in proportion to the force applied. If a certain force generates a certain motion, the motion will double if the force is doubled.

Action and Reaction Newton's third law states that for every action, there is an equal and opposite reaction. Forces come in pairs. Think about a balloon you have just inflated. The particles of air inside the balloon keep it inflated as you use your fingers to prevent the air from escaping. What happens when you let go of the balloon?

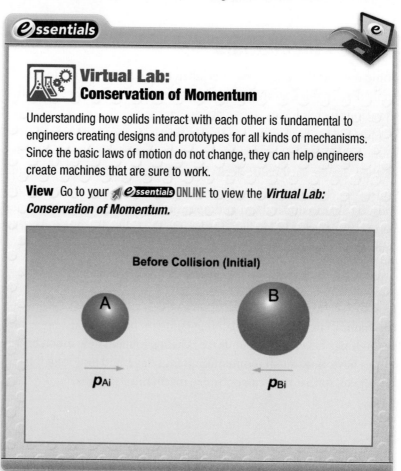

essentials

**Virtual Lab:
Conservation of Momentum**

Understanding how solids interact with each other is fundamental to engineers creating designs and prototypes for all kinds of mechanisms. Since the basic laws of motion do not change, they can help engineers create machines that are sure to work.

View Go to your *essentials* ONLINE to view the *Virtual Lab: Conservation of Momentum.*

Before Collision (Initial)

A

B

p_{Ai}

p_{Bi}

Statics and Dynamics

Mechanics is a branch of physics that studies motion and movement. **Statics** is the study of how forces affect non-moving objects. It can be used to describe loads and forces acting upon physical systems. Mechanical engineers in their pre-professional studies are often required to take an entire course in statics. Statics can be used to describe objects generally at rest or, as a scientist would put it, "in static equilibrium." Mechanical engineers need to understand what can and will happen within the systems they design when certain parts of the system are at rest.

Dynamics is the study of how forces affect moving objects. Often paired with the study of statics, dynamics helps describe scientifically how parts of a system function in a process. This may mean that certain parts of a system move, generate heat, or transfer energy of some sort. In order to design better and more efficient systems, mechanical engineers must understand how dynamics will affect the systems they design.

Energy Conversion and Thermodynamics

Thermodynamics is the study of the transformation of energy and how it relates to temperature, pressure, and volume. Mechanical engineers use their knowledge of thermodynamics when they design systems that change one form of energy to another. For example, automobile engines change the chemical energy stored in gasoline into the mechanical energy needed to move the vehicle.

The laws of thermodynamics are considered to be absolute. They apply to everything in our universe. These laws are important because they influence many aspects of the work of scientists and engineers.

Conservation of Energy
The first law of thermodynamics is usually referred to as the law of conservation of energy. It states that the total amount of energy within a closed system will remain constant. Another way to say this is that energy can neither be created nor destroyed. Matter or energy can change to another form, such as liquid to gas, but the total amount of matter and energy in the universe always remains the same. Energy can be transferred through and between parts of a mechanical device, but not without losses of energy at certain points in the process. Most of the time, a mechanical engineer attempts to minimize these losses by creating a more efficient system.

Increased Entropy
The second law of thermodynamics relates to the quality of matter and energy. This law is also known as the law of increased entropy. Although the quantity of energy in the universe remains the same, the quality of the energy deteriorates as it is used.

Absolute Zero
The third law relates to the state known as "absolute zero." Absolute zero is considered the lowest possible temperature, when molecular energy is at its minimum. It can be expressed on different scales:

PROJECT CONNECTIONS

Which parts of your launcher will be static and which will be dynamic?

✔ **Reading Check** **Explain** why the studies of statics and dynamics are grouped together by mechanical engineers.

PROJECT CONNECTIONS

Will losses of heat energy occur in your launcher due to friction? If so, how might you minimize this loss?

✔ **Reading Check** **Explain** how engineers use the law of absolute zero in their work on systems that involve energy.

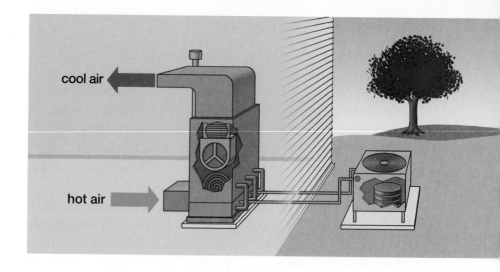

Fig. 9.2 Heat Pump This drawing shows a typical heat pump that helps to heat and cool a home. *What other device in your home may operate by the same principle?*

cool air

hot air

- 0 degrees Kelvin
- − 273.15 degrees Celsius
- − 459.67 degrees Fahrenheit

This law helps engineers understand how materials will react to temperature changes, particularly in ultra-low temperatures.

Thermodynamic Applications

Mechanical engineers design and develop a variety of energy conversion systems that utilize thermodynamic principles. These systems include heating, ventilating and air conditioning (HVAC), refrigeration, and power generation.

Heat Pumps

A heat pump operates on the same principle as air conditioners and refrigerators. Heat pumps perform the dual role of heating a home in winter and cooling it in summer. When the system is being used for cooling, a liquid is pumped through an evaporator coil. As the liquid moves through the coil, it changes to a gas as it absorbs heat from the air around the coil. A blower then pushes air around the cooled coil. The gas, now hot, passes through a compressor and liquefies. It goes to a condenser coil outside. The compressed gas releases its heat and returns to a liquid state. (See **Figure 9.2**.)

In cold weather, the process is reversed. Heat is extracted from the cold air outside and is released into the home. Heat pumps are not efficient when it is very cold outside, so most systems include an auxiliary electric heater on very cold days.

Power Generation

Electricity is vital to our daily life and economy. Nearly 50 percent of the electricity produced in the United States comes from coal-fired power plants. Other fossil fuel plants, such as natural gas and petroleum plants, are also common. Nuclear power plants generate a large percentage of the electricity in Europe. There is renewed interest in building additional nuclear plants in the United States.

Reading Check **Discuss** how a heat pump serves as both a heating and a cooling device.

Coal Plants Large coal plants can require more than 10,000 tons of coal per day, so frequent deliveries of coal are required. Many plants are located on rivers to facilitate cooling by water, and delivery of the coal by barge or ship. Rail cars or trucks also deliver coal. Usually the coal is crushed into a powder and burned in a boiler to heat water to about 1,000 degrees Fahrenheit to create steam. The steam is piped under high pressure to turbines. A **turbine** is a type of engine that gets power from a fluid such as water, steam, or combustion gases. The turbines spin generators at 3,600 revolutions per minute (RPM) to make alternating current. A cooling tower or nearby river helps condense the steam coming out of the turbines.

Natural Gas and Petroleum Plants Natural gas and petroleum power plants are similar to coal plants. They produce steam, or hot combustion gases, to turn turbines and generators. Many utilities use natural gas turbine plants to generate electricity during periods of peak demand. The turbines operate like jet engines. They compress the air, mix it with fuel, and ignite it in a combustion chamber.

Properties of Materials

All materials have unique thermal, magnetic, optical, acoustical, and electrical properties. Materials vary in density, and their mass differs according to their composition. They have different strengths and sensitivities in different situations and applications. Enormous amounts of information are dedicated to the study of materials and properties. Mechanical engineers must refer to many charts and diagrams to determine the properties of materials they use to design a device or system. A sample of such a chart is shown in **Figure 9.3**.

Engineers must always be aware of the properties of the materials they select. For example, an engineer who is designing a device to use in or near water must consider the electrical properties of the material

Property	Thermoplastics											Thermosets				
Materials	Abs	Acetal	Acrylic	Cellulosic	Fluorocarbon	Polyamide	Polycarbonate	Polyethylene	Polypropylene	Polyvinyl Chloride	Polyvinyl	Epoxy	Phenolics	Polyester	Silicone	Urea & Melamine
Tensile Strength	–	2	2	4	–	1	1	–	–	3	–	3	3	2	1	2
Flexural Strength	4	4	3	4	1	2	3	–	1	3	3	3	2	1	3	3
Weather Resistance	–	2	1	–	1	2	–	2	2	–	2	3	3	1	2	4
Resistance to Heat Expansion	2	–	3	–	–	1	2	–	–	2	3	4	2	2	1	3

Fig. 9.3 The Right Materials
This chart shows some of the properties that engineers consider when choosing materials for the machines and products they design. *Which of these materials is the strongest?*

he intends to use, as well as how its strength or other material properties might change when in contact with water. Regardless of the device or system, material properties are always important design considerations.

Hydraulics and Pneumatics

An understanding of hydraulics and pneumatics is essential to mechanical engineers. In fact, many engineers specialize in these areas. The term *fluids* describes both liquids (hydraulics) and gases (pneumatics). Fluids can be manipulated in different ways to do work. When they are not moving, fluids have no power. When they are put under pressure and moved to where they are needed, fluids can perform work.

Hydraulic Systems

Hydraulics involves fluid power systems that use oil or another liquid. Since liquids cannot be compressed, they can be used to transfer force. A common example of a hydraulic machine is a backhoe. Oil, a liquid, is pumped through tubes and hoses and into and out of hydraulic cylinders in a backhoe, in order to move the parts of this large machine. Depending on the size of the cylinders, the force within the pistons can change.

Hydraulic systems can also multiply force. The increase in force gained by using a machine is called mechanical advantage. Hydraulic systems are ideal when strength and accuracy are required. That is why hydraulic systems are effective in heavy equipment and are used to power material-moving devices in manufacturing systems.

Pneumatic Systems

Pneumatics involves systems that use air or another gas. Some common applications of pneumatics include pneumatic tools, air compressors, vacuum pumps, and air brakes on heavy vehicles. Pneumatic systems offer several advantages. They are generally cleaner than hydraulic systems, and they run on air, an ordinary available resource. If a pneumatic system leaks, there is nothing to clean up, and no hazardous materials are released. That is why pneumatic systems are used in food processing plants. But pneumatic systems have some disadvantages. They do not produce as much force as hydraulic devices, and many pneumatic devices are noisy.

Reading Check Discuss some advantages and disadvantages of hydraulic systems and pneumatic systems.

SECTION 9.1

Check Your Understanding

After You Read Perform the following tasks.

1. **State** the formula that describes the product of mass and velocity.

2. **Paraphrase** the law of conservation of energy.

3. **Determine** which method currently generates the most electricity in the United States.

Machines and Mechanisms

Simple Machines

To understand simple machines, you must understand the concept of mechanical advantage. Mechanical advantage is a mathematical expression of the way a machine multiplies the force put into it. Basically, a **simple machine** is a tool with a power system that helps us to do work. To understand mechanical advantage practically, consider the examples of simple machines in **Figure 9.4**.

Wheel and Axle

When a wheel is securely fastened to a smaller wheel, or an axle, mechanical advantage is achieved. Think of turning a doorknob to open a door. If the doorknob was very small, say the diameter of a coin, would it be harder to open the door? More mechanical advantage can be derived depending on how large the wheel is and how small the axle is. The exact mechanical advantage can be found by measuring the sizes of the wheel and the axle. There are, of course, limits to the materials that can be used to create this simple machine.

PROJECT CONNECTIONS

Which simple machines will you use to design your launcher?

Fig. 9.4 Simple Applications
Simple machines are tools with power systems for accomplishing work. *Give one example of a device that you have used today that incorporates one of these simple machines.*

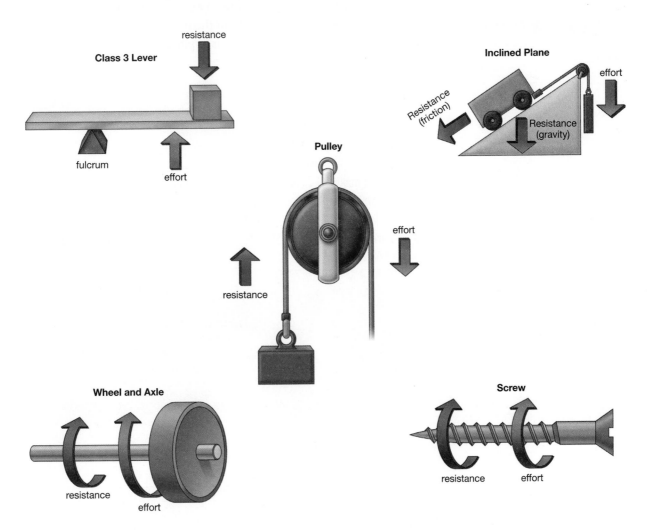

Class 3 Lever — resistance, fulcrum, effort

Inclined Plane — Resistance (friction), Resistance (gravity), effort

Pulley — resistance, effort

Wheel and Axle — resistance, effort

Screw — resistance, effort

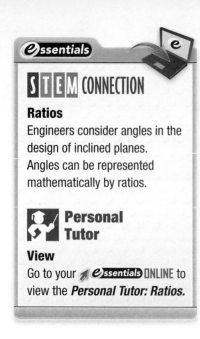
Reading Check **Explain** how an inclined plane achieves mechanical advantage.

Inclined Plane

Imagine that you had to move a heavy, oversized bowling ball that weighed 100 pounds to the second floor of a building by yourself. Would it be easier to try to lift it yourself or to roll it up a long, gradual ramp? The gradual ramp is also an inclined plane and provides the mechanical advantage of assisting with work.

Lever

There are three classes of levers, all of which are designed to do work and apply mechanical advantage. A lever has a fulcrum, or pivot point. The effort force, the result load, and the fulcrum position determine the class of the lever.

First-Class Lever An example of a first class lever is the *trebuchet*, a medieval siege machine. In a trebuchet, the fulcrum of the lever is placed between the effort force and the counterweight. The result load is at the projectile sling at the end of the opposing arm. If more weight can be applied, or if the arm can be made longer, the projectile will travel farther in the air.

Second-Class Lever An example of a second class lever is a wheelbarrow. The fulcrum of this type of lever is at one end, the load is in the middle, and the effort is at the other end. A load placed in a wheelbarrow is easier to move.

Third-Class Lever Tweezers are an example of a third class lever. In this case, the result load is less than the input force, which is desirable in some scenarios. The input force is applied between the fulcrum and the result.

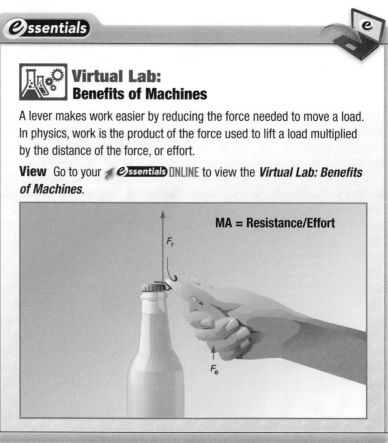

essentials

Virtual Lab: Benefits of Machines

A lever makes work easier by reducing the force needed to move a load. In physics, work is the product of the force used to lift a load multiplied by the distance of the force, or effort.

View Go to your *essentials* ONLINE to view the *Virtual Lab: Benefits of Machines.*

MA = Resistance/Effort

F_r

F_e

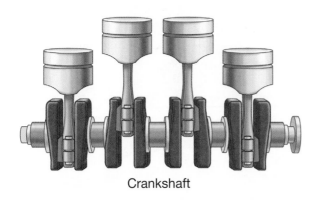

Crankshaft

Crank

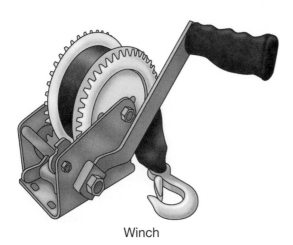

Winch

Ratchet and Pawl

Pulley

A simple pulley, also known as a *block* or *fixed pulley*, does not offer any mechanical advantage by itself, but it does change the direction of an applied force. Greater mechanical advantage can result when blocks are compounded and variously arranged in relation to the work they are designed to do. Cranes and winches are common applications of pulleys. They can have various applications, such as to lift and pull massive objects.

Mechanisms

A **mechanism** is a system made by combining parts, such as simple machines. Many mechanisms combine certain aspects of the simple machines described previously. In order to understand mechanisms and more complex machines, you must first understand the following five ways to describe types of motion and movement. (See **Figure 9.5**.)

- **Linear** – movement in a straight path in one direction
- **Reciprocating** – movement in a straight path, back and forth in opposite directions
- **Rotary** – movement in a circular path in one direction
- **Oscillating** – movement in a circular path, back and forth in opposite directions
- **Intermittent** – incremental movement in a circular or linear path

Fig. 9.5 Machines and Motion
Mechanisms are systems of simple machines that can produce motion. *What are the types of motion represented by each of the machines in these photos?*

PROJECT CONNECTIONS
Would you describe any part of your launcher as a "mechanism"? Why or why not?

Fig. 9.6 Using Gears Many different kinds and sizes of gears make up the machines that we use every day. *Which type of gear would change rotary motion to linear motion?*

Gears and Sprockets

A simple way to describe a gear is to say that it looks like a wheel with teeth. The technical term for a common type of gear is a *spur gear*. There are other types of gears, including crown gears, helical gears, and bevel gears, which can all be used in different ways. Regardless of the specific application, gears are generally used to transfer rotary motion. Gears can be used to increase or decrease the speed or torque of an axle. Different gears and arrangements can also change the direction of the rotary motion. (See **Figure 9.6**.)

A slight variation of a gear is a *sprocket*, which is somewhat like a flattened gear. Sprockets can be used for similar purposes as gears. However, sprockets are not meshed together as gears are. Sprockets are generally used together with chains, as in a bicycle, to transfer rotary motion over a distance.

Rack and Pinion

The rack-and-pinion device configuration is used to translate rotary motion into linear motion or vice versa. Most commonly found in motor vehicle steering applications, the pinion is generally a spur gear. The rack is a series of gear-like teeth on a flat plane, rather than in a circle.

Screws and Worm Gears

A screw is a combination of a wheel and axle and an inclined plane. A worm gear is one kind of screw. A worm gear is placed on an axle and can be turned. In a sense, a worm gear is one continuous gear tooth wrapped around a central point. When used with a spur gear, a worm gear can derive mechanical advantage and also change the direction of rotary movement. When a worm gear is used with a rack, it can also change rotary movement to linear movement.

Cams

Cams are very versatile devices. They change rotary movement to reciprocating, oscillating, or intermittent movement. A *follower* is an object or a part that makes constant contact with a cam as it rotates. In one of its simplest forms, an egg-shaped cam can translate rotary movement to reciprocating or intermittent movement. This type of cam is most commonly applied in a camshaft in an internal combustion engine. Cams along the rotating shaft are used to open and close intake and exhaust valves intermittently.

When a cam is used in conjunction with a third-class lever, it can create oscillating movement. This movement is found in many wind-up and other mechanical toys.

Cranks

A crank effectively combines a wheel and axle with a lever. Consider the example of a bicycle crank set at the pedals. In a way, simply bending an extension of the axle at two points combines the two simple machines. Moving the pedals (on which feet will apply the force) farther from the axle allows for more mechanical advantage.

Another common application of a crank is found in the crankshaft of an internal combustion engine. As the pistons in the engine reciprocate, this movement translates into the rotary movement of the crankshaft.

Ratchet and Pawl

The ratchet and pawl is a common mechanism, used when motion in one direction is desired and movement in the opposite direction is undesired. A ratchet and pawl is found in devices that tie down heavy loads to the bed of a truck, or in devices that hoist heavy items.

A ratchet looks like a gear with its teeth curved slightly in one direction. The pawl slips over each tooth as it moves in one direction. Then it locks, to prevent movement in the other direction.

Complex Mechanisms

Clutches, watch escapements, mechanical switches, winches, differentials, and transmissions are all examples of complex mechanisms. Complex mechanisms are simple mechanisms that have been optimized for different applications. It is important to remember that engineers use all mechanisms, regardless of their complexity, to control and translate movement, directionality, and power.

Visualization

Prototypes The design process requires visualization. This is often in the form of sketching, followed by the creation of more complex computer generated 2D drawings and 3D models. Virtual prototypes can also be made and tested in simulated conditions using computer tools before creating physical prototypes.

Go to your *essentials* ONLINE to learn more about developing models.

Group Workspace

Plan out the modeling process and visualize and sketch all the steps necessary in creating a finished model.

 **Reading Check** **Describe** how mechanical engineers use simple machines to create mechanisms.

Check Your Understanding

After You Read Perform the following tasks.

1. **Identify** an example of each of the three classes of levers.

2. **Describe** what kind of motion gears usually transmit.

3. **Analyze** why cams are used.

Review and Assessment

Problem-Solving Process

Identify

The XYZ Toy Design Company wants to develop simple mechanical toys for 3- to 5-year-olds. Of 10 models, three will be chosen. Your team will develop one model.

Set Up

1. Ground yourself in information about the project. Ask: *"What is really important about this project?"* and *"What criteria will make for a successful project?"*
2. Gather related background information. Research existing toys and disassemble some toys to see how they work.
3. Brainstorm potential solutions. Remember, there are no "bad" ideas in a brainstorming session. Record all thoughts on paper.
4. Choose the best solution. Base decisions on your previous criteria for success.

Execute

5. Plan the building of the solution with your team.
6. Keep sketching and recording ideas. These may become references later.
7. Build mock-ups of the solution, using different ways to carry out the building. You may try many ways of doing something before you find the best way.
8. Meet with your team at the end of each session to discuss accomplishments and set goals.

Evaluate

Determine which mock-up is best by testing the prototype with a group of children, your class, or a group of teachers. If your project is not successful, reevaluate your steps. Ask: *Did your group communicate effectively? Did you understand the project at the start?*

Share

Share your views on the importance of this project and the criteria that determined the success of the project. Discuss how well your team communicated and any difficulty you had with the project.

Critical Thinking

Key Concepts

1. **Identify** three different kinds of systems that mechanical engineers use.

2. **Summarize** Newton's three laws of motion.

3. **Compare and contrast** hydraulic and pneumatic systems.

4. **Evaluate** Newton's third law of motion and the first law of thermodynamics. Then discuss why and how they are related.

5. **Analyze** how mechanical advantage is achieved with a wheel and axle.

Teamwork   21st Century Skills

6. **Share** with your project team what you have learned about applied mechanics and how that information relates to your Discovery Project.

7. **Discuss** the use of simple machines in various systems and how to apply simple machines to solve a design problem in your Discovery Project.

essentials

Activity Center

Go to the **Activity Center** to review chapter vocabulary and key concepts.

Engineer's Toolbox

Go to the **Engineer's Toolbox** to:
- Access Academic Activities
- Access the Competitive Event Prep Activity

---

essentials

DISCOVERY PROJECT

Design and Build an Accurate Launcher Prototype

In this chapter's Discovery Project, you will create a launcher prototype that can launch a marshmallow at a target. Your team's launcher should be reliable and predictable. It should be able to adjust to targets at different ranges.

Go to your *essentials* ONLINE to view the video to learn about building and testing a trebuchet. Then complete the Discovery Project.

10

Manufacturing Engineering

ESSENTIAL QUESTION Why are designers of products and manufacturers of those products usually different people?

Manufacturing changes raw materials into finished goods, modifying those materials in a way that adds value. The term *manufacture* originally meant "make by hand." The manufacturing of products and tools made of wood and various metals began before 4000 B.C. Before the Industrial Revolution, manufacturing was done by skilled workers who were often assisted by apprentices. Today millions of different products are manufactured in factories all over the world.

*e*ssentials

DISCOVERY PROJECT

ENR
Engineering News-Record

Go to your *e*ssentials ONLINE to view a video that shows how a material mover assists a worker as he is building a wall.

Design and Build a Construction Material Mover

 21st Century Skills Describe how the integration of a lifting device can help a construction team function more smoothly.

Concrete blocks are popular materials used in commercial construction. Manually moving materials at construction sites is labor intensive and the largest cause of work-related injuries. The need to increase efficiency and reduce injuries presents an opportunity for engineers to design a better system for handling concrete blocks. See page 199 for a description of this project.

 Group Workspace

During the video, watch and listen for important facts about how a block wall is constructed. Write down some ideas about how an automated system might best be used to assist the workers.

 Engineer's Toolbox

Go to the Engineer's Toolbox to
- Access Note-Taking Activities
- Access Graphic Organizers
- Access Academic Standards met by this chapter

READING GUIDE

Before You Read What is the primary focus of manufacturing engineering? What are some of the main challenges that face manufacturing engineers?

Objectives

- **Discuss** the benefits of rapid prototyping.
- **Identify** four types of manufacturing systems and explain the benefits of each.
- **Explain** how quality control in manufacturing has evolved.
- **Compare and contrast** the roles of computer-aided manufacturing and computer-integrated manufacturing.
- **Analyze** the role of packaging in the manufacturing process.

Main Idea

In a manufacturing environment, engineers strive to develop ways to maximize safety of workers and the quality of products, while minimizing costs and the time required for producing a product.

Vocabulary

Content Vocabulary

- custom manufacturing
- intermittent manufacturing
- continuous manufacturing
- flexible manufacturing
- lean manufacturing
- just-in-time (JIT) manufacturing
- computer-aided manufacturing (CAM)
- computer-integrated manufacturing (CIM)
- automation
- industrial robots

Academic Vocabulary

- revolutionized
- assembled
- promotional
- expertise
- factors

Note-Taking Activity

Draw this table for each section. Write key terms and phrases under **Cues.** Write main ideas under **Note Taking.** Summarize the section under **Summary.**

Cues	Note Taking
•	•
•	•
Summary	

Graphic Organizers

Use graphic organizers to organize information as you read.

Go to your 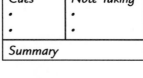 ONLINE for downloadable graphic organizers.

Manufacturing

ACADEMIC

Technology

ITEEA STL1.03 Inventions and innovations are the results of specific, goal-directed research.

ITEEA STL5.05 Humans devise technologies to reduce the negative consequences of other technologies.

Mathematics

NCTM Geometry Use visualization, spatial reasoning, and geometric modeling to solve problems.

Science

NSES E Students should develop abilities of technological design, understandings about science and technology.

ITEEA *International Technology and Engineering Educators Association*
NCTM *National Council of Teachers of Mathematics*
NSES *National Science Education Standards*

College & Career
READINESS

Writing Conduct short as well as more sustained research projects based and focused on questions, demonstrating understanding of the subject under investigation.

Speaking and Listening Present information, findings, and supporting evidence such that listeners can follow the line of reasoning and the organization, development, and style are appropriate to task, purpose, and audience.

Manufacturing Engineering Overview

STEM CONNECTION

Volume of a Composite Figure Manufacturing engineers often have to manage production lines. They will need to insure that all parts of the final product are able to work together. Often, it is necessary to place two parts together before completing the finishing of that product. Engineers may be required to solve problems regarding the individual parts or the composite item created by putting the individual parts together.

Personal Tutor

View
Go to your **essentials** ONLINE to view the *Personal Tutor: Volume of a Composite Figure.*

Manufacturing

Almost all of the products that we come into contact with every day are manufactured. Look around the room. Every book, computer, and almost everything else in the room was probably manufactured. In recent years, the numbers of U.S. manufacturing plants and of workers employed in those plants have declined significantly. Currently about 10% of the U.S. workforce is employed in manufacturing. Increasing the total amount of goods produced in the U.S. and exported would boost the U.S. economy and create additional jobs. The U.S. ranks behind many nations in industrial productivity, which is a measure of how efficiently products are made. The desire to increase productivity is one reason for the opportunities now available to manufacturing engineers.

What is Manufacturing Engineering?

More than one-third of all engineers are employed in manufacturing. Although many different kinds of engineers work in manufacturing plants, manufacturing engineers are an important part of the total engineering team. Manufacturing engineering focuses on the machinery and materials used in manufacturing. Manufacturing engineers work in facilities that manufacture products ranging from airplanes and computers to food and clothing. They are involved in all aspects of the manufacturing process, from the initial design to packaging and shipping. For certain items, such as equipment used for manufacturing other products, they may also supervise equipment installation and testing.

The work of a manufacturing engineer often begins with an electronic or physical prototype of a new product. Based on their experience, manufacturing engineers may suggest changes in the design of the product, to make it easier or less costly to produce. They recom-

Fig. 10.1 Workflow A manufacturing engineer works to maximize the efficiency of the workflow. *What are some factors an engineer might consider when developing recommendations to streamline a project?*

mend the best materials and design the most efficient processes for manufacturing. When necessary, manufacturing engineers also develop new processes and equipment. They solve problems that occur during production related to the quality of the products and environmental impacts of the manufacturing process or the product itself.

Product Design

Computer-Aided Design (CAD) has revolutionized product design and engineering. Solid modeling software makes it possible to create three-dimensional (3D) representations of individual parts that can be rotated and viewed from any angle. (See **Figure 10.2**.) Animation features of CAD software show how parts are assembled, or put together, into components and how the components are then combined into finished products. 3D CAD software can also be used to test and analyze the strength of materials and the behavior of parts and assemblies. CAD files can then be used to manufacture physical prototypes. When the design for a product has been finalized, manufacturing engineers use CAD to design the tools and machinery that will be used in the production process and also to design the layout of the manufacturing system.

Rapid Prototyping

Rapid prototyping is a technique used to produce physical models of parts and products in a short period of time. Compared to traditional machining and other model-making processes, rapid prototyping is fast and relatively inexpensive. The rapid prototyping process begins by using 3D CAD or animation software to design the part. The design data is then sent to a rapid prototyping machine which creates the model. Although the machines vary, they usually use a liquid, powder, or paper that can be built up in layers to create the exact shape of the part. Rapid prototyping can also be used to make molds for casting aluminum and other low-melting-temperature metals.

✓ Reading Check **List** two aspects of manufacturing that are the focus of manufacturing engineers.

PROJECT CONNECTIONS

Use CAD to create sketches and 3D drawings of the concrete blocks that will be moved by your model system.

PROJECT CONNECTIONS

If a rapid prototyping machine is available, use the CAD drawings to create the simulated concrete blocks.

Rapid prototyping has many practical applications. For example, a designer at a footwear company can design a new athletic shoe using CAD software. The data is sent electronically to the rapid prototyping machine, which layers material to create a prototype of the new shoe in the exact size and color desired. The prototype can then be used for additional study by the designers. When they are satisfied with the final prototype, it can be shared with potential customers.

Design for Recyclability

Some products are specifically designed so that they are easy to recycle. One way of designing for recycling ease is to create products that are easy to take apart. This can facilitate separating the materials that make up the product. At the end of their useful lives, more than 95% of U.S. automobiles are recycled. Unlike the U.S., in Europe automobile manufacturers are required to take back the automobiles they produced. This requirement has caused manufacturers to make major changes in the way their vehicles are constructed. They now make their vehicles using as many recycled materials as possible and also use materials that are easy to recycle. These manufacturers design vehicles that are easy to dismantle and try to avoid the use of hazardous materials. Although auto recycling is not as structured as it is in Europe, in the U.S. more than a third of steel produced is made with scrap steel from recycled automobiles. Using recycled steel greatly reduces the cost and pollution generated by using steel from newly mined ore.

Reading Check **Describe** special design considerations that are needed when designing for recyclability.

Fig. 10.3 Prototyping Machine
Rapid prototyping machines such as this one showing an engine block prototype are used to create physical models of parts and products in a short time. *What are two possible applications for rapid prototyping?*

Fig. 10.4 Designing Recycling
This photo shows an auto recycling center in Europe. The need to design products for recyclability can greatly affect decisions engineers make when creating a product. *How might some design choices for materials vary if recycling were required for all products?*

Production System Design

Competition requires manufacturing systems to be as efficient as possible. Manufacturing engineers need to choose the best systems to produce a particular item. They consider systems including custom, intermittent, continuous, flexible, lean, and just-in-time manufacturing.

Custom manufacturing is the manufacturing of items to fill a specific individual order. It is the oldest kind of manufacturing. The old-time shoemaker was a custom manufacturer. Today there are many companies that use modern manufacturing techniques to specialize in making custom products. For example, some window manufacturers specialize in making wood windows to order, and some machining companies make metal molds used for injection molding. Other companies make custom equipment needed to manufacture other products.

Intermittent manufacturing, or "batch production," is used to manufacture products in lots. It is often used by companies that make different models of the same basic product. For example, suppose a company that makes lawnmowers receives an order for 24,000 lawnmowers from a chain that has stores all over the country. Manufacturing engineers will design and set up a system to make sure that all the necessary parts are available where they are needed. They will also identify all the equipment needed for manufacturing the 24,000 mowers and determine the best way to arrange the production equipment. When that batch of lawnmowers has been assembled, the production system might be modified to produce a different model of lawnmower or possibly another product.

Continuous manufacturing produces products without interruption. An example is a production line that makes plastic shopping bags 24 hours per day, 7 days per week. This system would most likely be automated

PROJECT CONNECTIONS
Design the construction material moving system so that it can be easily disassembled to facilitate the reuse or recycling of materials from which it was made.

and require few people to run it. Automobile assembly lines are continuous production systems that combine conveyor systems with human labor and robotics as the vehicles are assembled.

Flexible manufacturing is designed so that changes are easy to make. In some flexible manufacturing systems, the same machines are used to make different products. In other cases, flexible manufacturing systems are designed to adjust as the size of production orders increases or decreases. Most flexible systems are based on robotics and other kinds of automated systems. An important advantage is the ability to handle changes in the kinds and quantities of products produced.

Lean manufacturing was originally developed by Toyota, and its goal is to eliminate waste in the manufacturing process. In lean manufacturing, anything that does not add value is defined as waste, including

- Producing more than is needed.
- Carrying an excess inventory of parts before they are needed.
- Having to inspect parts to correct manufacturing errors.
- Unnecessary movement of materials and workers.
- Having workers wait for materials or to use machines.

"Just-in-time" (JIT) manufacturing is an integral part of lean manufacturing. JIT increases productivity, lowers costs, and can help increase product quality. It is based on the idea that necessary resources – people, materials, and equipment – should be available at exactly the right time. Fast-food restaurants are an example of the difference between traditional manufacturing and JIT manufacturing. You have probably been to fast food

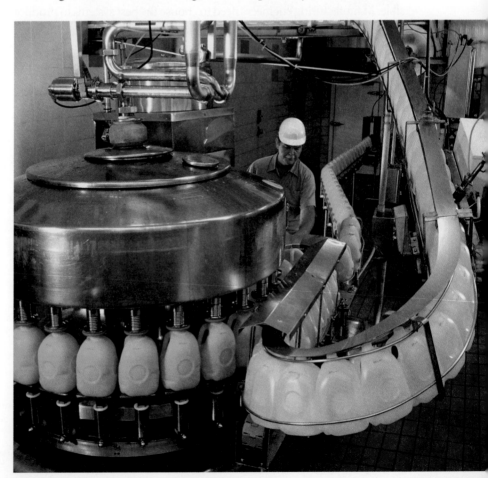

Fig. 10.5 Production Line This is a typical continuous production line for the bottling of orange juice. *What are two products that are probably manufactured using continuous production?*

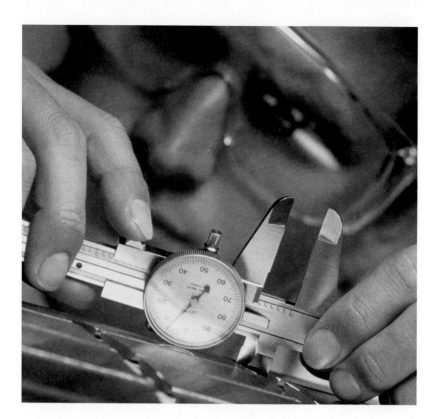

Fig. 10.6 Human Quality Quality control is often performed by a person, as shown here. *What are two additional methods of quality control?*

restaurants where hamburgers are pre-made and on display. If you want one of those, you can get it quickly. But if you want to custom order a burger, with no onions or extra pickles for example, it will take longer. Also, if too many burgers are made in advance, some will have to be thrown away. Other fast-food restaurants do not make burgers in advance. Instead they make the burger exactly as requested, and serve it as quickly as possible. How can this approach reduce waste?

Quality Control

For many years manufacturing quality control (QC) meant inspecting finished parts and products to identify those that were defective. Today QC is an integral part of the manufacturing process. Quality goals are established and manufacturing systems are designed with those goals in mind. Throughout the production process, data is collected and analyzed. For example, an automobile manufacturer will want to make sure that its painting system is applying the correct thickness of paint. By setting a certain standard and measuring the thickness of paint applied to vehicles periodically, the amount of paint being applied can be compared to the established standard. Looking for trends, such as determining that the thickness of paint applied to vehicles is within the acceptable range but a little less than desired, creates an opportunity to take corrective action before defective products are produced.

Marketing

Manufacturing engineers also consider marketing in their decision-making. When determining how to package a consumer product, these engineers may not only consider packaging that will protect their product

PROJECT CONNECTIONS
Discuss how your team can convince others that an actual system based on your model will improve the quality of commercial construction.

☑ **Reading Check** **Identify** the production design system that focuses on eliminating waste and adding value.

from damage, they may also consider how packaging would enhance the appeal of the product on a store shelf. Marketing also involves many kinds of promotional activities, such as advertising and meeting with customers. Some manufacturing engineers focus on selling to other companies. They utilize their technical expertise to understand how manufacturing processes work and recommend new equipment that will streamline production. Manufacturing engineers engaged in selling products need good communication and technical skills.

ssentials

Virtual Lab: Quality Control

Changing basic materials into finished products ready for consumer use is the main objective of manufacturing processes. In order to ensure the goods are safe and ready for consumer use, quality control systems are in place at every level of the manufacturing system and are integral components of the entire manufacturing process.

View Go to your *essentials* ONLINE to view the *Virtual Lab: Quality Control.*

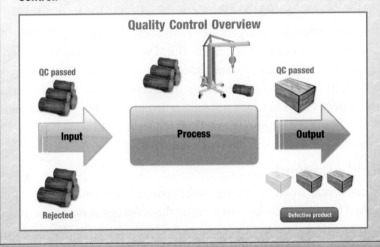

Quality Control Overview

Check Your Understanding

After You Read Perform the following tasks.

1. **Explain** how the role of quality control has changed, and describe the role of quality control today.

2. **Differentiate** six types of production systems.

3. **Discuss** the importance of marketing input to manufacturing systems.

Manufacturing Processes and Applications

Manufacturing Materials and Processes

As discussed in Chapter 6, engineers select materials on the basis of their properties, cost and availability. New materials are continually being developed. This requires that engineers keep up with the latest discoveries. The materials used in manufacturing include:

- **Ferrous metals:** various kinds of steel alloys made by adding carbon and other elements to iron.
- **Non-ferrous metals:** aluminum, copper, titanium, gold and other precious metals.
- **Ceramics:** glass, clay, and graphite.
- **Plastics:** thermoplastics that can be heated and reshaped, and thermoplastics that cannot be reheated and reshaped.
- **Engineered materials:** composites, fiber materials, and nanotechnology materials are stronger and more durable than other materials because their internal structure has been modified.

You will recall that while there are many processes used for manufacturing engineered products, they can be grouped into seven techniques. Those seven manufacturing techniques are casting, molding, forming, separating, joining, treating, and finishing. Manufacturing a single product will require the application of one or more of these processes. The choice of which technique or techniques to use when manufacturing a product will be influenced by the properties of the materials used, as well as other constraints such as cost and the desired properties of the finished product.

Consider the processes used to produce an automobile. Engine blocks are made by casting. Hundreds of individual plastic parts are made by injection molding. Forming processes used in automobile parts manufacturing include the forging of engine parts, and stamping to produce fenders and other body parts. Separating processes are used to cut the cloth or leather materials for seats. Automobile parts are joined using various techniques including nuts and bolts, adhesives, and welding. The glass in automobiles is tempered using a heat treating process to increase its strength.

Materials Processing Machines

Engineers must consider many factors when selecting the best process for cutting or shaping a material. These factors include the characteristics of the material itself, the material of the cutting tool, the shape of the cutting tool, the speed and depth of cut, and whether a fluid should be used to reduce friction during the cutting. Saws such as bandsaws and power hacksaws are used in manufacturing plants.

 Visualization

Flat Patterns After a product is manufactured, it often has to be packaged for shipping and sale. There are many elements to the design of packaging. Being able to visualize folding a 2D flat pattern into a 3D surface model is a fundamental visualization skill. The use of flat patterns is common in package design.

Group Workspace

Test your ability to visualize unfolded objects in 2D, called developments, and to match them to 3D objects, along with other exercises that involve visualizing folded paper and the rotation of 2D shapes.

Go to your ✐ *essentials* ONLINE to learn more about developing your 2D flat pattern visualization skills.

Whether working with metal, wood, or anther material, lathes and milling machines are used to remove material to produce items of various shapes. Using a lathe for turning is a common process. Turning produces pieces such as shafts or spindles. In this process, a piece of material rotates or spins while a cutting tool removes material to a certain depth as it travels along the rotating piece of material. Lathes are also used for other operations, including drilling holes and cutting threads.

Milling is used to shape materials with the use of cutters. In addition to complex shapes, milling machines are also used to make gears. Most milling machines are now computer controlled. Computer-controlled machines increase productivity and enhance the quality of parts produced because they can ensure that each piece milled is identical to the others. The milling machine pictured in **Figure 10.7** is being used to create a propeller blade for a ship.

Drilling machines are used to make holes. The vertical drill press is the most common drilling machine. Drill presses are versatile machines that are often oriented either vertically or horizontally, and come in many sizes. A vise or other device is used to prevent the material from moving or slipping as it is drilled.

Reading Check **List** factors engineers must consider when selecting the best process for cutting or shaping material.

Fig. 10.7 Materials Processing This milling machine is creating a ship's propeller blade. *What do saws, drills and milling machines have in common in the way that they process materials?*

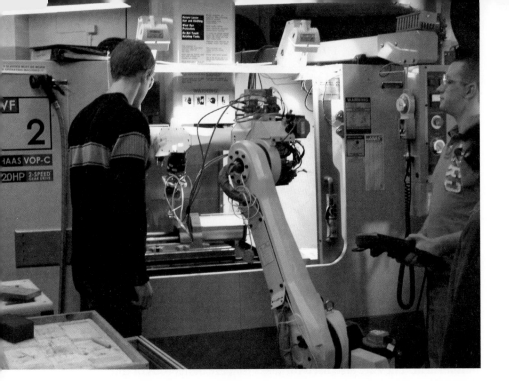

Computer-aided manufacturing (CAM) is the use of computer software to control machine tools such as milling machines. In many instances, the same software used for computer-aided design (CAD) can be used for machine control. When this process is fully integrated it is called CAD/CAM.

Computer-integrated manufacturing (CIM) is the use of computers to control the entire manufacturing process, including production, quality control, and inventory management. CIM systems use sophisticated communication systems as well as sensors and closed loop systems to create automated manufacturing systems. (See **Figure 10.8**.)

Automation and Robotics

Automation is the use of control systems to regulate equipment and processes. When automation is used in manufacturing, it results in higher quality products and reduces the need for human intervention. The initial cost of automating manufacturing is high. Over an extended period of time, however, it often turns out to be a good investment.

Programmable Logic Controllers (PLCs) are specialized computers used to automate manufacturing processes. PLCs are different from typical computers because they are designed to withstand harsh environments, including high temperatures or vibration. PLCs monitor almost every aspect of manufacturing, collect data, and make adjustments more quickly than humans can.

Industrial robots are devices that can be programmed to perform industrial tasks. They are part of modern manufacturing systems, and are often used to perform repetitive and unskilled tasks, freeing humans for tasks that take brain power or ingenuity. These robots do not resemble humans, but they are often programmed to move like a

Fig. 10.9 Robotic Perfection
Industrial robots like this one are used to perform tasks that are difficult for a human to perform consistently, such as spray-painting an automobile. *What are some advantages of using automation to perform tasks that used to be performed by humans?*

✔ **Reading Check** **List** common tasks performed by industrial robots in modern manufacturing systems.

human arm. They are also used for tasks that are dangerous or difficult for humans to perform consistently, such as spray-painting (see **Figure 10.9**), welding, and handling heavy items. Robots can also be used to move materials and for inspecting product quality.

*e*ssentials

Virtual Lab: Material Processes

As existing and new materials are chosen for manufacturing, various processes are used to transform the items into usable products. Engineers must choose the most appropriate processes and applications for materials. These processes include casting, molding, forming, separating, joining, treating, and finishing. Continually testing and evaluating emerging and existing materials is a constant challenge for manufacturing and materials process engineers.

View Go to your *e*ssentials ONLINE to view the *Virtual Lab: Material Processes.*

Plastics

Packaging

Packaging is the process of protecting products for shipping and sale. Packaging is an essential part of manufacturing and the third largest industry in the U.S. Some engineers work for companies that specialize in designing packages for other companies. Other engineers specialize in designing packaging processes and equipment. Some may work directly for the company that manufactures the product.

Packaging is designed to protect products against things such as damage due to dropping or extreme temperatures experienced during shipping. Most individual products made in manufacturing plants are packaged there for sale. A group of those packages is often placed in a carton and a large number of those cartons is then placed on pallets to facilitate shipping. In modern manufacturing, packaging is often an automated process. (See **Figure 10.10**.)

Fig. 10.10 A "Package Deal"
Packaging of consumer products can serve various functions including making the product look more attractive to customers and protecting it against damage. *What are some products you use every day that have unique packaging?*

Check Your Understanding

After You Read Perform the following tasks.

1. **Explain** the main benefits of using programmable logic controllers for manufacturing.

2. **Identify** five types of materials used in manufacturing.

3. **Evaluate** how CIM systems and automation might be both beneficial and detrimental to manufacturing.

Problem-Solving Process

Identify

Despite community and manufacturer reuse and recycling efforts, roughly one third of all residential waste is made up of packaging materials. To reduce packaging waste, GreenGoods, Ltd. is producing a line of school accessories that incorporate snack food packaging. Your manufacturing team must develop a pencil organizer that meets these criteria:

- You must use at least 50% recycled packaging materials.
- Produce a sample batch of at least 10 pencil organizers.
- Try to minimize the number of manufacturing operations.

Set Up

1. Research the project. Ask: *"What packaging materials can be easily reused?"* and *"What production method would be best?"*
2. Study features of existing products created from recycled materials. Consider the needs of your target audience.
3. Brainstorm potential solutions and develop sketches. Identify production techniques such as chemical or mechanical fastening.
4. Use a decision matrix to choose the best solution. Be sure to use criteria and constraints as guides in judging the best idea.

Execute

5. Plan the solution. Are recycled materials readily available? Is special equipment needed? What manufacturing process is best?
6. Keep sketching and recording ideas to improve your design.
7. Prepare models of the solution using different production methods. Perform periodic quality checks.
8. Meet with your group to discuss product development. Outline successful features and possible drawbacks of your designs.

Evaluate

Ask a group of potential users to use the prototype over a day or week. Ask them to critique the features, look, and finish of your design.

Share

Create a presentation about the product. Discuss the problems posed by packaging material and how your product could minimize them. Identify recycled materials and manufacturing processes that were used. Include the feedback from the stakeholders who tested the prototype.

Critical Thinking

Key Concepts

1. **Identify** five manufacturing systems and explain the benefits of each.

2. **Summarize** how automation affects quality in manufactured products.

3. **Compare and contrast** lean manufacturing and just-in-time manufacturing.

4. **Evaluate** four types of materials and explain how the properties of each type affect an engineer's choice of materials.

5. **Analyze** how industrial robots are used and the benefits of using them instead of human labor for certain processes.

Communication *21st Century Skills*

6. **Share** with your project team what you have learned about manufacturing decisions and distribution and how this connects to your Discovery Project.

7. **Discuss** how the development of your material mover will impact the process of constructing a commercial building and whether or not that will necessitate changes in the construction materials used.

Activity Center

Go to the **Activity Center** to review chapter vocabulary and key concepts.

Engineer's Toolbox

Go to the **Engineer's Toolbox** to:
- Access Academic Activities
- Access the Competitive Event Prep Activity.

---

essentials

DISCOVERY PROJECT

Design and Build a Construction Material Mover

Imagine that you work for a company that designs and builds materials handling equipment. To date the company has focused on equipment used in manufacturing plants. Now your company wants to expand its business by making materials handling equipment for the construction industry. Your task is to design a remotely controlled machine that can take concrete blocks from a pallet and move them into the correct position in a wall that is being built.

Go to your **essentials ONLINE** to complete the Discovery Project.

11

Biomedical Engineering

ESSENTIAL QUESTION How are engineers like physicians?

Biomedical engineering is a field that is focused on improving the health and safety of all of us. Using as their foundation the principles of biology and medicine, biomedical engineers develop and improve systems and devices from consumer products and safety equipment to cutting-edge medical instruments and imaging systems. Items as varied as a desk chair and an artificial heart have been made possible by the contributions of biomedical engineers. This branch of engineering has also greatly improved the efficiency and effectiveness of surgery and other medical procedures.

essentials

DISCOVERY PROJECT

Design an Artificial Human Hand

21st Century Skills — Discuss why teamwork is an important part of designing, building, and testing a model prosthetic hand.

What concepts of biomedical engineering come into play when designing an artificial limb such as a replacement for the human hand? In this chapter's Discovery Project you will research the human hand and create a model to mimic its construction. Modeling systems (such as LEGO® and K'NEX®) can be used as the basic building materials.

 Group Workspace

Summarize how engineers must consider the principles of biomedical engineering when creating replacements for human body parts.

 Engineer's Toolbox

Go to the Engineer's Toolbox to
- Access Note-Taking Activities
- Access Graphic Organizers
- Access Academic Standards met by this chapter

ACCESS Science
Inspiring Science Discovery

Go to your *essentials* ONLINE to view the video to learn about the development of an improved artificial human eye.

READING GUIDE

Before You Read How is biomedical engineering an extension of traditional medicine? How do biomedical engineers find solutions to address the physical needs of patients?

Objectives

- **Identify** the roles of engineers in biomechanics and ergonomics.
- **Compare and contrast** the various types of medical imaging systems.
- **Discuss** the purposes served by artificial organs and tissues.
- **Explain** the contributions of engineering to medical instruments and equipment.

Main Idea

Biomedical engineering is a branch of engineering that has made major contributions to the medical and health care industries. Engineers develop and refine systems that help doctors diagnose and treat medical conditions more efficiently and effectively.

Vocabulary

Content Vocabulary

- homeostasis
- musculoskeletal
- minimally invasive surgery
- robotic surgery
- biomechanical
- inverse
- computed tomography (CT, CAT)
- magnetic resonance imaging (MRI)
- ultrasound imaging
- isotopes
- tissue engineering
- transplant
- biomaterials

Academic Vocabulary

- image
- adjustments

Note-Taking Activity

Draw this table for each section. Write key terms and phrases under **Cues**. Write main ideas under **Note Taking**. Summarize the section under **Summary**.

Cues	Note Taking
•	•
•	•
Summary	

Graphic Organizers

Use graphic organizers to organize information as you read.

Go to your  **ONLINE** for downloadable graphic organizers.

ACADEMIC

Technology

ITEEA STL10.01 Research and development is a specific problem-solving approach that is used intensively in business and industry to prepare devices and systems for the marketplace.

ITEEA STL14 Students will develop an understanding of and be able to select and use medical technologies.

Mathematics

NCTM Data Analysis and Probability Formulate questions that can be addressed with data and collect, organize, and display relevant data to answer them.

Science

NSES F Students should develop understanding of personal and community health; population growth; natural resources; environmental quality; natural and human-induced hazards; science and technology in local, national, and global challenges.

ITEEA *International Technology and Engineering Educators Association*
NCTM *National Council of Teachers of Mathematics*
NSES *National Science Education Standards*

College & Career READINESS

Writing Conduct short as well as more sustained research projects based on focused questions, demonstrating understanding of the subject under investigation.

Biomedical Engineering Overview

What is Biomedical Engineering?

Biomedical engineering is the application of knowledge from engineering, biology, and medicine to improve human health. Biomedical engineering is one of the newest and fastest-growing fields within the engineering profession. There will almost certainly be excellent career opportunities in this field during the coming decade. These include conducting research at the university level and developing new and improved products for companies in the health care industry. Some biomedical engineers work with physicians to develop new medical devices and instruments. Pharmaceutical companies employ biomedical engineers to develop manufacturing processes for new medications. They are also employed by hospitals to maintain complex devices such as robotic surgical systems. Important medical advances made possible by biomedical engineering include improved imaging systems, artificial joints, pacemakers, and computerized blood analysis systems.

Biology

Biology is the study of life and living organisms. This field of study dates back to at least 350 B.C. Areas of biology related to biomedical engineering include cell theory, genetics, **homeostasis** (the stability of the body's systems), and energy. Biomedical engineers need to understand each of these areas as well as the human body as a system.

Cell theory is based on the concept that all living things are made up of cells and that those cells came from other cells through the process

Fig. 11.1 Biomedical Engineers
Biomedical engineers work on a wide range of projects, such as research and development of new medicines. *Which biomedical careers involve more time spent "in the field" rather than in laboratories?*

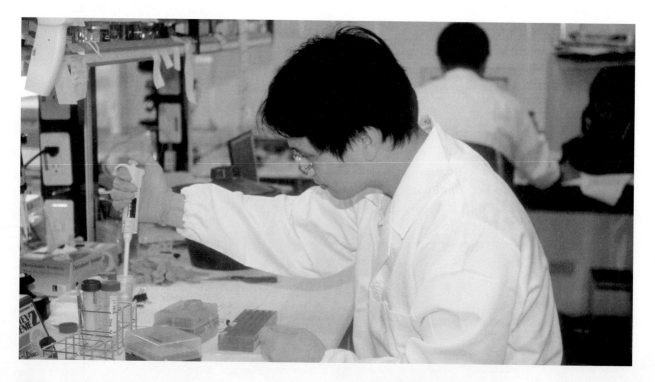

of cell division. Cell theory is important for understanding the causes of, and possible treatments for, many illnesses.

Genetics is the study of heredity. We know that humans and other living things inherit traits from their parents. Genetics, along with experience, determines how organisms, including humans, look and behave.

Homeostasis refers to the ability of an organism to regulate its internal environment. For example, to regulate your internal body temperature, you perspire when exercising and shiver when you are cold. Related to homeostasis is the understanding of energy as it applies to biology. Humans and all other living things need a source of energy. Most of our energy comes from chemicals contained in the foods that we eat.

Medicine

Medicine is the profession that focuses on the diagnosis and treatment of illnesses. A good understanding of human biology is necessary for professionals in the medical field. The Greeks established a medical school around 700 B.C. The Greek physician Hippocrates is considered to be the father of modern medicine. He studied illnesses and developed treatments for them. He also performed surgery and shared his knowledge by teaching others. The Romans also made important contributions to medicine, particularly in developing medical instruments. Modern versions of many Roman medical instruments are still used by physicians today.

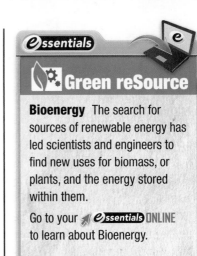

Green reSource

Bioenergy The search for sources of renewable energy has led scientists and engineers to find new uses for biomass, or plants, and the energy stored within them.

Go to your *essentials* ONLINE to learn about Bioenergy.

Group Workspace

Bioenergy uses plant-based materials, such as wood or agricultural waste, as an energy source. Discuss some sources of Bioenergy and how they can be used to create energy.

essentials

Virtual Lab: Ergonomics

Engineers in the field of ergonomic design (which is also known as human factors design and engineering) study physiology, engineering, and psychology to encourage the harmony of form, function, and performance. Ergonomics improves product design to help humans avoid repetitive stress injuries and other unhealthy consequences of unnatural or uncomfortable movements.

View Go to your *essentials* ONLINE to view the *Virtual Lab: Ergonomics.*

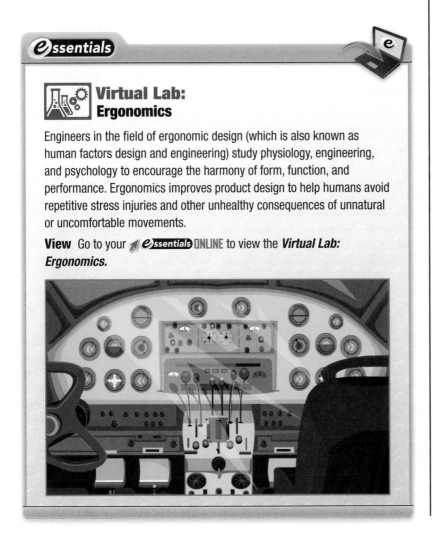

Fig. 11.2 Robotic Surgery The da Vinci surgical robot in the center of the photo below converts the surgeon's hand movements (at left) into the movement of surgical instruments, which are monitored on the screen (at right). *What advantages does this system provide over traditional surgery?*

An undergraduate degree in biomedical engineering is good preparation for the study of biomedicine. The fields of medicine and biomedical engineering include many related specialties. For example, orthopedic medicine is concerned with the functioning of the **musculoskeletal** system, which includes bones, joints, tendons, ligaments, and muscles. Patients with musculoskeletal problems seek treatment from orthopedic surgeons. Orthopedic engineers work with orthopedic surgeons to create devices such as artificial hips and knees. Since people are living longer than ever before, there is an increasing need for devices that function well for a long time, so that patients do not need to undergo additional surgery to replace those devices.

Biomedical engineers have played an important role in improving surgery through the development of new surgical equipment. Two important and related advances are **minimally invasive surgery** and robotic surgery.

Minimally Invasive Surgery One development that has revolutionized the field of surgery in recent years is that of minimally invasive surgery, also known as endoscopic surgery. This technique usually involves the use of small incisions and very small surgical instruments designed for this purpose. An endoscope, which is a long, flexible tube that has a light and camera at its end, is inserted into the patient's body through one incision, while surgical tools are inserted through other incisions. The endoscope allows the surgeon to monitor the procedure on a screen as he or she works.

Compared to traditional surgery, minimally invasive surgery offers the advantages to the patient of reduced blood loss, shorter hospital stays, more rapid recovery, and smaller scars. There are also disadvantages. In some cases, surgical procedures using minimally-invasive techniques can take longer than traditional surgeries, and not all surgeons have the training and experience necessary to use these techniques.

Robotic Surgery Robotic surgery is growing increasingly common as more companies manufacture robotic surgical systems and more

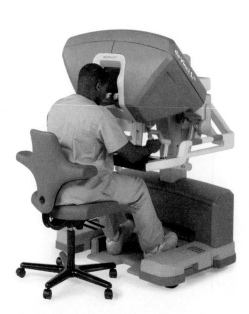

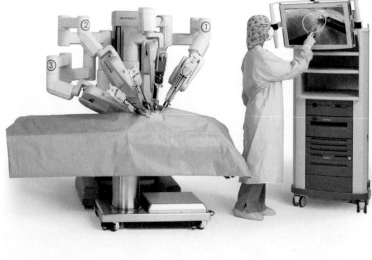

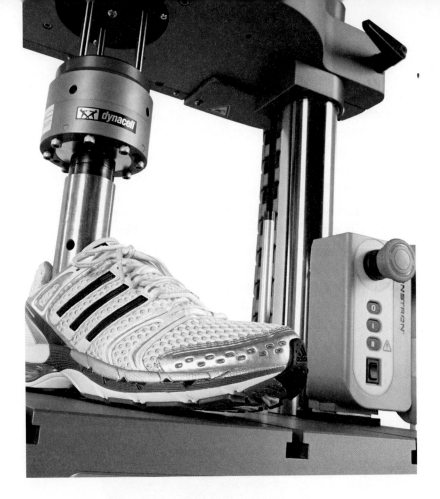

Fig. 11.3 Product Testing These shoes are tested extensively before being manufactured in order to protect athletes from injury. *Which parts of a shoe must be most carefully and thoroughly tested?* Photo courtesy of Instron®

physicians are trained to use them. Robotic systems are currently being used for heart, orthopedic, and other kinds of surgery. Such procedures are minimally invasive, allow greater precision than is possible with traditional surgery, and remove the need for the doctor to look away from the monitor when performing an operation.

The da Vinci surgical robot is currently the most popular system of this type. It includes three main components: a workstation for the surgeon, a robot that is placed next to the patient, with four arms to hold and control surgical instruments, and a three-dimensional vision system. The surgeon's hand movements are electronically converted into the movement of small, specially-designed surgical instruments. (See **Figure 11.2**.)

Biomedical researchers are also working on smaller robotic surgical devices following recent advances in the field of nanotechnology. Tools at the cellular level will someday assist in diagnosis, imaging, and surgical procedures. Such applications are already being developed in the areas of orthopedics, heart surgery, spinal surgery, and plastic surgery.

Rehabilitation Rehabilitation engineers usually work with physicians and other medical professionals such as physical therapists to design devices that help people cope with, or recover from, disabilities. Many rehabilitation engineers modify devices or create new devices for individual patients. For example, rehabilitation engineers can customize an electric wheelchair's seating and control systems for maximum comfort and ease of operation by the patient. They can also design modifications

Make an illustration that shows the bones of the hand. Describe the importance of muscles and tendons for movement. Decide which parts of the hand will be the most important to the design of your prosthetic hand.

that will allow the patient to drive a motor vehicle and can recommend architectural changes in the home to increase accessibility.

Biomechanics

Biomechanical engineers focus on the mechanics of the human body. They are interested in how bones, muscles, tendons, ligaments, and joints work within the body, and they use this knowledge to design replacement body parts. They must take into consideration constraints such as friction, wear, elasticity, strength, and stress.

Biomechanical engineers also design equipment for consumers and athletes. For example, although running is healthy exercise, many runners suffer impact injuries. Athletic shoe companies study the effects of impact when designing new kinds of running shoes that will help athletes perform well, enjoy greater comfort and less fatigue, and reduce injuries. (See **Figure 11.3**.)

Biomechanical engineers also design consumer safety products such as bicycle helmets. Lightweight, stylish, and comfortable helmet

Non slip surface upholstery

Adjustable Backrest Height

Adjustable Forward/Backward Backrest

Seat swivels 360°

Adjustable Height

Minimum 5 Rungs On Wheels

Fig. 11.4 Ergonomic Features
This chair is meant to provide its user with both comfort and safety. *What features of a chair must be designed with ergonomics in mind?*

designs have encouraged more riders of all ages to wear helmets. The helmets use energy-absorbing materials to reduce the force of impacts to the head. To test helmets, manufacturers drop them from a height of several meters and use electronic instruments to measure how much protection the helmets provide. Similar tests are used to study the helmets designed for football and hockey players.

Ergonomics

Ergonomics, sometimes referred to as human factors design and engineering, is the process of ensuring that there is a good fit between technology and its users. Human factors that engineers in this field must consider include the specific task that needs to be done, the equipment needed to complete the task, and information about the user's physical needs.

Ergonomics can be applied to the design of relatively simple items such as desk chairs that can be adjusted for the comfort of the user (see **Figure 11.4**) or for complex items such as the cockpit and instrument panel of an airliner. In an airliner, it is important for the pilot to be seated comfortably for an extended period of time. The pilot also needs a good view of the airplane's instruments and must be able to reach the controls required for takeoff, landing, and cruising from his or her seat.

The field of ergonomics uses knowledge from a number of other fields, including biomechanics, psychology, mechanical engineering, and medicine. It is a factor in the avoidance and treatment of conditions such as carpal tunnel syndrome and some types of arthritis, as well as numerous types of injuries. Ergonomics is also a consideration when designing and furnishing workspaces, from office computer stations to industrial assembly lines, as such considerations play a part in maintaining workplace safety and the health and comfort of employees. Elements of ergonomics are addressed by occupational therapists as well as engineers.

Reading Check **Explain** the advantages of minimally invasive surgery.

Check Your Understanding

After You Read Perform the following tasks.

1. **List** some career opportunities in the field of biomedical engineering.

2. **Identify** ways in which biology is the foundation of the field of medicine.

3. **Analyze** the role that biomechanical engineers play in the testing of new consumer products.

Types of Biomedical Engineering Projects

Biomedical engineers are involved in many aspects of developing new medical devices and techniques that may dramatically improve medical care in the coming years. They develop new and improved diagnostic equipment that is designed to monitor human health. The equipment that they design is used in laboratories, hospitals, physicians' offices, and patients' homes. Examples of common diagnostic equipment include blood pressure monitors, surgical instruments, microscopes used to examine tissue samples, and equipment to monitor heart and brain activity.

Imaging systems that can look inside the body are among the most important tools available to physicians. Biomedical engineers both develop new imaging systems and improve the quality of existing imaging systems. Tissue engineering, which makes use of continuing advances in biology and engineering, offers the possibility of creating new organs from a patient's own skin cells. This is of particular importance for patients who have suffered serious burns. New biomaterials are making it possible to improve contact lenses for millions of users and to enhance the performance of prosthetic limbs used by athletes.

Medical Imaging Systems

Some biomedical engineers specialize in designing equipment that generates an image that can be used for diagnostic purposes. The images create visual representations of something inside the body. X-rays, CT scans, MRIs, ultrasound, nuclear medicine, and endoscopy are the major types of imaging systems. Imaging technology is a rapidly advancing field, and improved versions of these systems and entirely new systems are constantly under development.

X-Rays

X-rays were the first kind of medical imaging that made it possible to see inside a living body. Traditional x-ray machines have a source that emits x-rays in the form of a beam. The beam penetrates the body to expose photographic film that is on the other side of the person. Modern x-ray systems use electronic detectors instead of photographic film. X-rays create inverse images. For example, when a chest x-ray is taken, less dense areas such as the lungs appear dark in the inverse image, while bones such as the ribs appear light. X-rays are convenient and relatively inexpensive compared to other medical imaging techniques. A major concern is that repeated exposure to the radiation produced by x-rays can cause biological damage to the patient. Another major limitation of traditional x-rays is that the images produced are two-dimensional.

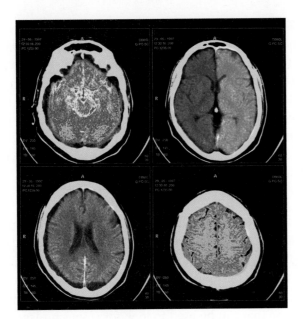

Computed Tomography

Computed tomography, commonly called a CT or CAT scan, is a special x-ray technique that produces three-dimensional images by moving a narrow x-ray beam around the body while the patient remains still. The separate images are computer processed to produce a high quality three-dimensional image. Unlike standard x-rays, the CT scan can detect soft tissue as well as bone and other dense materials. It requires the use of machinery that is larger and more expensive than x-ray machines. (See **Figure 11.5**.)

Magnetic Resonance Imaging

Magnetic resonance imaging (MRI) uses a strong magnetic field and radio waves to produce images. The MRI's magnetic field aligns the hydrogen atoms of the water inside the body. Radio waves alter the alignment of the hydrogen atoms to create a rotating magnetic field that the scanner detects. MRIs are good for imaging soft tissues of the brain, heart, and other organs. They are not good for getting images of bones. Functional MRIs, which are relatively new, are designed for tasks such as looking at blood flow in the brain and detecting oxygen levels in the blood. MRIs are considered to be safe for the patient.

Ultrasound Imaging

Ultrasound imaging scanners are based on the use of high frequency sound. They use a probe and a gel that is spread between the probe and the patient's skin. Sound waves are sent into the body and reflected by tissues within the body. The reflected sound waves are processed to create a digital image. Ultrasound imaging is a valuable diagnostic tool for monitoring the heart, especially the function of heart valves. Ultrasound is also commonly used during pregnancy to monitor the health of the baby developing within the mother's body. Although it does not produce images of the same quality as other imaging techniques, it provides real-time information. Another advantage of ultrasound is that it is inexpensive. Several manufacturers have designed small, portable ultrasound scanners. (See **Figure 11.6**.)

Nuclear Medicine

Nuclear medicine uses radioactive **isotopes** for imaging and treatment. A radioactive chemical is taken orally or injected so that a particular organ and its functioning can be studied. For example, a person might be given radioactive iodine to produce images that show how the thyroid gland is working. Similar techniques can also be used to map brain activity. The amount of radiation ingested during this procedure is very low and is safe for most patients; however, some doctors advise against repeated use of this technique over a short period of time.

Optical Imaging

Optical imaging techniques use light to see what is happening inside the body. Endoscopy, which means "looking inside," is based on the use of an endoscope. Endoscopes use fiber optics. They have a light source and a lens to focus the light and bring the image back to a physician or technician. In a common procedure, patients are sedated and swallow an endoscope that can be used to look for stomach ulcers. After the procedure, the patient usually recovers very quickly.

Biological Applications

Some of the most important applications of biomedical engineering are those that can improve the lives of people with serious health conditions. From tissue research at the cell level to the development of high-tech prosthetic devices, engineers are constantly changing and improving the way in which a variety of conditions are treated.

Tissue Engineering

Tissue engineering is an engineering technique that uses cells and special materials to repair or replace tissues such as skin, bone, or blood vessels. Patients with severe burns are at high risk for developing infections. For this reason, skin grafts taken from another part of the body are used to replace the skin in damaged areas. Occasionally skin from another individual can also be used for the grafts. But now biomedical engineers are improving techniques that take just a few skin cells from an individual to grow the millions of skin cells needed to create new skin.

Reading Check **Identify** which imaging technique is most useful for viewing soft tissue inside the body.

PROJECT CONNECTIONS

Investigate why hand x-rays are taken and what they can show. How do the bones of the hand appear in the x-ray? What else can be seen?

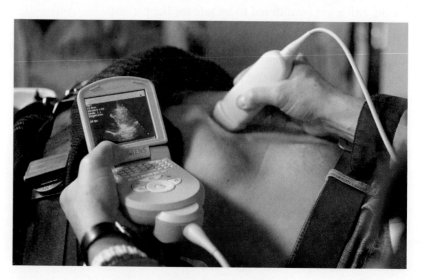

Fig. 11.6 Portable Ultrasound Machines This ultrasound system is being used to make a quick assessment of an accident victim. *What makes ultrasound more useful for this purpose than an MRI?*

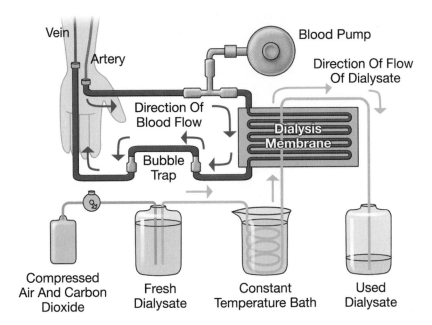

Vein

Artery

Blood Pump

Direction Of Flow
Of Dialysate

Direction Of
Blood Flow

Dialysis
Membrane

Bubble
Trap

Compressed
Air And Carbon
Dioxide

Fresh
Dialysate

Constant
Temperature Bath

Used
Dialysate

Fig. 11.7 Dialysis Machine
This dialysis machine replaces the function of a patient's kidneys. *What other artificial organs are available to doctors and hospitals?*

There are diseases that cannot be treated with drugs or surgery. When an entire organ such as the heart, liver, or kidney fails, the only option may be a **transplant**. Currently about 75,000 people in the United States are waiting for kidneys, and 16,000 are waiting for livers. Biomedical engineers are working on a variety of solutions to this problem. When a person has a heart attack, the heart has only a limited ability to heal. One possible solution may be to perform a biopsy and remove cells from a healthy part of the heart. These cells are then grown in a laboratory to create a patch to repair the damaged tissue. A problem with this approach is that it can take several weeks. For that reason, other solutions such as artificial organs are needed.

Artificial Organs

Artificial organs are human-made devices that replace a natural organ that is not functioning properly. Dialysis machines, heart-lung machines, the artificial heart, and cochlear implants are examples of artificial organs. To date, the dialysis machine, which replaces kidney function for patients with kidney failure, has been the most widely used artificial organ. There are several dialysis techniques. Hemodialysis is the most common. In hemodialysis, the patient's blood is pumped into a dialysis machine, which uses a filter and solution to remove waste and excess water. The cleaned blood is then returned to the patient's body. Treatment can take three to five hours and is usually repeated several times per week. (See **Figure 11.7.**)

The heart-lung machine is a vital piece of operating-room equipment. It is used during heart surgery to maintain blood flow and respiration while the heart is stopped for surgery. One reason for the heart-lung machine's importance is that it is difficult to operate on a beating heart. Coronary bypass surgery is the most common heart operation. During that surgery, the heart-lung machine replaces the function of the patient's heart and lungs. The machine removes carbon dioxide from the blood, delivers oxygen to the blood, and helps maintain the desired body temperature.

Success in using heart-lung machines for several hours during surgery has encouraged research to develop an implantable artificial heart. This research is important because there is a shortage of human hearts available to people suffering from total heart failure. To date, there has been only limited success with permanent, implantable artificial hearts. However, the use of artificial hearts to maintain the life of patients while they wait for a heart from a suitable donor has been successful in more than 1,000 patients. Developing an implantable heart is a challenging task. It must be made from materials that are compatible with the human body, it needs to be the right size for the patient's body, it must not damage the patient's blood or other organs, and it must have a reliable, long-lasting power supply.

The cochlear implant is a device that enables some deaf or severely hard-of-hearing patients to hear. Deaf children and adults who have lost their hearing due to illness and who have a functioning auditory nerve are good candidates for the surgery. The device is implanted under the skin behind the ear. It includes a microphone that detects and filters sound, and a transmitter that sends the sound to a receiver connected to the cochlea of the ear by electrodes. Several weeks after the surgery, the device is turned on and adjusted. Following successful surgery, it can take between several months and several years for young children to achieve hearing and speaking levels comparable to those of hearing children of a similar age. (See **Figure 11.8**.)

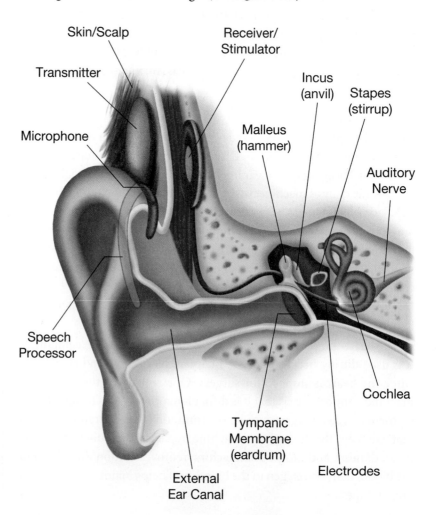

Fig. 11.8 Cochlear Implant
A cochlear implant can restore hearing to some patients. *What type of hearing loss benefits from this device?*

Prosthetic Devices

Prosthetic devices are artificial parts designed to replace a part of the human body that is missing or damaged due to a birth defect, an illness, or an accident. Their use can greatly improve the quality of life of their users. Common prostheses include replacement limbs and teeth. The use of artificial teeth and limbs goes back more than two thousand years. Extensive research and development by biomedical engineers is helping to produce better-quality and less-expensive prosthetic devices.

The first prosthetic limbs were made of natural materials such as wood. Today, prosthetic limbs make use of modern, lightweight materials such as carbon fibers. These limbs are customized for each patient using computer-aided design and manufacturing. Runners who use prosthetics may have several different kinds of prosthetic limbs, such as one for daily use that cosmetically resembles a natural foot and another that is specifically designed for competitions. Some prosthetics use computers and sensors to make adjustments according to the needs of the user. The needs of people injured in military service have driven the development of prosthetic arms that operate robotically. These arms use a series of computer-controlled motors with pressure sensors built into the "skin" of the device. (See **Figure 11.9**.)

Fig. 11.9 Prosthetic Leg Though this prosthetic leg does not look like a natural leg, it is ideally suited for athletic events. *What constraints might the designers of this prosthetic leg have taken into consideration?*

PROJECT CONNECTIONS

Identify several major challenges that a biomedical engineer would face in designing a prosthetic hand.

Reading Check **List** types of artificial organs that are not located in the patient's body.

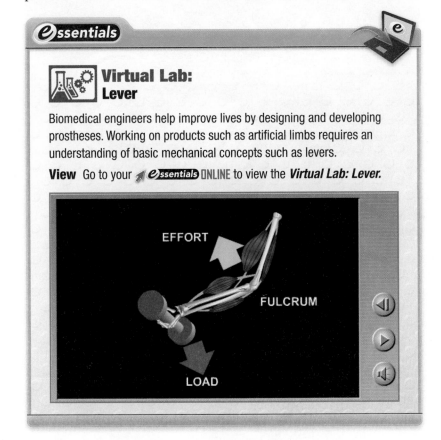

essentials

Virtual Lab: Lever

Biomedical engineers help improve lives by designing and developing prostheses. Working on products such as artificial limbs requires an understanding of basic mechanical concepts such as levers.

View Go to your *essentials* ONLINE to view the *Virtual Lab: Lever.*

EFFORT

FULCRUM

LOAD

PROJECT CONNECTIONS

Investigate the kinds of materials that are used in making prosthetic hands. What are some important reasons for the choice of those particular materials?

Biomedical Materials and Equipment

Engineers must draw upon their knowledge of materials and their properties in order to create new materials for medical and health care purposes and to develop and improve medical equipment.

Biomaterials

Biomaterials are natural or synthetic (human-made) materials that are used for medical applications. Biomaterials must be compatible with the human body. Common medical applications of biomaterials include using silicon rubber for finger joints, titanium for hip joints, and polymers for contact lenses. The first contact lenses were made of glass. Today most contact lenses are made of hydrogels, which are polymers made up mostly of water. Bone cement, another common biomaterial, is used for joining artificial joints and natural bone.

Some biomaterials, such as those used to make replacement heart valves, are chosen or designed so that they do not react negatively with the body. Heart valves can be replaced using mechanical valves or valves from pigs that have been chemically treated to make them compatible with the human heart. (See **Figure 11.10**.) Other biomaterials are engineered so that they interact with the body in a specific way. For example, new materials are being designed to locate and destroy cancer cells. The biomaterials field is growing rapidly, with excellent career opportunities expected in the coming years.

Fig. 11.10 Artificial Heart The artificial heart is a device that is constantly being evaluated for improvements by biomedical engineers. *What components of an artificial heart are most essential to its successful functioning?*

Fig. 11.11 AED Many places of business have acquired automated external defibrillators (AEDs) for emergency use. *How can an AED effectively save lives in the absence of trained medical responders?*

Medical Instruments and Equipment

Biomedical engineers contribute to medicine by designing medical instruments and equipment used to improve the health care of patients and the general public. Some surgical instruments, such as scalpels, are used for general surgical purposes. Other instruments are designed for special applications such as minimally invasive surgery.

Cardiac monitoring devices are one example of the lifesaving equipment designed by biomedical engineers. Cardiac monitoring is used by physicians who use electrocardiograph (EKG or ECG) machines in their offices to monitor heart rhythm during routine physicals, by paramedics treating possible heart attack patients, and in hospitals during surgery and recovery. An important recent development has been the development and use of automated external defibrillators (AEDs). AEDs are portable devices that can detect abnormal heart rhythms and, if necessary, provide a shock to restore normal rhythm. They are routinely used by medical personnel, and are now made available in many public places. The AEDs that are located in facilities such as schools and stadiums provide audible directions so that they can be used by untrained personnel. Public AEDs have been credited with saving many lives. (See **Figure 11.11**.)

> **✓ Reading Check** **Explain** why engineers need to know the properties of biomaterials that are to be used inside the body.

Check Your Understanding

SECTION **11.2**

After You Read Perform the following tasks.

1. **Discuss** the ways in which several different medical imaging systems are used.

2. **Summarize** how the continuing development of new types of artificial organs is changing the ways in which doctors treat their patients.

3. **Debate** this statement with a partner: The use of prosthetics by some athletes in competitions is unfair.

Review and Assessment

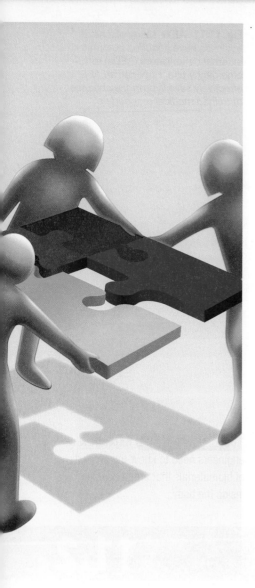

Problem-Solving Process

Identify

For people who suffer from arthritis, musculoskeletal disabilities, or hand injuries, many daily activities present a challenge. To assist these individuals, biomedical engineers use ergonomics to develop innovative solutions. Griponomics, a specialty houseware company, has asked your team to create a line of kitchen utensils for people with limited hand function. The line must meet the following constraints:

- Fit the average adult hand
- Have a force-absorbing grip
- Be at an ergonomically correct angle

Set Up

1. Research the project. Ask: *"What are the physical limitations of the user?"* and *"How can the input force be multiplied?"*

2. Research existing products created for people with weak grips. Evaluate the dimensions of an average adult hand.

3. Brainstorm potential solutions and develop sketches. Identify hand positions, dimensions, and possible materials.

4. Use a decision matrix to choose the best solution.

Execute

5. Plan the solution. What materials can provide a supple, yet firm grip? What techniques can be used for production?

6. Keep sketching and recording ideas to improve your design.

7. Prepare models using various production techniques. You may develop models with different handles to optimize your design.

8. Meet with your team to discuss product development. Analyze your progress and consider ways to improve fit and finish.

Evaluate

Evaluate the design by having several people use the redesigned utensil along with a standard utensil. Ask users for feedback on the effort required to perform common tasks with each. Modify the design as necessary.

Share

Create a commercial for your solution. Identify prospective users and their problems with standard kitchen utensils. Describe how your design reduces stress and improves life for users with physical limitations.

Critical Thinking

Key Concepts

1. **Identify** the roles of engineers in biomechanics and ergonomics.

2. **Summarize** the situations and conditions that call for artificial organs and tissues.

3. **Compare and contrast** several biomaterials and their uses.

4. **Evaluate** the advantages and disadvantages of the various types of medical imaging systems.

5. **Analyze** how biomedical engineers have changed the way in which doctors perform surgical procedures.

Teamwork 21st Century Skills

6. **Share** with your project team what you have learned about artificial organs and tissues, and how that information connects to your Discovery Project.

7. **Discuss** what you have learned about biomechanics, ergonomics, artificial organs, prosthetic devices, and biomaterials. Decide with your team members how you will use this information in your Discovery Project.

Activity Center

Go to the **Activity Center** to review chapter vocabulary and key concepts.

Engineer's Toolbox

Go to the **Engineer's Toolbox** to:
- Access Academic Activities
- Access the Competitive Event Prep Activity

DISCOVERY PROJECT

Design an Artificial Human Hand

What concepts of biomedical engineering come into play when designing an artificial limb such as a replacement for the human hand? In this chapter's Discovery Project, you will research the human hand and create a model to mimic its construction. Modeling systems (such as LEGO® and K'NEX®) can be used as the basic building materials.

Go to your *essentials* ONLINE to view the video to learn about the development of an improved artificial human eye.

CHAPTER 12

Chemical Engineering

ESSENTIAL QUESTION **Does chemical engineering harm or help the environment?**

Chemical engineering involves changing raw materials into useful substances. Chemical engineers must have a thorough understanding of science, especially chemistry and physics. Chemical engineers work with other engineers to research, develop, and design products. The water you drink each day is clean because of chemical engineers. The foods you eat may contain substances that have been chemically engineered. Chemical engineers even played a role in making the paper and ink used in this book. Can you think other chemical engineering projects? This chapter will help you learn more about the work of chemical engineers.

essentials

DISCOVERY PROJECT

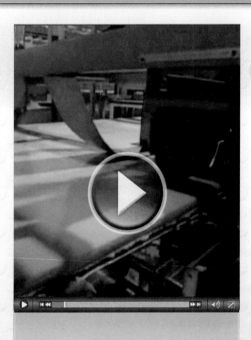

Go to your ✈ *essentials* ONLINE to view the video to learn about one of the uses for adhesives.

Make the Strongest Natural Glue

 21st Century Skills **Why do chemical engineers need to be flexible when creating adhesives?**

Chemical engineers use the chemical process when designing adhesives, such as glue. Before synthetic materials were used to make glue, natural materials were used. You will take on the role of a chemical engineer to create your own natural glue. See page 233 for a brief description of this project.

 Group Workspace

How can adhesives be used to make a material stronger?

 Engineer's Toolbox

Go to the Engineer's Toolbox to:
- Access Note-Taking Activities
- Access Graphic Organizers
- Access Academic Standards met by this chapter

READING GUIDE

Before You Read What role do chemical engineers play in research and development? What types of projects involve chemical engineers?

Objectives

- **Summarize** the field of chemical engineering.
- **Evaluate** chemical production and process design.
- **Identify** key technical concepts of chemical engineering.
- **Compare and contrast** chemical byproduct disposal and chemical recycling.
- **Discuss** the role of chemical engineers in food production.

Main Idea

Chemical engineering involves the processing of chemicals to create products. Chemical engineers work on a variety of projects.

Vocabulary

Content Vocabulary

- pharmaceuticals
- byproducts
- deinking
- resin
- equilibrium
- entropy
- enzymes
- distillation
- filtration
- dissolved
- diluted

Academic Vocabulary

- environmental
- structure
- professional
- refined
- physical
- constant

Note-Taking Activity

Draw this table for each section. Write key terms and phrases under **Cues**. Write main ideas under **Note Taking**. Summarize the section under **Summary**.

Cues	Note Taking
•	•
•	•
Summary	

Graphic Organizer

Use graphic organizers to write and organize information as you read. Go to your  ONLINE for downloadable graphic organizers.

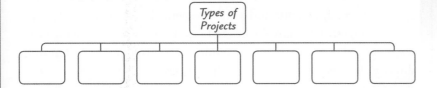

Types of Projects

STANDARDS

ACADEMIC

Technology

ITEEA STL19.06 Chemical technologies provide a means for humans to alter or modify materials and to produce chemical products.

Mathematics

NCTM Algebra Analyze change in various contexts.

Science

NSES B Develop an understanding of the structure of atoms, structure and properties of matter, chemical reactions, motions and forces, conservation of energy and increase in disorder, and interactions of energy and matter.

ITEEA *International Technology and Engineering Educators Association*
NCTM *National Council of Teachers of Mathematics*
NSES *National Science Education Standards*

College & Career READINESS

Reading Interpret words and phrases as they are used in a text, including determining technical, connotative, and figurative meanings, and analyze how specific word choices shape meaning or tone.

Chemical Engineering Overview

What Is Chemical Engineering?

Chemical engineering focuses on the processing of chemicals, and the handling of liquid, gas, and air. An engineer in this field could also specialize in environmental, health, and safety issues and projects. Chemical engineers apply knowledge of chemistry and physics. They might also deal with some biological knowledge. Chemical engineers are in charge of converting raw materials to more useful substances, such as foods and beverages, pigments and dyes, plastics, adhesives, and petroleum products. Some chemical engineers today are working with emerging technologies such as nanotechnology applications, non-traditional energy production, and biomedical engineering.

Chemical engineering has developed alongside research in chemistry since the 1800s. Early matter and atomic structure discoveries provided knowledge that could be applied to meet human wants and needs.

Education

A chemical engineer in the United States has an undergraduate degree. The undergraduate degree requires study in physics, chemistry, mathematics, and other courses unique to chemical engineering. Many chemical engineers choose to engage in advanced study at the Master's or Doctoral level.

Licensure and Credentials

Though not required to be a practicing engineer, a Professional Engineer (P.E.) license is necessary for a chemical engineer who offers his or her services directly to the public. The P.E. license is granted by a state and can be endorsed by other states if a chemical engineer chooses to work in another state. A Chemical P.E. candidate must take a Fundamentals of Engineering exam as well as a written exam in chemical engineering after having worked in the field. The National Council of Examiners for Engineering and Surveying (NCEES) develops and standardizes the P.E. national tests. However, individual states can set their own passing scores and can also have more specific requirements for licensure.

Research and Development

Many chemical engineers, especially those who work in chemical processing and **pharmaceuticals** (prescription drugs), spend much of their time in research and development (R&D). The approach to R&D in a project is very systematic and sometimes entails teams of many people working together toward the desired results. Since many scientists are also engaged in R&D, chemical engineers involved in R&D often work directly alongside scientists and other professionals.

essentials

Career Center

Chemical Engineer GPS systems give us driving directions. Nuclear technology is used to generate power for homes and businesses. The networking of computers led to the creation of the Internet as we know it today. These things were initially created by the military, NASA, or other government agencies. Watch the video on how an invention is helping the British military provide clean water to troops operating in less than sanitary conditions. Consider how this invention could have wider uses.

Go to your *essentials* ONLINE to learn more about the education, career paths, and future of a chemical engineer.

Chemical Production

Most chemical engineers work in the chemical production industry. The chemical production industry develops and produces plastics, rubber products, textiles, paper products, metals, alloys, and other items. The monitoring and testing of chemical plant outputs may be among the chemical engineer's responsibilities.

Plastics are used in a variety of commercial, industrial, and consumer goods. Chemical engineers may develop new plastics and polymers. These types of products include polyethylene, polyethylene terephthalate, polystyrene, polycarbonates, PVC, and polypropylene. You may recognize these substances by the recycling markings and numbers imprinted on them. (See **Figure 12.1**.)

Chemical engineers may also work in the production of basic chemicals for many common applications. The chemicals for use in pools and the chemicals used in cleaning products, as well as those used in items such as fertilizer, all begin as raw materials. These materials are then refined or processed in a chemical plant.

Process Design

Chemical engineers are more interested in the process of creating or refining chemicals than in the machines and equipment used to perform that process. The planning of procedures that are used to bring about the physical and chemical transformation of materials is known as process design.

*e*ssentials

STEM CONNECTION

Exponential Growth

Chemical engineers not only have to be familiar with the chemical make-up of elements but also must be aware of how the elements react with their environments. Engineers should be able to predict the reaction of these elements as they work through the engineering design process. It is important for engineers to do the research necessary to project the outcome of these reactions.

Personal Tutor

View

Go to your *e*ssentials ONLINE to view the ***Personal Tutor: Exponential Growth.***

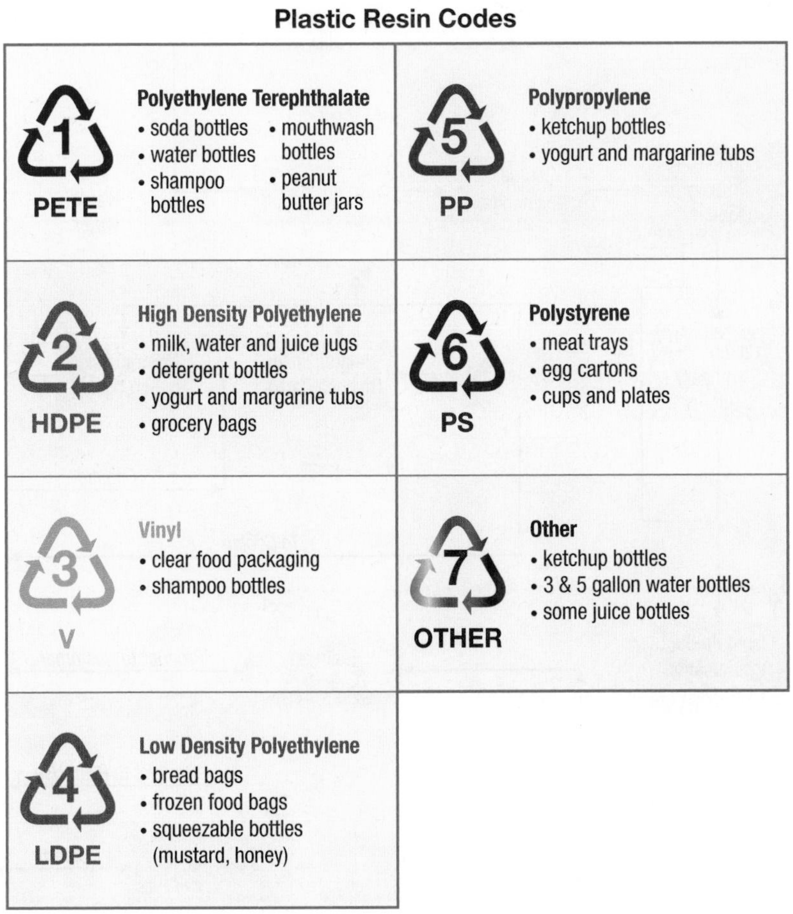

Plastic Resin Codes
1
PETE
Polyethylene Terephthalate
• soda bottles
• water bottles
• shampoo bottles
• mouthwash bottles
• peanut butter jars
5
PP
Polypropylene
• ketchup bottles
• yogurt and margarine tubs
2
HDPE
High Density Polyethylene
• milk, water and juice jugs
• detergent bottles
• yogurt and margarine tubs
• grocery bags
6
PS
Polystyrene
• meat trays
• egg cartons
• cups and plates
3
V
Vinyl
• clear food packaging
• shampoo bottles
7
OTHER
Other
• ketchup bottles
• 3 & 5 gallon water bottles
• some juice bottles
4
LDPE
Low Density Polyethylene
• bread bags
• frozen food bags
• squeezable bottles (mustard, honey)

PROJECT CONNECTIONS

Draw a diagram outlining the process for making your glue.

Fig. 12.1 Types of Plastics Chemical engineers have designed a variety of plastics. *What is the purpose of the numbers on plastic products?*

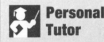

PROJECT CONNECTIONS

Will the production of your glue create any byproducts? How will you dispose of them?

Imagine all of the things that can be used to transform things chemically. Heat, pressure, other chemicals, and time are all things that can be used to treat and engineer chemicals. A chemical engineer works to optimize each of these things in a systems approach. To show how components of the process work together, a chemical engineer uses block flow diagrams and process flow diagrams. These types of diagrams are essential in chemical engineering. (See **Figure 12.2**.)

Byproduct Control and Disposal

Chemical engineers also work on the disposal of process **byproducts** and other waste products. For example, when coal is burned to generate electricity, it produces byproducts that can be harmful to the environment. A team of chemical engineers may be in charge of designing and maintaining the systems that are used to control the levels of mercury and other toxic elements that are byproducts of the coal-burning process.

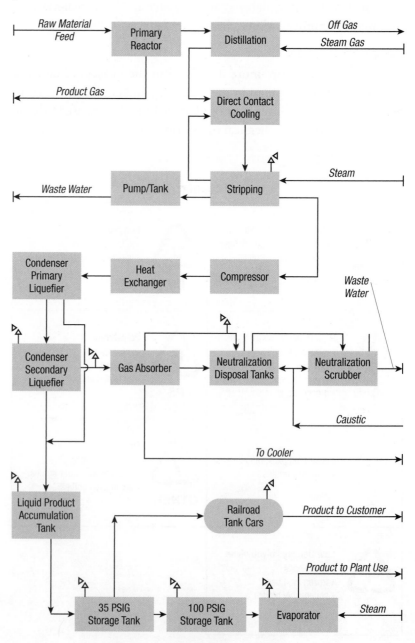

Fig. 12.2 Block Flow Diagram
Chemical engineers use a block flow diagram to show the components of a process. *How could this diagram help a chemical engineer?*

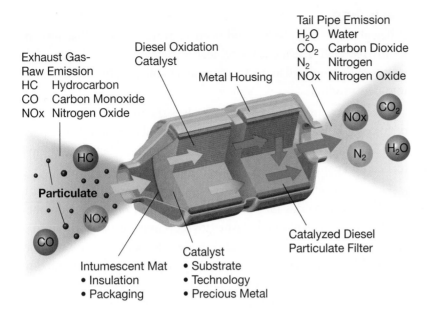

Exhaust Gas-
Raw Emission
HC Hydrocarbon
CO Carbon Monoxide
NOx Nitrogen Oxide

Diesel Oxidation
Catalyst

Metal Housing

Tail Pipe Emission
H_2O Water
CO_2 Carbon Dioxide
N_2 Nitrogen
NOx Nitrogen Oxide

Particulate

Intumescent Mat
• Insulation
• Packaging

Catalyst
• Substrate
• Technology
• Precious Metal

Catalyzed Diesel
Particulate Filter

Fig. 12.3 Catalytic Converter
Chemical engineers help design
catalytic converters to control the
release of harmful compounds. *What
other field of engineering would be
involved in creating this device?*

As another example, when an internal combustion engine in a car
or other vehicle burns fuel, it releases unburned gasoline, carbon monoxide, and nitrogen oxides. In a motor vehicle, a catalytic converter is
used to prevent much of these harmful compounds from getting into
the atmosphere. A chemical engineer works with other engineers to
create an effective design for catalytic converters and similar devices.
(See **Figure 12.3**.)

Reading Check **Determine**
when chemical engineers work with
scientists and other professionals.

⟨e⟩ssentials

**Virtual Lab:
Byproduct Recycling/Disposal**

Chemical engineering allows people to recycle and dispose of toxic
waste in a variety of ways. Chemical engineers use chemistry and
chemical processes to turn raw materials into useful substances and
potentially harmful substances into functional products. Chemical
engineering processes can also ensure that hazardous waste and
byproducts are disposed of safely.

View Go to your *⟨e⟩ssentials* ONLINE to view the *Virtual Lab:
Byproduct Recycling/Disposal.*

Recycling

Paper, glass, metals, plastics, and electronics are all things that are commonly recycled. A chemical engineer is involved in the design of the processes that are used to treat these products and turn the used materials into new products.

The process of paper recycling involves the removal of any writing or coloration from the paper by a process called **deinking**. The paper is then reduced to pulp, and new fibers must be added before the pulp is turned into paper again.

Plastics recycling processes vary because there are different types of plastics. (Resin codes indicate the type of **resin**, or sticky substance, used to create each plastic.) Plastics for recycling are often separated by color, then shredded, melted, and made into pellets to use as a raw material for making other products. Newer plastic recycling processes put the plastic material through a reverse of the chemical process that was used to create it. Chemical engineers are currently working to create new methods of recycling various types of plastics. (See **Figure 12.4**.)

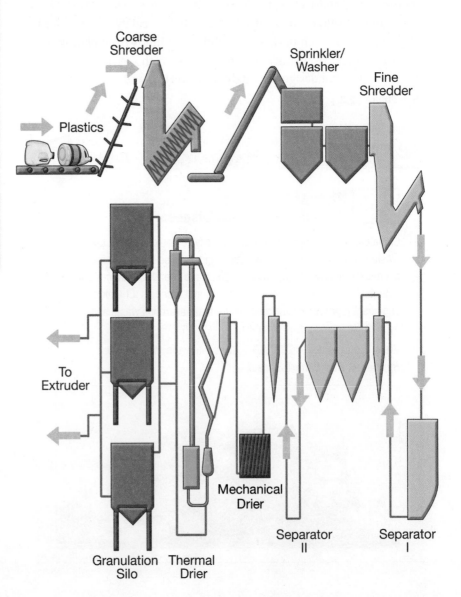

Fig. 12.4 Plastic Recycling The process of plastic recycling involves several stages. *Name the major stages of the recycling process shown here.*

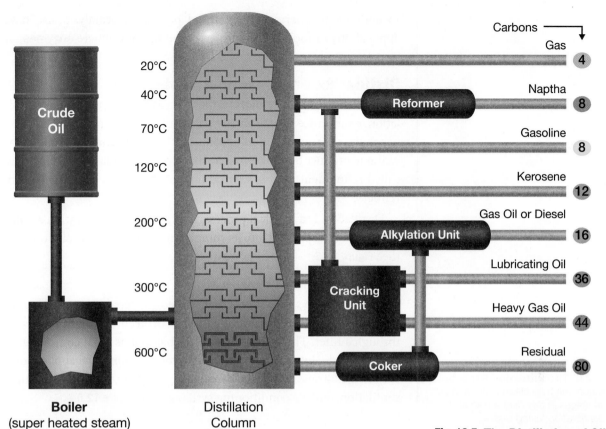

Fig. 12.5 The Distillation of Oil
Distillation is used to separate crude oil. *What do the colors in the distillation column indicate?*

Key Technical Concepts

To understand the applications of chemical engineering, one must understand key technical concepts used by chemical engineers.

Thermodynamics and Conservation of Energy

Thermodynamics involves the study of variables of temperature, pressure, and volume. In chemical reactions, all of these variables can change as a change in physical state takes place and as other properties of materials change. There are four laws of thermodynamics that concern conservation of energy, thermal **equilibrium** (balance), **entropy** (loss of energy), and absolute zero of temperature.

Especially important to chemical engineering is the first law of thermodynamics, which is also known as the law of conservation of energy. It states that energy can neither be created nor destroyed, or that energy in an isolated system will remain constant over time.

Catalysts

A catalyst is a substance that changes the rate of a chemical reaction. A catalytic substance or material can either be an inhibitor, meaning that it slows down the chemical reaction, or a promoter, meaning that it speeds up the chemical reaction.

In the field of energy, catalysts are used in petroleum refining to change oil into more useful substances. In chemical processing, oxygen is used as a catalyst to create nitric acid from ammonia, and ammonia itself is made from nitrogen using another type of catalyst.

In addition to energy and chemical processing, catalysts also have applications in food processing and food biology, where **enzymes**, or proteins, can be used as catalysts.

Distillation and Chemical Separation

Distillation is a physical process rather than a chemical reaction. In distillation, a substance is heated to separate out its components. Distillation has many commercial applications. It is used to separate crude oil as well as to produce beverages that contain alcohol. Distillation is sometimes called refinement, as it is when crude oil is processed at a petroleum refinery.

Distillation is a physical process, but in chemical separation a compound can be separated into its component parts by chemical processes. (See **Figure 12.5**.)

Filtration

Filtration is a physical process that is used for separating solid matter from liquids or gases. In filtration the raw, or "feed," substance is passed through a filter. The filtrate, or filtered material, is what comes out on the other side. Filtration has many common commercial applications, such as the filtration of water and coffee, and the use of filters for heating, ventilation, and air conditioning systems. (See **Figure 12.6**.)

Fig. 12.6 The Filtration Process
Filtration can help clean water and air. *What stages in this diagram show actual filtration taking place?*

Water Filtration System

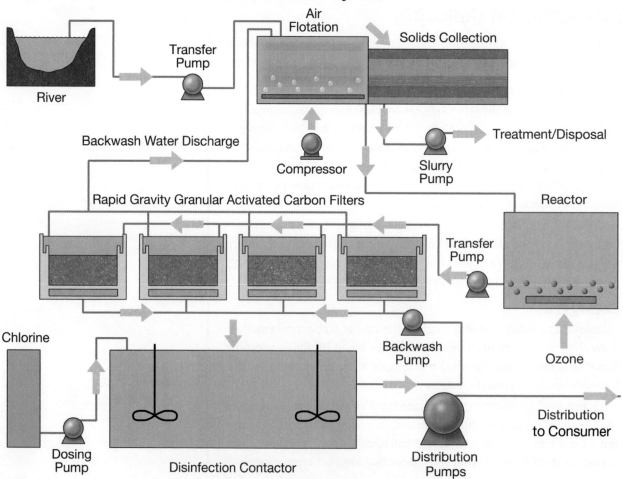

Chemical Reactions and Chemical Synthesis

A chemical reaction happens when two or more molecules interact and a chemical change occurs. Some chemical reactions happen naturally in the environment. For example, when something made from steel rusts over time the iron in the steel is interacting with the oxygen in the air.

Chemical reactions that are forced or designed have been chemically engineered. Chemical engineers have a good understanding of chemical reactions and how they can be applied to achieve a desired material. Computers are important tools in chemical engineering today, because software can be used to simulate chemical reactions.

Chemical synthesis occurs when chemicals combine. Using chemical reactions to synthesize chemicals is at the core of the chemical engineer's work.

Simulation Software Some chemical processes are modeled, or simulated, using computer software, which can be an integral part of chemical design and production. Chemical process modeling and simulation is used to analyze processes, systems, and reactions as part of the chemical engineer's design process. Simulation software is extremely important because it allows the chemical engineer to experiment without risk of causing or suffering physical harm.

Conservation of Mass

The law of conservation of mass states that the mass of a substance in a closed or isolated system will remain constant over time. In the context of chemical engineering, it is important to understand that as chemicals are treated, synthesized, and separated, their total mass will remain constant. That mass cannot be created or destroyed.

Fluid Dynamics

A chemical engineer must understand the concepts of fluid dynamics. Different types of liquids and gases behave differently when they are in motion. Viscosity is the measure of the resistance of a fluid, which can be thick or thin. The way fluids behave when they are moving or changing state is at the heart of the study of fluid dynamics.

PROJECT CONNECTIONS

Does any chemical reaction take place during the making of your glue?

Reading Check Identify the key technical concepts of chemical engineering.

Check Your Understanding

After You Read Perform the following tasks.

1. **Evaluate** whether a catalyst is necessary for a chemical reaction. Discuss your reasoning.

2. **Compare and contrast** the law of conservation of mass and the law of conservation of energy.

3. **Analyze** how the recycling of chemical products affects the environment.

Chemical Engineering Applications

Types of Projects

Chemical engineers work on projects related to the creation and optimization of ceramics, fuels, fertilizers, plastics, explosives, detergents, fragrances and flavors, diet supplements, and pharmaceuticals. They also work with paints and coatings, inks, adhesives, and many other items.

Chemical engineers design the processes and materials used in distillation, filtration, synthesis, and other chemical operations. They focus on the process while other engineers and professionals design the actual machinery involved in the process.

Food and Beverages

Chemical engineers are involved in various aspects of the diverse world of the food and beverage industry. Some are involved in the early stages of growing food, by creating the fertilizers and insecticides used to treat crops. Others are responsible for the development of food processing systems, in which various substances are combined into something edible and consumable.

Some chemical engineers work to develop additives for taste and appearance. Artificial sweeteners and substances used for food coloration are chemically engineered products.

The creation and use of additives and the design of processes for food purification or preservation are other chemical engineering specialties. Drinking water purification systems and systems used for processes such as milk homogenization and pasteurization are also chemical in nature. Chemical engineers also develop the systems used to add desired items into foods and beverages, such as when vitamins are added to foods and drinks.

Pigments and Dyes

Pigments and dyes are substances used to add color to other materials. The difference between a pigment and a dye is that dyes are **dissolved**, or mixed with a liquid, in a solvent whereas pigments are insoluble. The ancient Egyptians, Greeks, and Romans mastered the use of dyes that came from natural sources, such as plants, animals, and minerals.

The use of synthetic dyes began in the mid-nineteenth century. This practice became more prevalent during the second half of the century and into the twentieth century. The dye industry and the knowledge it produced became the basis for other industries, including pharmaceuticals and plastics.

Today, synthetic dyes are used in many items, including textiles, foods, and paper. Synthetic pigments are used in paints and other types of coatings. Pigments are also used in printing inks and as a colorant for some plastics.

essentials

Visualization

Details and Shapes Have you ever thought about how you orient yourself in the world, whether you are reading, writing, sketching, walking, or even arranging your books and papers and any other items you need to complete your homework? Since we are used to looking at the world in a particular way, we have pictures in our minds of how things should look that may cause us to ignore details.

Go to your *essentials* ONLINE to learn more about focusing on details and shapes.

Group Workspace

Sketch letters and objects in various orientations. Describe any difficulties you had in visualizing the images.

Adhesives

An adhesive, or glue, is a product that adheres or bonds things together. While some adhesives come from natural sources such as starches, acids, and vinegars, most commercially available adhesives today are from synthetic sources. Some have been developed using highly sophisticated engineering.

Some common consumer synthetic glues include polyvinyl acetate (PVA, also known as white glue), rubber cement, silicone, epoxy, and cyanoacrylate.

Medical Applications

The pharmaceutical industry is largely based on biology, biological science, and medical science. However, the development of certain medicines may involve pharmaceutical engineering, which is often considered a subfield of chemical engineering. A chemical engineer in the pharmaceutical industry is in charge of the design process for the chemical production of pharmaceuticals.

PROJECT CONNECTIONS

Compare and contrast your glue with white glue (PVA).

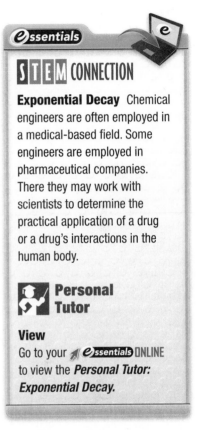

STEM CONNECTION

Exponential Decay Chemical engineers are often employed in a medical-based field. Some engineers are employed in pharmaceutical companies. There they may work with scientists to determine the practical application of a drug or a drug's interactions in the human body.

Personal Tutor

View
Go to your *essentials* ONLINE to view the *Personal Tutor: Exponential Decay.*

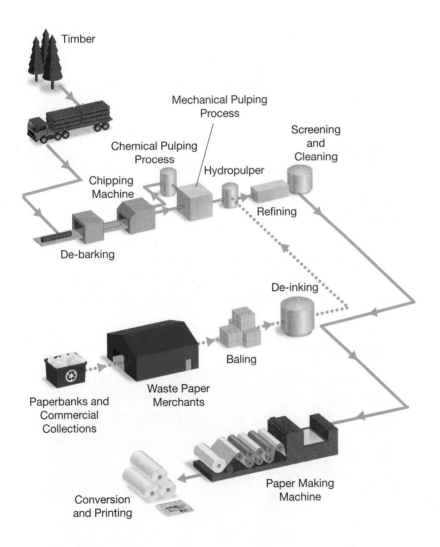

Timber

Mechanical Pulping Process

Chemical Pulping Process

Screening and Cleaning

Hydropulper

Chipping Machine

Refining

De-barking

De-inking

Baling

Paperbanks and Commercial Collections

Waste Paper Merchants

Conversion and Printing

Paper Making Machine

Fig. 12.7 The Papermaking Process There are several steps in the process of making paper. *List the papermaking steps you see here.*

PROJECT CONNECTIONS

How does your glue interact with the cardboard used for testing? Use specific descriptive terms in your analysis.

Pulp and Paper

The pulp and paper industry is one of the largest industries worldwide. Chemical engineers are employed in various stages of the processes used to make paper for printing, packaging, and other applications. At one time most paper was made from cutting down trees without regard to the effect this would have on the environment. Thanks to chemical engineers and the paper recycling process, today fewer trees are destroyed to make paper.

The process of papermaking includes several steps. Fiber materials from wood or reclaimed sources are dissolved, thickened, **diluted** (thinned), refined, cleaned, and mixed into pulp. Next, chemical additives or pigments are added to bleach or color the pulp. Then several mechanical processes, such as rolling, pressing, and drying, are used to turn pulp into paper. After the pulp has been converted to paper, other chemicals may be added to surface or smooth it before it is cut or rolled for the consumer. (See **Figure 12.7**.)

Cosmetics, Soaps, and Fragrances

Companies that make cosmetics, soaps, and fragrances employ many chemical engineers. Polishes, gels, deodorants, perfumes, lotions, powders, shampoos, and other cosmetic products are derived chemically. Most chemical engineers in this industry are involved in the research and development of new products.

Virtual Lab: Nanotechnology

Nanotechnology is the engineering of functional systems and products at the molecular level. One nanometer is approximately one billionth of a meter, or about 1/80,000 the width of a human hair. Typically structures that are considered to belong to nanotechnology are 100 nanometers or smaller in at least one dimension.

View Go to your *essentials* ONLINE to view the *Virtual Lab: Nanotechnology.*

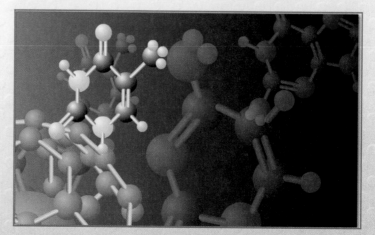

Fragrances also have applications outside of the cosmetics industry. For example, air deodorizers are engineered chemical compounds, as are the fragrances in many cleaning supplies. Sometimes, odorants are added to dangerous, naturally odorless substances, such as natural gas and hydrogen, so that people will be able to tell when there is a leak in a system. Many products that you encounter on a daily basis contain fragrances. Take a look at a few ingredient labels to see if fragrances are used in your favorite products.

Nanotechnology

Nanotechnology deals with engineering on a molecular scale. Nanoparticles, nanotubes, and nanofilms are all types of nanomaterials with one or more nanosized dimension. They may occur in nature or be manufactured.

Chemical engineers are among the leaders in this emerging field. New processes and terminology have accompanied the development of nanotechnology. Nanocatalysts and nanofiltration are new studies that are likely to have major effects in the field of chemical engineering.

Physicists, biologists, chemists, engineers, and other professionals have greatly expanded their research and work at the nanoscale level over the past quarter century. The U.S. National Nanotechnology Initiative was established in 2001 to encourage cooperation among these and other fields.

Nanotechnology has already played a part in developing new molecules and polymers. This work has led to new and improved consumer products such as new types of batteries, films and coatings, paints, food and food storage, clothing, cosmetics, sunscreens, and personal care products. However, some concern has arisen over the possible consequences of nanotechnologies. As with any technological development, desired results may come with unanticipated negative consequences.

Reading Check Compare and contrast pigments and dyes.

Check Your Understanding

SECTION **12.2**

After You Read Perform the following tasks.

1. **Identify** the major types of chemical engineering projects.
2. **Summarize** the papermaking process.
3. **Predict** how nanotechnology will affect chemical engineering and the world.

Problem-Solving Process

Identify

America's dependence on oil is high, while the world's supply is becoming harder to extract. Increased offshore drilling raises the possibility of spills. AbsorbAll, a chemical company specializing in environmental cleanups, has hired your firm to develop an environmentally friendly product to remove oil from water. It must meet the following criteria.

- It must be made from natural or non-toxic ingredients.
- It must cause oil to clump and be easily removable from water.
- It must be dispersed on a spill easily, without special equipment.

Set Up

1. Research the project. Ask: *"What are the chemical properties of oil?"* and *"What chemicals will bond to oil but not to water?"*
2. Analyze methods and products used to clean up oil spills. Research products that interact with oil to make it easier to clean.
3. Brainstorm potential solutions. Describe how each product can be spread over the oil and how it might interact with the oil.
4. Use a decision matrix to choose the best solution. Be sure to use criteria and constraints as guides in judging the best idea.

Execute

5. List chemicals and components you will need to produce the solution. Determine if a special work environment is required.
6. Keep developing and recording ideas to improve your design.
7. Prepare samples of the solution, using various techniques.
8. Discuss how the solution is produced, transported, and used. How will that affect your final design? Plan your next steps.

Evaluate

Model a shoreline environment for an oil spill, including elements such as sand, rocks, and plant life. Introduce oil, and then spread the solution over the spill. Observe and record the interaction between the oil slick and the product.

Share

Post pictures of the oil spill before and after you applied your solution. Describe outcomes and possible tradeoffs, as well as how product refinement could improve quality. Include background information, a list of solutions, testing methods, and an evaluation of the final product.

Critical Thinking

Key Concepts

1. **Identify** key technical concepts of chemical engineering.

2. **Summarize** the field of chemical engineering.

3. **Explain** the types of projects chemical engineers are involved in and what role they play in each project.

4. **Compare and contrast** chemical byproduct disposal and chemical recycling.

5. **Evaluate** chemical production and process design. Then discuss why and how they differ.

Information Literacy *21st Century Skills*

6. **Share** with your project team what you have learned about chemical reactions and how that information connects to your Discovery Project.

7. **Discuss** the role of chemical engineers in food and beverage production. Describe how it differs from their roles in the production of other chemical products.

⊘ssentials

Activity Center

Go to the **Activity Center** to review chapter vocabulary and key concepts.

Engineer's Toolbox

Go to the **Engineer's Toolbox** to:

- Access Academic Activities
- Access the Competitive Event Prep Activity

⊘ssentials   DISCOVERY PROJECT

Make the Strongest Natural Glue

In this chapter's Discovery Project, you will create a natural glue. To make a natural glue you must use all-natural materials such as milk, vinegar, baking soda, water, cornstarch, flour, or corn syrup. Your challenge is to make the strongest glue for cardboard. The strength of the glue will be tested by the number of pieces of cardboard held together and the amount of glue used.

Go to your ⊘ssentials ONLINE to collaborate with your team on this Discovery Project.

Specialties and Emerging Disciplines

What is the most exciting new engineering discipline?

The field of engineering includes the four major areas of civil, electrical, mechanical, and chemical, which employ the most people. There are also some specialty fields, which may or may not fall under the umbrella of one of the major fields. It is important to understand what these specialty fields are, what the associated terminology means, and how the specialties fit under the larger umbrella of engineering.

essentials

DISCOVERY PROJECT

Reducing Energy Consumption

 21st Century Skills

How can you use creativity to improve the energy efficiency of an existing device or system?

While it is difficult to identify specific developments that will have the most impact on the future of engineering, there are trends that are sure to continue. You will now revisit one of your earlier projects or a new device with two goals in mind:

- Work to make the device more efficient and reduce the energy required while maintaining performance; and
- Identify future uses for the materials it contains after it reaches the end of its useful life.

 Group Workspace

During the video, watch and listen for important facts about the constraints of the project. Write down some ideas about the projects you have completed so far in this course and how you might apply some of the ideas from the video.

 Engineer's Toolbox

Go to the Engineer's Toolbox to
- Access Note-Taking Activities
- Access Graphic Organizers
- Access Academic Standards met by this chapter

ENR
Engineering News-Record

Go to your *essentials* ONLINE to view the chapter 13 Discovery Project Launcher Video to learn about engineering for efficiency.

READING GUIDE

Before You Read What are some career paths that are common to engineering graduates as they enter the workforce? What are some career options they have once they have gained experience as practicing engineers?

Objectives

- **Describe** three levels of education that can prepare a person for an engineering career.
- **List** the qualifications required for a project manager.
- **Discuss** the knowledge required for agricultural engineers.
- **Name** five types of systems that are part of industrial engineering.
- **Identify** the three main focus areas of environmental engineers.
- **Describe** the role of ocean engineers and the devices they work on.
- **Discuss** the qualifications required of systems engineers.

Vocabulary

Content Vocabulary

- engineering technology
- optimization
- project manager
- logistics
- environmental engineering
- remediated
- systems engineering
- security engineering
- cryptography
- physical security systems
- information security systems

Academic Vocabulary

- technologists
- economics
- statistics
- emerging
- coordination

Note-Taking Activity

Draw this table for each section. Write key terms and phrases under **Cues**. Write main ideas under **Note Taking**. Summarize the section under **Summary**.

Cues	Note Taking
•	•
•	•
Summary	

Graphic Organizers

Use graphic organizers to organize information as you read.

Specialties
1 2 3 4 5

Go to your **essentials ONLINE** for downloadable graphic organizers.

ACADEMIC

Technology

ITEEA STL2.02 Systems, which are the building blocks of technology, are embedded within larger technological, social, and environmental systems.

ITEEA STL2.04 Selecting resources involves trade-offs between competing values, such as availability, cost, desirability, and waste.

Mathematics

NCTM Problem Solving Solve problems that arise in mathematics and in other contexts.

Science

NSES E Students should develop abilities of technological design, understandings about science and technology.

ITEEA *International Technology and Engineering Educators Association*
NCTM *National Council of Teachers of Mathematics*
NSES *National Science Education Standards*

College & Career READINESS

Reading Read and comprehend complex literary and informational texts independently and proficiently.

Writing Produce clear and coherent writing in which the development, organization, and style are appropriate to task, purpose, and audience.

Engineering Specialties

Specialty Fields

Though there are many more specialties, this section introduces six common specialty areas and discusses the varied qualifications required to pursue these career paths. These specialties include a variety of education levels. For instance, general engineers and engineering technicians may have either a 2-year or 4-year degree. Most people in engineering management have earned degrees at the master's level or higher, while the more specific fields of agricultural and architectural engineering often require additional specialty area education.

General Engineering

The term "general engineering" usually refers to a college level associate's degree program or introductory coursework at the bachelor's level. This is a general program designed to introduce students to many fields and disciplines of engineering, and also to some of the themes that are common to all areas of engineering. Students who major in general engineering often transfer to a bachelor's level program or a more specific major within one of the engineering fields.

Engineering Technology

Engineering technology is a common bachelor's level program that involves a less rigorous study of mathematics and science than a general engineering program. Graduates of engineering technology programs are generally not eligible for professional certification. Graduates of these programs are often referred to as engineering technologists, and they specialize in applications of engineering rather than the theory. Engineering technologists usually focus on research, production, and operations related to engineering projects.

Engineering Management

Some people who have already received university degrees in engineering later choose to pursue an advanced degree in the field. Engineering Management is one advanced degree area in which someone can study at the master's level. Coursework in this area can be described as about half business-related, because the introductory courses in the program are very much like those in a Master of Business Administration (MBA) program, combined with an advanced study of engineering.

Engineering management students learn mostly about the management of manufacturing and industrial operations and facilities. They also study business administration, accounting and financial management, human resources, and information systems. Part of the degree program typically will focus on optimization, or making the best use of a situation, product, or resource, and quality control (QC). Engineering management also deals with health, safety, and environmental issues.

Project manager is a title held by engineers in manufacturing, construction, industrial applications, and other fields. A project manager is a professional responsible for planning and carying out a project in any field. An advanced degree is not required to hold this title, but a degree such as Master of Engineering Management shows that a person has the background to understand project management requirements.

Architectural Engineering

Architectural Engineering is very closely aligned with the work of an architect, but an architectural engineer holds a degree in engineering and is eligible to be certified as a Professional Engineer (PE).

An architectural engineer may be in charge of the design of buildings and other large structures. This field is closely related to fields such as civil and structural engineering, but will often be treated separately in university programs and professional certification.

Where architects focus on form and esthetics, architectural engineers focus on functional elements of a building, such as structure, HVAC, building systems, acoustics, lighting, and energy use. Architectural engineers apply knowledge of materials, including steel, wood, concrete, and masonry, and plan for implementation and maintenance.

Reading Check **Differentiate** between architectural engineering and architecture.

Fig. 13.1 Designing for Harsh Weather Architectural engineers must consider environmental factors when designing a project. These factors include the type of soil, as well as the weather conditions in the area. *What are some factors an architectural engineer must consider when a building is being constructed near the coast, where hurricanes are more likely?*

Fig. 13.2 Agricultural Equipment
Agricultural engineers may be involved in all aspects of farming including those related to crops, animals and equipment. *What are three types of systems that are common to the work of agricultural engineers?*

Architectural engineers are specialists on material strengths and applications, structural concepts, sustainability, and structural stability. They may also be identified as experts on buildings, their ability to support loads, and their ability to withstand weather and extreme natural events such as earthquakes or hurricanes (see **Figure 13.1** on page 237).

Architectural engineers often work with other engineers and architects, so they need to have good verbal and written communication skills. They should also be detail oriented, creative, and analytical.

Agricultural Engineering

The term "agriculture" is used to describe the production of food and other goods through the process of farming. Plant and animal production is the focus of farmers and also of agricultural engineers.

Agricultural engineers apply their knowledge to the development of physical systems and machines, buildings, and biological systems. They are responsible for designing many of the systems used in farming. These systems include physical systems such as pumps, hydraulics, machinery, and irrigation. Because many of the systems they

Virtual Lab: Architectural Engineering

Engineering specialty areas are becoming more and more prevalent with the rapid development of new technologies and the merging of existing engineering disciplines. New branches of engineering specialty areas, such as nanotechnology, computer engineering, and software engineering, are constantly emerging and evolving. Better-known engineering specialty areas include architectural, industrial, and agricultural engineering.

View Go to your **essentials** ONLINE to view the *Virtual Lab: Architectural Engineering*

Green reSource

Greenhouse Gas Emissions
Conventional buildings are "energy hogs." It takes great amounts of energy to heat, cool, illuminate, and provide power to commercial and residential buildings. Buildings are responsible for almost half of all greenhouse gas emissions into the atmosphere.

Group Workspace

Emissions are released during the construction, operation, modification, and destruction of a building. Engineers and architects are working to reduce the impact to our environment during each of these phases. What are some steps that can be taken to reduce greenhouse gas emissions during construction?

Go to your **essentials** ONLINE to view a Conversation with Werner Sobek.

design and implement involve electrical systems, agricultural engineers should also have good knowledge of electrical circuits, controls, and instrumentation.

Many chemicals are typically used in farming. An agricultural engineer might therefore also implement hazardous material handling and storage systems.

An agricultural engineer may be in charge of designing the machinery used in farming, such as harvesters, planters, sprayers, milking machines, and sorting machines. Agricultural engineers must know about mechanical design, materials, and power systems, including engines, motors, and transmissions.

Health and safety, economics, and statistics are also part of the general knowledge required of an agricultural engineer. They are involved in the design of livestock environments, ventilation and air quality systems, and water and water quality systems. Agricultural engineers may even design buildings to house livestock or plants.

Agricultural engineers must also have expert knowledge of soil, water, and plant life, which, of course, are all related to the sciences of biology and geology. Agricultural engineers understand hydrology, soil-water relationships, erosion, nutrients, contaminants, and biological materials (see **Figure 13.2**).

In recent years, a movement toward more sustainable food sources has required more involvement and attention from agricultural engineers. Engineers working in these areas have driven new developments in organic agriculture, aquaculture, and hydroponics.

Industrial Engineering

Industrial engineering is another specialty area of engineering. Industrial engineers typically work with facilities, systems design, plant logistics, safety systems, and quality control (QC).

Facilities planning requires optimal utilization of building space. An industrial engineer will work to optimize process flow, which includes all of the subcomponent systems used to transform raw materials into useful products. This means that he or she will select an appropriate site for work to be done, design the very best layout for the processes to be done at that site, and develop specific plans for materials handling at that site. This requires a solid understanding of systems design, which may involve any number of inputs, processes, and outputs to complete a task. Industrial engineers need to understand all of the fabrication processes in order to maximize the performance of related systems.

Industrial engineers should be experts in **logistics**, which is the study of production planning and forecasting, scheduling, inventory control, distribution, storage, shipping, and routing. In designing systems to accomplish these tasks, they apply knowledge of safety and ergonomics to minimize risk of injuries from noise and other exposures. Industrial engineers incorporate human-machine interface design, which is based on anthropometric data that records the typical sizes of human beings and their features.

Quality Control Quality control is often part of the work of an industrial engineer. He or she must understand and design for reliability, make improvements to existing systems, take predictive and preventive approaches to maintenance, and carry out failure analysis when systems break down.

Reading Check **Identify** some of the factors industrial engineers must consider as they design manufacturing and distribution systems.

Check Your Understanding

After You Read Perform the following tasks.

1. **Describe** three steps engineers might take as they advance in their careers.

2. **Identify** six engineering specialties of concern to agricultural engineers.

3. **Predict** the positions architects and architectural engineers are likely to take if they disagree on the question of form versus function.

Emerging Engineering Disciplines

Five Emerging Disciplines

The broadest areas of engineering, such as civil, electrical, and mechanical engineering, can trace their professional roots back to the nineteenth century. However, certain areas of engineering are newer or even still emerging today. These include environmental engineering, ocean engineering, software engineering, systems engineering, and security engineering.

Environmental Engineering

Environmental engineering began as an accepted term and discipline in engineering during the second half of the twentieth century. Although environmental engineering is a relatively young discipline, a PE exam is available for it from the National Council of Examiners for Engineering and Surveying (NCEES). (See **Table 13.1** on page 242.) Environmental engineers implement systems for water, air, and waste, and provide other services intended to improve the natural environment.

The work of environmental engineers is often related to water. Environmental engineers might deal with wastewater, storm water, potable water, and related resources. These engineers are experts in hydraulic movement, collection, biology, microbiology, chemistry, and sampling and measurement systems. They may also be responsible for the design of systems for pollution remediation, treatment, and management. Some environmental engineers work for public utilities and focus on areas related to watershed management and reservoirs.

Other environmental engineers work primarily on projects related to air. They may draw upon knowledge of meteorology and the atmosphere. Environmental engineers often design control, treatment, and transport systems for emissions and odors. They may also head up pollution minimalization and prevention projects and services for companies.

Environmental engineers are also involved in the storage, collection, and management of waste. They design systems for the handling and treatment of municipal solid waste, and commercial and industrial waste. They also design, implement, and maintain recycling systems. In addition, they may deal with the storage, collection, and transport of hazardous materials, including radioactive waste.

When an area or environment becomes polluted, it needs to be **remediated**, which means that as much of the pollutant as possible must be removed from the site. Environmental engineers perform services such as site assessments, and remediation technique development. They also provide input to to agencies such as the Environmental Protection Agency to assist with public health and safety issues.

Career Center

Environmental Scientist
Do you pay much attention to the ground beneath your feet? Is it sandy, or full of clay, or is there solid rock just a few feet below the surface? Have you ever seen a sinkhole or experienced an earthquake or a flood? What part does soil play in various fields of engineering design? Watch the video on soil testing, and think about the ground in the area where you live and how it may influence everything from construction to transportation.

Go to your *essentials* ONLINE to learn more about the education, career paths, and future of an environmental scientist.

Reading Check Identify which of the major engineering disciplines are most likely to be involved in environmental engineering, based on the tasks of an environmental engineer described here.

Table 13.1 PE Certifications
The National Council of Examiners for Engineering and Surveying offers professional Engineer certification exams and grants PE licensure in the listed specialties.

PE exams available from NCEES
Agricultural
Architectural
Chemical
Civil: Construction
Civil: Geotechnical
Civil: Structural
Civil: Transportation
Civil: Water Resources and Environmental
Control Systems
Electrical and Computer: Computer Engineering
Electrical and Computer: Electrical and Electronics
Electrical and Computer: Power
Environmental
Fire Protection
Industrial
Mechanical: HVAC and Refrigeration
Mechanical: Mechanical Systems and Materials
Mechanical: Thermal and Fluids Systems
Metallurgical and Materials
Mining and Mineral Processing
Naval Architecture and Marine
Nuclear
Petroleum

Ocean Engineering

Often linked to a mechanical engineering program, ocean engineering is a new specialty and is also the title of some specialized university degree programs. A PE exam for ocean engineeering has not yet been established by the NCEES. Ocean engineering involves offshore mechanics, marine robotics, sensors and forecasting systems, and structures and vessels. Ocean engineering requires scientific knowledge of fluid mechanics, hydrodynamics, ocean currents, materials science, and acoustics.

Much of the work of ocean engineers is in the area of the design of structures and vessels. The development of platforms, supertankers, transoceanic cables, and deep submersibles all may involve an ocean engineer. Ocean engineers sometimes work on the design of sonar and navigation systems. Some work may require special knowledge of marine power and propulsion. Some specialties within ocean engineering are classified in the area of environmental protection.

Reading Check **Identify** the types of systems that are the focus of ocean engineers.

Software Engineering

Software engineering is a relatively new specialty discipline of engineering. The NCEES did not approve the development of a PE exam for software engineering until 2009. Software engineering combines knowledge of mathematics and computer science in the area of software development (a field concerned with the design, development, implementation and maintenance of computer software). Many who hold the title of software engineer may actually have a degree in computer science. Not to be confused with software engineer, the term "computer engineer" refers to individuals who deal more with computer hardware.

Software engineering goes beyond knowledge of computer programming. It also requires knowledge of customer requirements, design, and testing. Where programmers' focus includes software systems, networking, databases and artificial intelligence, software engineers focus on design, quality, processes, management, and maintenance.

Software engineers design better, more affordable, and quickly-developed software that is ideal for its purpose. Software engineering specialties include requirements, design, development (implementation), testing (verification), maintenance, and management.

essentials

Virtual Lab: Environmental Engineering

Environmental engineering often involves complicated issues affecting everyone worldwide. Environmental engineers apply scientific and technological principles to solve environmental problems such as pollution or other human-created disasters. Environmental engineers mainly focus on providing a continuous supply of healthy water, air, and land for humans, animals, and plants. Recycling, reducing waste, waste management, pollution control, and other public health or environmental issues are just a few of the daily challenges facing environmental engineers.

View Go to your *essentials* ONLINE to view the *Virtual Lab: Environmental Engineering.*

essentials

STEM CONNECTION

Make Conjectures from Data Engineers will often have to make conjectures based on data provided. This data may be provided in the form of tables or graphs. Engineers may have to collect the data or it may be provided through report mechanisms. Engineers need to be well versed in using data to make conclusions. One example would be in a cost analysis to determine the break-even cost of an item in production.

Personal Tutor

View
Go to your *essentials* ONLINE to view the *Personal Tutor: Make Conjectures from Data.*

 **Explain** the difference between software engineers and computer engineers.

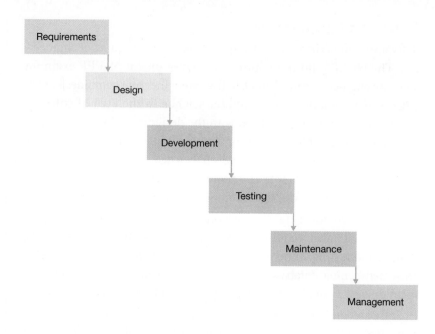

Fig. 13.3 Waterfall Model of Software Engineering This waterfall model illustrates the steps in the software engineering process. *What other engineering disciplines can you think of to which this model might apply?*

PROJECT CONNECTIONS

Can you identify several subsystems in your project? Can one or more of them be optimized to reduce energy consumption?

Systems Engineering

The field of **systems engineering** began in the mid-twentieth century due to a increasing need to manage engineering projects that were growing larger and much more complex. As an emerging discipline, systems engineering is largely defined by how disciplines and systems merge or integrate. Because its main function is to facilitate project work across disciplines, systems engineering involves a good deal of project management.

Systems engineering focuses on the relationships among the systems and subsystems of complex projects. Larger projects such as those to develop a space mission to Mars, mass transit systems, new jet airliners, mass manufacturing plants, and telecommunications systems may all involve systems engineers. Engineers involved with jet airliner design, for example, must ensure that the computer systems for communication and ignition are compatible with one another, and also compatible with outside systems such as weather monitoring or air traffic control systems.

A systems engineer can have an undergraduate degree in any engineering discipline and also needs to have a keen interest in, and knowledge of, other specialty fields. Because systems engineers are the primary managers of major projects, they must have strong organizational, communication and leadership skills. The Federal Aviation Administration (FAA), NASA, defense contractors, and many other large industries employ systems engineers for their major large-scale projects.

Systems engineers should be experts in the logistics, coordination, and automation of large and complex processes. They may specialize in content areas such as biological applications and human communication, or in computer, control, environmental, or structural systems. Many systems engineers have advanced degrees in their specialty area.

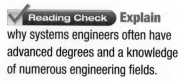

Reading Check **Explain** why systems engineers often have advanced degrees and a knowledge of numerous engineering fields.

Security Engineering

Security engineering is similar in nature to systems engineering, but it also draws upon knowledge of social science and psychology. It is used both for physical systems and for information systems. **Cryptography**, or the science or study of the techniques of secret writing, especially code and cipher systems, methods, and the like, is one specialty of security engineers.

Security engineers plan for and analyze the requirements for the operations and maintenance of security systems. Most of the work done by a security engineer would fall into one of two categories: physical security or information security.

Physical security systems provide for the protection of physical spaces such as residences, commercial offices, and other facilities, or even of entire geographic areas such as countries. Physical security is not a modern concept. In fact, the concept of physical security systems includes city walls, moats, etc. You probably encounter numerous physical security devices and systems every day. Modern systems range from door locks and driveway gates and fences to video monitors and alarm systems for buildings and vehicles. Human guards and guard dogs can also be considered physical security systems.

Information security systems are also known as cyber security and are used to protect electronic data in a networked or online environment. Security engineers utilize knowledge of computer software and encryption techniques in order to protect personal and private data sources. The little lock symbol that you sometimes see on web pages indicates that an information security system is being used to protect your information while you are online.

Security engineering as a profession emerged quite recently, but grew especially rapidly after the events of September 11, 2001. The United States Department of Homeland Security now employs many engineers to carry out tasks and develop programs related to domestic security.

essentials

Visualization

Visualizing Objects
Engineering education is a specialized field of study. The development of spatial abilities is enormously important in this field. Being able to visualize is an important part of being a successful engineering and technology student. It is vital to find the best way to develop these skills.

Group Workspace

View pictorial drawings and match them to their top, front, and side orthographic views.

Go to your *essentials* ONLINE to learn more about developing your ability to visualize objects in both 2D projections and 3D orientations.

✓ Reading Check **Differentiate** between the two main types of security engineering.

Check Your Understanding

After You Read Perform the following tasks.

1. **Identify** three main areas of focus for environmental engineers.

2. **Recall** the six steps in the waterfall model of software specialties.

3. **Justify** why some engineering systems probably required input from a systems engineer.

Review and Assessment

Problem-Solving Process

Identify

A great deal of money is spent each year on shoreline replenishment. GeoTech, an environmental engineering firm, has been hired by a community to reduce its shoreline erosion, and they have asked your team to develop a low-impact solution to their problem. The criteria are:

- Low visual impact
- Made of natural material
- Reduce soil erosion by 25%

Set Up

1. Research the project. Ask: *"What esthetic impact will the material have?"* and *"What materials best resist water erosion?"*
2. Learn about shoreline erosion. Investigate modern solutions to gain information on how it is currently being handled.
3. Brainstorm solutions. Develop sketches for an overall design. Identify materials and structures that can reduce erosion rate.
4. Use a decision matrix to choose the best solution.

Execute

5. Plan your model environment and solution. What is needed to represent the shoreline? How will your solution be assembled?
6. Keep recording ideas to improve design and quality.
7. Prepare models of the solution. You may have to develop several.
8. Discuss the solution. Analyze the model and its effectiveness.

Evaluate

Develop a testing environment to obtain baseline information. Test your solution in the same environment. Observe the impact of the solution and calculate the new erosion rate.

Share

Create a report on the activity. The report should include:

- a summary of the problem situation
- sketches and photographs of the solution
- a description of your testing process
- a summary of your evaluation

Discuss the relationship of environmental engineering with other specialties. What is similar? What challenges does the field present?

Critical Thinking

Key Concepts

1. **Identify** the three levels of education that workers in the engineering field commonly achieve.

2. **Summarize** the primary responsibilities of architectural engineers.

3. **Compare and Contrast** the fields of environmental engineering and ocean engineering.

4. **Evaluate** the role of the development and testing stages of the software development process.

5. **Predict** the future demand for systems engineers. Explain your reasoning.

Problem Solving

6. **Explain** why industrial engineers must understand the tasks as well as the people and equipment involved in a production process.

7. **Examine** with a classmate why security is an engineering specialty.

Activity Center

Go to the **Activity Center** to review chapter vocabulary and key concepts.

Engineer's Toolbox

Go to the **Engineer's Toolbox** to:
- Access Academic Activities
- Access the Competitive Event Prep Activity

DISCOVERY PROJECT

Redesigning for Reduced Energy Consumption

In this chapter's Discovery Project, you will revisit one of your earlier projects or a new device with two goals in mind. First, you will make the device more efficient and reduce the amount of energy it consumes while still maintaining appropriate performance. You will also identify future uses for the materials in the device after it reaches the end of its useful life.

Go to your **essentials** ONLINE to collaborate with your team on this Discovery Project.

Review  College & Career READINESS

Critical Thinking

Key Concepts

1. **Identify** the chemical, mechanical, and physical properties of materials used in the engineering process.

2. **Summarize** civil, electrical, mechanical, and chemical engineering.

3. **Compare and contrast** the effects of social, financial, and environmental constraints on the engineering field.

4. **Evaluate** the resources used to create electricity in your local power plant and the ways in which electrical generation affects your community.

5. **Predict** how a failure of materials can lead to a faulty product.

Problem Solving 21st Century Skills

6. **Share** your ideas on how to develop or improve a product.

7. **Discuss** how engineering design problems can be solved by the correct selection of materials based on their chemical, mechanical, biological, electrical, and physical properties.

Design and Build a Model of an Earthquake-Resistant House

Project Process

IDENTIFY

1. List the main design goals of designing and building an earthquake-resistant single-family home for a developing country you select.

2. Summarize the main challenges, including criteria and constraints, when designing homes of this type.

3. Outline the concepts from this unit that your design will use.

SET-UP

4. Brainstorm and research the possible ideas and solutions for your building.

5. Choose the best solution to model.

EXECUTE

6. Design a detailed layout and structural plan for the building.

7. Create a model of the home that you sketched.

8. Document your design by taking a photograph of the model you created.

SHARE

9. Present your model to the class. Discuss how the home that you modeled will save lives and possessions.

EVALUATE

 Group Workspace

10. Write about how your design may have changed from initial concept through the modeling stage of development. Explain why your model represents a better home for the country you selected.

Project Evaluation Chart

 Go to the Engineer's Toolbox to access the Project Evaluation Chart.

ENR
Engineering News-Record

Go to your *essentials* ONLINE for Challenge Project details.

The World of Engineering

Engineers need strong communication and leadership skills in order to be effective team members when implementing their designs and projects. They must cooperate with a number of different professionals in order to accomplish their work and complete their projects.

As engineering and its tools and materials continue to change, engineers today are poised to help solve a number of significant challenges worldwide. Environmental and energy needs are among those challenges, as are calls to assist communities in the developing world and protect us all from the threat of terrorism. Numerous professional and student organizations exist to help keep engineers and students informed about these and other challenges.

As you complete this unit project, do the following:

- **Identify** the main design goals for modeling a Mars habitat.

- **Explain** the main challenges in modeling a Mars habitat.

- **List** the key steps needed to design and model a Mars habitat.

- **Develop** possible ideas and solutions for your Mars habitat.

- **Share** your ideas for a Mars habitat.

Designing and Modeling a Mars Habitat

KEY QUESTION What are the main constraints to consider when designing and modeling a Mars habitat?

For nearly 20 years, NASA has been interested in the human exploration of Mars. Although unmanned missions, which began in the 1960s, have provided valuable information about the planet, many technological challenges will need to be solved in order for humans to be able to travel to Mars or build a habitat on that planet. Since transporting supplies to Mars will be expensive and time-consuming, it will be desirable to create a habitat that is largely self-sufficient. Ideally, the habitat will include systems that can produce the food, water, and oxygen needed by the crew. During this Challenge Project, you will learn about the Mars environment and design a prototype habitat for a crew of six astronauts.

Remember that as you work through the Unit 3 Chapter Discovery Projects, you will gain knowledge and skills that will help you complete the Unit 3 Challenge Project.

In Partnership With

Engineering News-Record

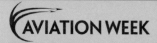

Inspiring Science Discovery

GreenSource

Engineers must successfully communicate and work with others in order to meet 21st century challenges such as the human exploration of Mars.

Go to your  ONLINE to view the video about the future of renewable energy. Learn about ways to generate power without fossil fuels and decide which of those methods could be used on Mars as well as on Earth. Then answer the question in the Engineer's Blog. See page 305 for a brief description of the steps you will follow to complete this unit project.

Group Workspace

What forms of renewable energy could be used during space travel and in a Mars habitat?

Go to your *essentials* ONLINE for Challenge Project details.

ESSENTIAL QUESTION **What is the most important engineering skill?**

Teamwork is a much-discussed ideal in almost every working environment. In the field of engineering, it is a crucial skill needed by engineers as they plan and carry out projects in which a number of different professionals are involved. A wide range of interpersonal skills, from basic communication abilities to familiarity with the global business world, is important in making teamwork possible. Engineers are striving to build a more diverse workforce in their field that more accurately reflects the world around them.

essentials

DISCOVERY PROJECT

Go to your *essentials* ONLINE to learn about the problem faced by the Apollo 13 astronauts.

Square Peg, Round Hole

21st Century Skills **Explain why engineers must interact effectively with the people who put their designs into place.**

The Apollo 13 astronauts and mission control were faced with a problem that required teamwork. They had to design an adapter that would fit a square cartridge into a hole made for a round cartridge. The astronauts had a limited amount of materials available on board the spacecraft. In this project, you will design and make an adapter based on the spacecraft's problem, using a limited amount of materials. You will then communicate verbally the procedures for reconstructing the device to your teammates, none of whom will have actually seen your solution.

Group Workspace

Explain how leadership is an important factor in creating and sustaining an effective project team.

Go to your *essentials* ONLINE for Discovery Project details.

Engineer's Toolbox

Go to the Engineer's Toolbox to
- Access Note-Taking Activities
- Access Graphic Organizers
- Access Academic Standards met by this chapter

READING GUIDE

Before You Read How have the engineering workforce and the skills needed to work with others in the engineering field changed over time?

Main Idea

Engineers must develop communication and related skills in order to be effective team members when implementing their designs and projects.

Objectives

- **Identify** the professionals and team members who work with engineers.
- **List** the communication skills that engineers must develop in order to work successfully with others.
- **Examine** the additional safety, information technology, cultural, and business skills that are important to the engineer's working life.
- **Analyze** the need to diversify the engineering workforce.

Vocabulary

Content Vocabulary

- technician
- engineering technician
- draftsperson
- risk assessment

Academic Vocabulary

- roles
- aspects

Note-Taking Activity

Draw this table for each section. Write key terms and phrases under **Cues.** Write main ideas under **Note Taking.** Summarize the section under **Summary.**

Cues	Note Taking
•	•
•	•
Summary	

Graphic Organizers

Use graphic organizers to organize information as you read.

Go to your **essentials ONLINE** for downloadable graphic organizers.

Project Team Members

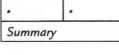

ACADEMIC

Technology

ITEEA STL3.02 Technological innovation often results when ideas, knowledge, or skills are shared within a technology, among technologies, or across other fields.

ITEEA STL17.05 There are many ways to communicate information, such as graphic and electronic means.

Mathematics

NCTM Problem Solving Monitor and reflect on the process of problem solving.

Science

NSES A Students should develop abilities necessary to do scientific inquiry, understandings about scientific inquiry.

ITEEA *International Technology and Engineering Educators Association*
NCTM *National Council of Teachers of Mathematics*
NSES *National Science Education Standards*

College & Career READINESS

Reading Integrate and evaluate content presented in diverse formats and media, including visually and quantitatively, as well as in words.

Writing Develop and strengthen writing as needed by planning, revising, editing, rewriting, or trying a new approach.

The Team Members

Biomimicry Biomimicry is a design principle rooted in nature. Many successful products and processes are created by studying efficiencies in the natural world. Olympic swimmers such as Michael Phelps wear sharkskin-inspired swimsuits. An inventor created Velcro® after removing plant burrs from his dog's fur.

Go to your *essentials* ONLINE to *Going Green, Step by Step* and learn how Interface created a sustainable business model.

Group Workspace

Airplanes were first invented—and are continually being made more efficient—by studying the flight patterns of birds. Illustrate some of the ways birds have inspired human flight.

The Engineer and the Team

Engineers often function as members of teams. They regularly team with others outside of their own profession: scientists, technicians, technologists, and skilled workers. They also work with other engineers, either within or outside their own disciplines. An engineer's interpersonal skills and his or her ability to function as a member of a team are essential job skills. While the people who are involved in a project may all have unique and important roles, the engineer is often right in the middle, contributing to important discussions and making key decisions.

Scientists

There is a long-standing debate about the roles played by science and technology in developing new ways of doing things. One side of that argument holds that scientific discovery leads to new technology. The other side says that technological development drives science to new discoveries about the natural world. In reality, each drives the other.

Fig. 14.1 Scientists Scientists provide the foundation for the work of engineers. *How do scientists and engineers depend on each others' work?*

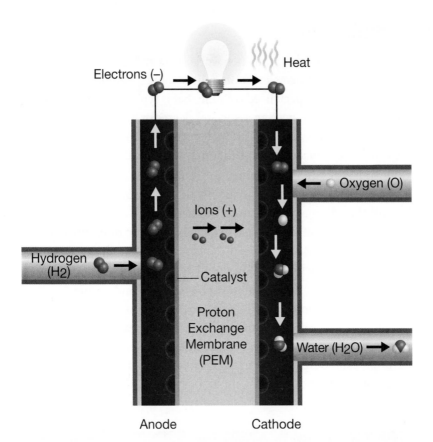

Electrons (–)

Heat

Oxygen (O)

Ions (+)

Hydrogen (H2)

Catalyst

Proton
Exchange
Membrane
(PEM)

Water (H2O)

Anode   Cathode

Some engineers work closely with scientists. Often the two distinct fields and knowledge bases overlap. For the most part, when an engineer works directly with a scientist or someone who holds a degree in one of the pure sciences, they do so in either of two settings: at an educational institution or similar establishment, or in industrial research and development (R&D).

While a scientist is primarily concerned with advancing our understanding of the natural world, an engineer works to design technological devices and systems. However, scientists and scientific knowledge have always had a hand in developing new technologies. Imagine a major project with the goal of creating new, more efficient methods of producing a hydrogen fuel cell. This type of cell uses the hydrogen from water to produce an electrical current. It works through a process called electrolysis, which separates hydrogen atoms from water. A scientist might be asked to research this process in great detail and conduct a series of related experiments. An engineer working on this project would consider the results of these experiments when designing the system that will be used to capture the hydrogen as usable fuel. (See **Figure 14.2**.)

As you can imagine from the above scenario, there is significant overlap between the work of scientists and that of engineers. In the most effective teams and partnerships, scientists are involved in the design and construction of devices that are based on their knowledge of how the world works. There are also engineers who make important scientific discoveries through their experiences and work.

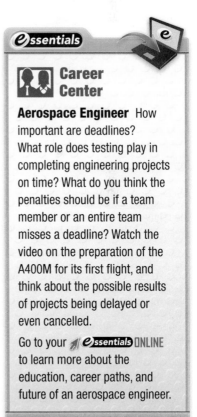

Career Center

Aerospace Engineer How important are deadlines? What role does testing play in completing engineering projects on time? What do you think the penalties should be if a team member or an entire team misses a deadline? Watch the video on the preparation of the A400M for its first flight, and think about the possible results of projects being delayed or even cancelled.

Go to your *essentials* ONLINE to learn more about the education, career paths, and future of an aerospace engineer.

Reading Check **Identify** the settings in which an engineer typically works directly with scientists.

Reading Check **Compare** the relationship of technicians to engineers.

Technicians

A **technician** is a person who often works with, and reports to, engineers on projects. Technicians most often have a high-school education, as well as additional specialized training that is typically obtained on the job. They might also have an associate's degree or have received further training in a trade or technical school program. Engineers typically plan the work of technicians, though they may not actually oversee the work.

Technicians need a practical understanding of the systems with which they work. They also should be skilled and knowledgeable beyond their immediate area of expertise. Their work is much more hands-on than that of a typical engineer. They are often in charge of lab testing and related equipment. They test ideas, analyze results, and solve problems during the course of their work. (See **Figure 14.3**.)

Combining the responsibilities of engineers and technicians, an **engineering technician** might construct the equipment to be used for an engineering project. He might also carry out experiments, collect data, and collate results. Some engineering technicians are involved in the design and development of engineered products, especially if their hands-on experience will be helpful to a project. Engineering technicians usually specialize in a particular type of engineering.

Fig. 14.3 Engineers and Technicians Technicians help to implement an engineer's plans for a project. *In what way does an engineering technician perform the responsibilities of both an engineer and a technician?*

Virtual Lab:
Engineering Teams

Engineering teams have become more common as engineering problems become more complex. No longer can people work in isolation without consulting or collaborating with a number of people over time to solve challenging engineering issues. Engineering team members may include the lead engineers themselves, scientists, technologists, technicians, contractors, consultants, drafting and design specialists, and other skilled workers. Teams must work together cohesively to get complicated jobs done successfully.

View Go to your ✐ **e**ssentials ONLINE to view the *Virtual Lab: Engineering Teams.*

Engineering Technologists

Engineering technologists focus on the application and implementation of the work of engineers. They usually have a bachelor's degree, and generally work more closely in a supporting role with engineers than a technician would. They may help coordinate and manage human and material resources as well as special equipment and machinery. An engineering technologist will also assist in the design of engineering concepts.

The typical degree program for engineering technology (often subdivided into programs such as manufacturing technology and industrial engineering technology) involves some study of mathematics and science, but is focused more on practical applications. Core courses in this field of study may include classes in technical drawing and computer-aided design, materials science, statics and dynamics, project management, and manufacturing processes. Graduates of engineering technology programs are generally not eligible for the same professional certification as engineers.

Engineering technologists usually focus on research, production, and operations related to engineering projects. They might also be involved in some project management tasks. The focus of their work

Fig. 14.4 Project Workers
Large projects involve teams of workers from numerous professions. *What skills make it possible to work successfully with other project workers?*

typically includes product improvement and the detailing of fabrication processes.

Skilled Workers

An engineer typically works with a number of skilled workers—people who hold a specific skill set. These are the people who are responsible for the actual manufacturing or construction of the engineer's design or product.

For example, a **draftsperson** will often directly assist an engineer by helping the engineer complete technical drawings. Some of these drawings may be hand drawn, but more often they would be completed using a computer-aided design (CAD) software package. A draftsperson is an expert in visualization and drawing processes. He or she may be required to resolve problems in both the early and advanced stages of design.

✔ **Reading Check** **List** types of resources an engineering technologist manages.

Engineers also need to understand the work of various skilled workers who are hired to carry out the manufacturing or construction of their projects. As orchestrators of the work, engineers implementing a design need to be aware of how skilled workers such as construction workers or factory employees and managers operate if they hope to complete their projects successfully. The people performing the manufacturing or construction of an engineering project may have a wide range of practical experience and professional training in numerous fields, making it especially important for engineers to be able to clearly communicate the project's details and instructions to those workers. (See **Figure 14.4**.)

Outside Contractors, Subcontractors, and Consultants

Engineers often interact with various outside contractors and consultants who are engaged to work on specific phases of a project. For example, a construction management firm might be brought in as a consultant to take care of cost estimates and other factors in the design of a large project. The engineer must communicate with these people regularly to ensure success in the project.

Another area of responsibility is the financial management of the construction or manufacturing process. Cost engineers, accountants, and bankers may be responsible for monitoring and managing the numerous costs and expenses of the project. Those financial variables are often some of the most important constraints of an engineering project.

As part of the same project, various contractors and subcontractors may be employed to hire and manage the labor for a particular job. It is largely up to the engineer and engineering management to make sure that the lines of communication between all of these team members remain clear and open throughout a project.

✔ Reading Check Explain why engineers need to understand the tasks of skilled workers.

Check Your Understanding

After You Read Perform the following tasks.

1. **List** the professionals with whom engineers often work on a regular basis.
2. **Summarize** the ways in which engineers work with scientists.
3. **Compare** the educational requirements for technicians and engineering technologists.

PROJECT CONNECTIONS

One key to effective teamwork is to define clearly established roles for each team member. Which role will each member of your adapter design team take on?

STEM CONNECTION

Data Analysis Engineers may be asked to collect data from experiments or tests, or to analyze data already collected. In each case, engineers should use their content knowledge to make conclusions about the data provided. Engineers must be knowledgeable about the processes used as well as the constraints imposed on the process or design in question. They should also insure they are abiding by the National Society of Professional Engineers (NSPE) Engineering Code of Ethics.

Personal Tutor

View
Go to your *essentials* ONLINE to view the *Personal Tutor: Data Analysis.*

Skills for Engineering

The most important skills for today's engineers are problem-solving, communication, interpersonal, leadership, decision-making, and time management skills. The engineer needs to be able to solve practical problems as well as mathematical ones. He or she must be able to communicate effectively with and lead other people working on projects. The engineer must also be willing to accept personal responsibility and accountability for all aspects of his or her project.

Teamwork

Engineers regularly interact with many types of people. They manage teams, work with clients, and set up the work of laborers. These tasks require strong interpersonal skills and the ability to communicate clearly and effectively with others. As described in Section 14.1, an engineer will often work with other engineers as part of a larger team. This teamwork also involves working with managers, contractors, consultants, cost estimators, and others. (See **Figure 14.5**.)

When working with other engineers, an engineer needs to be willing to learn from individuals with more experience as well as from those who have a different range of experience. A good team can teach a newer engineer and help him or her adapt to a new job title or role.

Engineers working together on a project share their insights and contribute both to a larger knowledge base and to project success. This can help develop mutual trust among professional engineers as they discuss projects in depth and brainstorm solutions to problems together.

Fig. 14.5 Teamwork Members of a project team must regularly meet to stay informed about all aspects of the project. *What communication skills does a person need to function well in a meeting?*

Fig. 14.6 Communicating through Presentations The ability to speak to a group and to use technology to enhance presentations are both important skills for engineers to have. *When might an engineer need to make a presentation to others?*

Communication Skills

Good communication abilities are essential in engineering. Speaking, reading, and writing clearly and effectively are all critical parts of the engineer's skill set.

Speaking Engineers often speak with clients about a project's needs and requirements, as well as its progress toward implementation. Engineers also need to be able to speak directly with the project's managers and other team members to communicate important facts about their work.

A related skill is that of public speaking. Professionals in many fields, including engineering, must often speak before small or large groups of people. This can include making formal presentations about a project as well as leading informal discussions. (See **Figure 14.6**.)

Reading Reading is a regular part of an engineer's job. Engineers must be able to read and interpret technical documents, legal documents, plans and specifications documents, manuals, engineering control documents, and trade journals. Engineers often learn of new technologies by reading about them in journals and materials provided by vendors.

Writing Engineers must also be able to write both technical materials and non-technical documents such as letters and memos. Engineers may write about the methods and procedures that will be used to implement their designs. They may also be responsible for creating reports on project progress and specifications for cost estimates for projects.

Time Management

Engineers must not only be responsible for the management and use of their own time, but also often take on the planning of the time of other individuals and groups of people. This is especially true if they assume management roles. They must meet deadlines set by their own superiors and have the ability to plan realistic deadlines for others.

Decision Making

Engineers must exhibit strong decision-making skills. They must factor cost, risk, ethics, and other requirements into their designs and projects.

PROJECT CONNECTIONS

Verbal communication of project procedures will be important to the success of the adapter design project. How do written and oral communication of the same material differ?

PROJECT CONNECTIONS

One limiting factor of the Apollo 13 adapter was time. How will you use the time that you have to complete this project effectively?

Engineers must also keep the overall goals and constraints of projects in mind as they make important decisions as the work progresses.

Safety and Accountability

Engineers must thoroughly understand the consequences of their work. They know that each of their designs will have both intended and unintended consequences (desired and undesired outcomes). Therefore, engineers must understand **risk assessment** and management. They take responsibility for important issues such as those related to safety. They are also accountable for making sure that projects conform to government regulations, so their knowledge of specific local and federal laws and codes is of great importance.

In addition to traditional engineering skills, such as the ability to apply mathematic, scientific, and technological knowledge to solve problems and design systems, today's engineers are faced with a number of contemporary skill requirements.

Information Technology

Hardware, software, and information technology are an integral part of the work of engineers. They must be able to use software to write and develop documents, share and revise those documents, enhance presentations, develop models, analyze data, run simulations, and communicate with others.

The ability to find and analyze information pertinent to a project is crucial to engineering today. Engineers must also be able to use information technology to determine the costs and benefits of their own work.

Global and Cultural Awareness

Engineering is increasingly becoming a global profession. It is not uncommon for engineers, even if they are newcomers to the profession, to work with companies and individuals from other parts of the world. For this reason, global awareness and cultural understanding are important parts of an engineer's skill set. This can include learning about the customs of people in other countries as they apply to business and professional conduct.

Business and Entrepreneurship

In recent years, engineers have become more responsible for common business tasks than ever before, especially those related to management. Some colleges and universities are now making business and entrepreneurship courses part of the core coursework for undergraduate engineering programs. Engineers are responsible for developing good and reliable systems, but also have to ensure that they are marketable and transferable ones. They must also take into account the costs of materials and labor when planning a project.

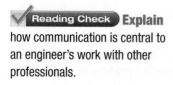 **Reading Check** Explain how communication is central to an engineer's work with other professionals.

Diversity in Engineering

Increasing diversity in the engineering field is an ongoing pursuit. As the United States becomes less homogenous every year, professional fields such as engineering are constantly examining their own efforts to reflect that demographic trend.

Women

The number of women receiving bachelor's degrees in engineering has increased in the past few decades. (See **Figure 14.7**.) However, women are still underrepresented in engineering, even though they comprise nearly half of the overall workforce in the United States.

The percentage of women receiving bachelor's degrees in engineering varies from discipline to discipline. As of 2006, women earned over 40% of bachelor's degrees in bioengineering and biomedical engineering. About a third of bachelor's degrees awarded in chemical, industrial, and materials engineering were earned that year by women. The traditional areas of civil, mechanical, and electrical engineering included women to an even lesser extent. Women earned less than 25% of civil engineering degrees, and less than 15% of mechanical and electrical engineering degrees. (Figures are from the American Association of Engineering Societies.)

In an effort to address this issue, some engineering societies have created affiliated groups within their organizational structures. For example, the Institute of Electrical and Electronics Engineers (IEEE) has a "Women in Engineering" community as part of its organization. There is also an entire engineering society for female engineers, the Society of Women Engineers (SWE).

African American and Hispanic Engineers

African American and Hispanic engineers are also currently underrepresented in engineering. In fact, while the number of women entering undergraduate engineering programs has steadily increased over the past several years, the number of African American and Hispanic engineering students has decreased, despite the increase in their overall participation in higher education. According to the American Society

Visualization

Complete and Incomplete Views It is very important for everyone working with technical drawings to be able to read and understand the drawings. They need to notice if something is wrong and correct any errors before production begins. It takes practice to be able to visualize a complete three-dimensional object from a two-dimensional drawing and notice any errors.

Group Workspace

Examine orthographic views of objects. Complete a third view from two complete orthographic views or add lines that are missing from incomplete orthographic views.

Go to your *essentials* ONLINE to learn more about developing your ability to finish incomplete views.

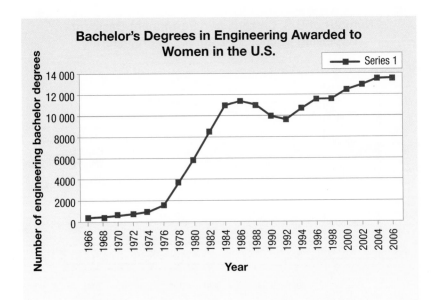

Fig. 14.7 Women in Engineering This chart shows the number of bachelor's degrees awarded to women in the U.S. over the past several decades. *Which decade saw the most dramatic increase in this category?*

Virtual Lab: Engineering Skills

Certain skills are needed to achieve success in such a multifaceted discipline as engineering. Because engineers routinely work with a large number of people and must communicate their ideas effectively, excellent interpersonal communication and cooperation skills are indispensable. Exceptional decision-making abilities and a thorough knowledge of safety factors and accountability are also integral to a successful engineer's skill set.

View Go to your *essentials* ONLINE to view the *Virtual Lab: Engineering Skills.*

Reading Check **Identify** the engineering fields of study in which women are best represented.

for Engineering Education, in schools where African American students make up about 11% of overall undergraduate students, they account for only about 5% of engineering students. (See **Figure 14.8.**)

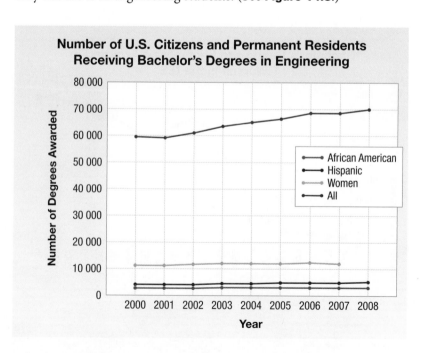

Number of U.S. Citizens and Permanent Residents Receiving Bachelor's Degrees in Engineering

Fig. 14.8 Diversity This chart shows the number of engineering degrees awarded to women, African Americans, and Hispanics. *What is the trend of each of these three groups of graduates?*

The National Science Foundation confirms these trends with regard to women, African Americans, and Hispanics not only in the engineering workforce, but also in technical fields in general. Considering the importance that those groups will have in the workforce of the future, many outreach programs have been developed to address these issues. Some high school courses, competitive events, and institutional outreach programs have shown positive results in introducing and retaining underrepresented groups in engineering-related activities.

Engineers in the workforce today must also develop attitudes favorable to diversity in their personal activities and actions, as some stereotypes still exist in the world of engineering.

Fig. 14.9 Diversity Increasing diversity in engineering departments at universities will lead to further diversity in the engineering work force. *What groups are the primary focus of movements for diversity in engineering in the U.S. today?*

Check Your Understanding

SECTION **14.2**

After You Read Perform the following tasks.

1. **Identify** several ways in which teamwork is a part of an engineer's professional life.

2. **Summarize** the types of communication that are central to an engineer's work.

3. **Propose** what additional efforts could be made to increase diversity in the engineering workforce.

Review and Assessment

Problem-Solving Process

Identify

During the late 19th and early 20th centuries, over 50 Fabergé eggs were produced for the Russian imperial family. SolidCase Ltd. is a manufacturer that has won a contract from the Kremlin Armory Museum in Moscow to develop transport cases for this priceless collection. SolidCase has asked you to create a container meeting the following specifications:

- The container must be developed by a team that includes a material scientist, lead engineer, engineering technologist, draftsperson, and fabrication technician.
- The container must survive a drop from 15 feet.
- The length, height, and width of the container must be eight inches or less, and must securely hold a Fabergé egg roughly the size of an extra-large hen's egg.

Set Up

1. Research the project. Establish the means by which team members will communicate with each other.
2. Analyze commercial carrying cases and their components.
3. Brainstorm potential solutions. Develop refined criteria for the project and preliminary ideas to share with the engineering team.
4. Choose the best solution.

Execute

5. Plan the solution with your team.
6. Keep sketching and recording ideas to improve the design.
7. Prepare prototypes of the solution.
8. The team should communicate progress made every day, and work to continually refine and develop the best product.

Evaluate

Test the designs by having volunteers carry a raw egg in the container for 24 hours. After the test, examine the product to see which held up best and what might need to be redesigned. Record your findings.

Share

Share your work with others by developing a wiki page about the product and the team experience. Be sure to describe the various roles of the team members and how well they communicated.

Critical Thinking

Key Concepts

1. **Identify** several of the professionals who might be involved in an engineering project.

2. **Summarize** the types of communication that the engineer should have in his or her skill set.

3. **Outline** the ways in which the engineering field is less diverse than the workforce as a whole.

4. **Evaluate** contemporary engineering skills that have brought changes to the field in recent years.

5. **Examine** why diversity in engineering is a worthwhile goal to pursue.

Teamwork 21st Century Skills

6. **Share** with your project team what you have learned about working with various types of project team members and how that information connects to your Discovery Project.

7. **Discuss** what you have learned about the interpersonal skills that engineers need. How will you use this information in your Discovery Project?

Activity Center

Go to the **Activity Center** to review chapter vocabulary and key concepts.

Engineer's Toolbox

Go to the **Engineer's Toolbox** to:
- Access Academic Activities
- Access the Competitive Event Prep Activity

---

essentials

DISCOVERY PROJECT

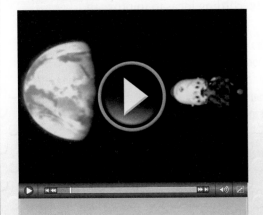

Square Peg, Round Hole

In this project, you will use a limited amount of materials to design and make an adapter based on a problem faced by the Apollo 13 astronauts. You will then have to communicate verbally the procedures for reconstructing the device to your teammates, none of whom will have actually seen your solution.

Go to your **essentials ONLINE** to learn about the problem faced by the Apollo 13 astronauts. Then collaborate with your team to complete this Discovery Project.

Preparing for an Engineering Career

ESSENTIAL QUESTION What makes a good engineer?

Successful engineers are expected to possess a high level of academic and technical skill. Being a successful engineer, however, requires much more than academic learning and technical skills. Because most projects involve teams and require a high degree of project management skill in addition to design abilities, successful engineers need to master a variety of "soft" skills in addition to their technical knowledge of engineering. "Soft" skills include creative abilities, communication skills, and leadership skills. These skills are also known as 21st Century Skills.

essentials

DISCOVERY PROJECT

AVIATION WEEK

Go to your *essentials* ONLINE to watch a video about how engineers consider constraints and goals when completing a project.

Solve an Engineering Problem

 21st Century Skills **Analyze your role as a team member and your contribution to moving your project forward.**

Work in teams to select an engineering area of interest. Draft a proposal that identifies a problem that can be solved using available resources. Once the proposal is approved, work as a team to complete the project. Each project will be judged by a panel of teachers and engineers who will review the project material and interview each team about their project.

 Engineer's Blog

During the video, watch and listen for facts about how engineers apply information about constraints and project goals to projects. Write down some ideas about the projects you have completed so far in this course, and how you might apply some of the ideas from the video to your culminating project.

 Engineer's Toolbox

Go to the Engineer's Toolbox to
- Access Note-Taking Activities
- Access Graphic Organizers
- Access Academic Standards met by this chapter

READING GUIDE

Explain why professional organizations in the engineering field are important to the profession. Also explain how the numerous professional and student organizations provide information, and also promote specific engineering disciplines to prospective engineers.

Objectives

- **Discuss** how technical skills should increase with experience.
- **Explain** why creativity and communication skills are important.
- **Describe** how a student might decide on a specialty.
- **Describe** the role of engineering societies in continuing education.
- **Discuss** the roles of the Technology Student Association and the Junior Engineering and Technical Society.
- **List** three organizations for minorities in engineering.

Vocabulary

Content Vocabulary

- specialized
- esthetically
- extensively
- extracurricular
- prospective
- practicing
- profiles

Academic Vocabulary

- emphasize
- differentiate
- format
- conflicts
- virtual

Note-Taking Activity

Draw this table for each section. Write key terms and phrases under **Cues**. Write main ideas under **Note Taking**. Summarize the section under **Summary**.

Cues	Note Taking
•	•
•	•
Summary	

Graphic Organizers

Use graphic organizers to write and organize information as you read.

Go to your **essentials** ONLINE for downloadable graphic organizers.

Personal Inventory

Inventory
| 1 | 2 | 3 | 4 |

STANDARDS

ACADEMIC

Technology

ITEEA STL3.02 Technological innovation often results when ideas, knowledge, or skills are shared within a technology, among technologies, or across other fields.

ITEEA STL13.01 Students will develop the ability to collect information, and evaluate its quality.

Mathematics

NCTM Data Analysis and Probability Formulate questions that can be addressed with data and collect, organize, and display relevant data to answer them.

Science

NSES A Students should develop abilities necessary to do scientific inquiry, understanding about scientific inquiry.

ITEEA *International Technology and Engineering Educators Association*
NCTM *National Council of Teachers of Mathematics*
NSES *National Science Education Standards*

College & Career READINESS

Writing Gather relevant information from multiple print and digital sources. Assess the credibility and accuracy of each source, and integrate the information while avoiding plagiarism.

Speaking and Listening Integrate and evaluate information presented in diverse media and formats, including visually, quantitatively, and orally.

Personal Inventory

Reading Check **List** two areas in which engineers need to possess technical skills in addition to their content knowledge.

Technical Skills

Undergraduate engineering programs emphasize the development of technical skills in science and mathematics, and of **specialized** skills, or skills adapted for a particular purpose, related to the engineering discipline studied. Engineers are problem solvers. Most engineering programs emphasize the engineering process because it is a valuable tool that is used regularly.

Many programs also emphasize graphic communication. This involves expressing ideas using sketching and computer-aided design (CAD). It also includes drawing illustrations of ideas. Hand drafting, orthographic projection, and isometric projection are useful skills. Knowledge of CAD and graphics software programs may also be useful. Engineers are often asked to use drawings prepared by others.

Technical skill development continues throughout a professional career. A civil engineering major will graduate with a good general background in the discipline. However, there is still a lot for this engineer to learn after graduation. A new engineer may be assigned to a small portion of a large project, such as designing access roads to a new power plant. As the engineer gains experience, the level of responsibility assigned to him or her for a project tends to increase. In addition to learning on the job, this engineer will continue to learn by reading technical journals and taking continuing education courses to learn about new technologies. Many firms provide financial support for engineers interested in earning graduate degrees.

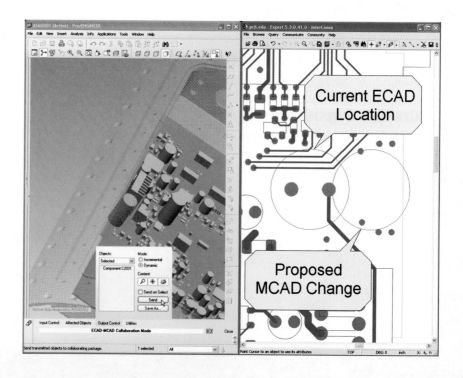

Fig. 15.1 Collaboration Software
Engineers often work together on projects using specialized collaboration software such as your project software for this course, or this engineering software. *How has using software to collaborate helped you with your Unit Challenge and Chapter Discovery projects in this course?*

Fig. 15.2 Modern Methods
The old San Francisco-Oakland Bay Bridge (left) stretches alongside the construction of a new replacement bridge. The new bridge is of a much different design. *Why might a bridge that has functioned well for a long time be replaced with something entirely different?*

Software Skills

Engineers should be skilled users of common software products for word processing, spreadsheets, and presentations. Engineers are often also skilled in the use of specialized computer-aided design and modeling software. Instead of testing designs by building physical models, many designs are tested through computer modeling. Some software packages also allow engineers in different locations to collaborate on designs and testing. (See **Figure 15.1**.)

"Soft" Skills

Engineers often lead project teams. These jobs require a high degree of project management skill. Successful engineers should master a variety of "soft" skills including creative abilities, communication skills, and leadership skills. These skills are also known as 21st Century Skills.

Creative Abilities

In addition to having the technical skills necessary to solve complex problems, it is often desirable for engineers to propose creative solutions to problems. Engineers develop and enhance their creative abilities through practice. Using the engineering design process helps. Imagine that an engineering firm is asked to design a replacement for a 50-year-old suspension bridge. One solution is to construct a bridge that is very similar to the existing bridge. A better solution, however, might be to challenge the team to take advantage of the availability of new materials, and new design and construction techniques to create a new bridge that stays within the available budget and is both functional and **esthetically** pleasing, which means it is appealing to the eye. (See **Figure 15.2**.)

Engineers not only solve problems, they also look for new opportunities. In recent years engineers have developed many new electronic products that have created new industries and tremendous demand. Examples include smart telephones that function as computers to access hundreds of applications, challenging video games with realistic graphics, and flat-screen televisions with lower prices and higher-quality images. (See **Figure 15.3**.)

Communication Skills

Successful engineers are good communicators. Communication includes listening, speaking, and writing skills. Since engineering education focuses primarily on developing technical skills, engineering students sometimes need to develop communication skills on their own. One way to become a more effective communicator is to make sure you get plenty of practice in listening, speaking, and writing.

These skills can be developed by working hard on compositions for any class, and perhaps taking a speech or business communication class. In addition, students can participate in student organizations that provide them with opportunities to practice their communication skills and conduct formal meetings. Some of these organizations include opportunities for students to work on project teams and to assume leadership roles. Information on specific student and professional organizations is provided in Section 2 of this chapter.

Engineers often work in teams to solve complex problems. As teams develop solutions, two-way communication among team members is

Fig. 15.3 Building Technology
This building design for an apartment tower in Dubai is an application of the concept of cybertecture, a living accommodation intended to seamlessly interact with modern technology. It is even designed to resemble a high-tech electronic device. *What are some other products that demonstrate the use of creative design and engineering?*

Fig. 15.4: Teamwork at Work
Engineering team members communicate their concerns and ideas about a project. *What are three project areas that benefit from good communication among project team members?*

important. Listening to other views helps each team member understand what the others are thinking. Careful listening helps the engineer understand a problem, and provides time for thinking of possible solutions. Solutions may involve agreeing or disagreeing with others and possibly adding to or combining the ideas contributed by others. Being a good listener is key, since team members often appreciate a colleague with good listening skills and are more likely to value the suggestions he or she offers. (See **Figure 15.4**.)

Engineers speak regularly with other members of their team, as well as with managers and clients. Effective speaking skills help engineers both with their current projects and with career advancement. It is important to speak clearly and at a pace that makes it comfortable for others to listen. Effective speakers also know how to emphasize the important points and differentiate between facts and opinions. They know when to stop talking and listen to others. When called upon to deliver formal presentations, effective speakers choose the words they know will help their audience understand what they are explaining (especially if the audience is not all engineers). They may also use materials such as PowerPoint presentations and handouts that add value, contribute to understanding, and hold the attention of their audience.

Engineering managers often plan and conduct meetings. Emails are often used to inform others that a meeting will be held. In these communications, it is important to let attendees know when the meeting will start, what needs to be covered in the meeting, and when the meeting will end. This can be accomplished by sending an agenda in advance of the meeting. During the meeting the leader should follow the agenda and practice effective communication, which means being a good speaker as well as a good listener.

Engineers should strive to be effective writers of emails, business letters, reports, memos, and proposals. The primary difference between speaking and writing is that writing can be a permanent reminder of effective or ineffective communication skills. General guidelines for effective writing include:

- **Be brief** – reread what is written and eliminate unnecessary words
- **Be clear** – use complete sentences and easily understood vocabulary
- **Avoid errors** – check and double-check spelling and grammar

Most engineers use email **extensively**, or in a widespread way. It is vital to review emails to make sure that they convey the desired message, are error-free, and are sent to the correct person or persons.

Memorandums ("memos") must state their message clearly and tell the recipients if they need to take action based on the memo. Many firms have a standard format for business letters. Engineers should learn and follow the required style.

Engineers also write reports to describe their work on projects. It is often helpful to create an outline of the report content, and it is important to make sure that the finished report is free of errors. Young engineers should review high-quality reports written by others and seek suggestions from colleagues whenever possible.

✓ **Reading Check**) **Describe** how skills such as creativity, communication, and leadership can help an engineer advance into a management position over an engineer who only has strong technical skills.

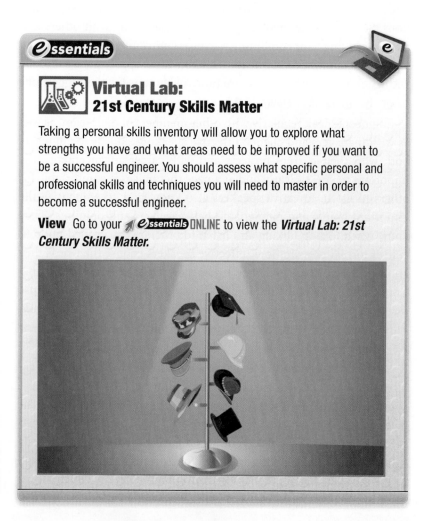

e⟩ssentials

🧪⚙️ **Virtual Lab:**
21st Century Skills Matter

Taking a personal skills inventory will allow you to explore what strengths you have and what areas need to be improved if you want to be a successful engineer. You should assess what specific personal and professional skills and techniques you will need to master in order to become a successful engineer.

View Go to your ⟋ **e⟩ssentials** ONLINE to view the *Virtual Lab: 21st Century Skills Matter.*

Leadership Skills

Experienced engineers can advance their careers by developing the leadership skills needed to coordinate the work of dozens or sometimes hundreds of engineers and others working on complex projects. Project management skills can be developed through formal education and by looking for opportunities to assume increasingly complex responsibilities. Engineers who demonstrate good leadership qualities such as the ability to motivate others and to resolve conflicts may be given the opportunity to advance to management-level positions. These positions often come with a significant increase in salary.

Assessing Your Abilities

Think carefully about your own interests and abilities. You do not have to be a math or physics genius to do well as an engineering student, but you should have a sincere interest and good grades in these subjects and be willing to study and develop your knowledge about them. If you are a pretty good student in these classes and enjoy developing creative solutions to problems, then engineering may be for you. Some students are interested in a career that enables them to help others. Biomedical engineering is one field that attracts students who wish to use engineering to develop products and services that help others through improved health care.

Check with your guidance counselor about career preference tests that might provide you with helpful information. The Myers-Briggs personality inventory is one instrument that many prospective engineers find helpful. Free, short versions of Myers-Briggs tests are available online. In the next section of this chapter you will learn about the courses that will help you prepare to be a successful engineering student and about organizations that provide information to assist you in making informed career decisions.

PROJECT CONNECTIONS

Work as a team to determine the format of the portfolio that will be used to document the culminating project. Create an outline that identifies the content of the portfolio along with a list of individual responsibilities.

Reading Check **List** some tools engineering students can use to help identify an engineering discipline that is a good match for them.

Check Your Understanding

After You Read Perform the following tasks.

1. **Identify** three main skill areas that are important for students to develop if they want the best chance for upward advancement in their engineering career.

2. **Explain** why creative abilities and communication skills are important attributes of successful engineers.

3. **Predict** how technical skills required of an engineer might change as he or she gains more career-based experience.

Preparation for an Engineering Career

Types of Courses

This engineering class and this text have provided you with information and experience related to engineering. Preparation for any career begins with the selection of courses that will be taken throughout high school. The following courses are recommended for students considering a career in engineering:

- **Mathematics** – algebra I and II, geometry, trigonometry, and calculus
- **Science** – biology, chemistry, physics
- **Technology and Engineering** – engineering design, computer-aided design
- **English** – four years
- **Advanced Courses** – take advantage of advanced-placement and honors courses in science, mathematics, and engineering if they are offered.

In addition to course work, a good way to prepare for an engineering career is to become involved in **extracurricular** activities, or activities that are not part of the standard academic curriculum, which are

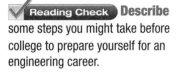
Reading Check Describe some steps you might take before college to prepare yourself for an engineering career.

Fig. 15.5 Competition FIRST
Students entering FIRST robotics competitions work in teams to develop their projects for competitions held at various levels. *What major benefit do students gain from participating in competitions such as FIRST?*

Fig. 15.6 Applied Learning
High school students can enhance their engineering experience by participating in a summer engineering program. *Search the Internet to find out if there are any engineering schools in your state that offer summer engineering programs for high school students.*

related to robotics and other aspects of engineering. Organizations such as FIRST (www.usfirst.org) sponsor team-based competitions at the local, state, and national levels, and provide an opportunity to develop technical and leadership skills. FIRST offers programs throughout the United States that include opportunities for students to work with practicing engineers who provide technical assistance to the high school teams. Other organizations that sponsor engineering-related competitions include VEX Robotics (http://robotevents.com) and the Technology Student Association. (See **Figure 15.5**.)

Many colleges sponsor engineering summer programs for high school students. Often intended for students who have completed 11th grade, these programs vary in length and give students a chance to experience engineering classes and projects (See **Figure 15.6**.). Many of these programs can be found through the Web sites of the organizations, as well as through individual colleges and universities. Some of these programs require the payment of tuition, but others are funded by grants, or offer scholarships for students. Another way to gain knowledge and experience in STEM-related careers is to volunteer at a science center or children's museum. At the science center or museum you will be surrounded by interesting exhibits and people who are knowledgeable and interested in engineering and science.

Engineering Organizations		
Discipline or Specialty	**Engineering Society**	**URL**
Agricultural	American Society of Agricultural and Biological Engineers	www.asabe.org
Architectural	Architectural Engineering Institute	www.aeinstitute.org
Biomedical	Biomedical Engineering Society	www.bmes.org
Chemical	American Institute of Chemical Engineers	www.aiche.org
Civil	American Society of Civil Engineers	www.asce.org
Computer/Software	IEEE Computer Society	www.computer.org
Electrical	Institute of Electrical and Electronic Engineers	www.ieee.org
Environmental	American Academy of Environmental Engineers	www.aaee.net
Industrial	Institute of Industrial Engineers	www.iienet2.org
Manufacturing	Society of Manufacturing Engineers	www.sme.org
Mechanical	American Society of Mechanical Engineers	www.asme.org
Systems	International Council on Systems Engineering	www.incose.org

Table 15.1

Information Resources

Because of the need for engineers in most engineering disciplines, many organizations are eager to provide information and activities that will encourage high-school students to consider engineering as a career. Many of the organizations also offer programs for elementary and middle-school students as well as for parents of **prospective,** or likely, engineers. Categories of these organizations include engineering societies, organizations that promote engineering through hands-on activities and competitions, and organizations for minorities.

Engineering Societies

Engineering societies are professional organizations that support their members in a variety of ways. They promote the particular discipline

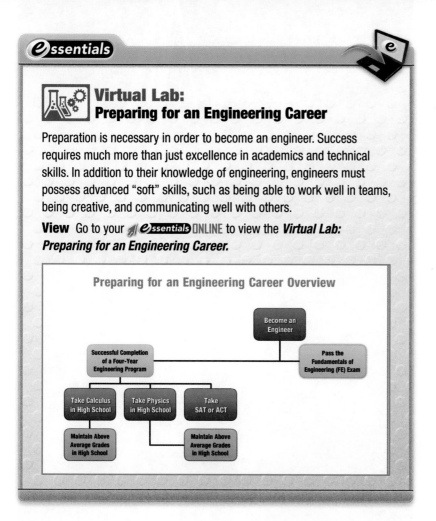

Virtual Lab:
Preparing for an Engineering Career

Preparation is necessary in order to become an engineer. Success requires much more than just excellence in academics and technical skills. In addition to their knowledge of engineering, engineers must possess advanced "soft" skills, such as being able to work well in teams, being creative, and communicating well with others.

View Go to your *essentials* ONLINE to view the *Virtual Lab: Preparing for an Engineering Career.*

Preparing for an Engineering Career Overview

or specialty that they represent, and serve members of the profession by publishing journals and newsletters with information about the latest technologies. They also offer continuing education through traditional and online courses. Many of these organizations have chapters for undergraduate engineering students, and Web sites that include information helpful to high-school students interested in the field. Look for links to "students" or "K-12 outreach" when you visit their Web sites. **Table 15.1** contains the names and Internet addresses of professional societies for each of the engineering disciplines and specialty fields described in this book.

Student-Oriented Organizations

Technology Student Association (TSA) The Technology Student Association (www.tsaweb.org) is an organization for students interested in technology and engineering. Currently more than 2,000 schools and 150,000 students participate in TSA activities. TSA has a twofold mission: technological literacy, and leadership. These skills are developed through chapter activities and nearly 40 STEM-related competitive events. TSA students work in class or after school to prepare for competitions that are held at the state and national level. Some states also have regional competitions to select those who will advance to the state competition. Many students who win at the state level then go on to compete at the national TSA competition, which is held in late June each year. Each

PROJECT CONNECTIONS

Conduct research to learn more about a society in an engineering field related to the topic of your culminating project.

Fig. 15.7 TSA Contest Students often work in teams to create models of their designs in competitions held by TSA and other organizations. *What are some advantages of working on TSA teams?*

Green reSource

Renewable Energy Traditional sources of energy — coal, natural gas and oil — are derived from a finite supply of fossil fuels. Renewable energy relies on the infinite resources of nature such as the sun, wind, and water to power our world.

 **Group Workspace**

Biofuels are a type of renewable energy that is derived from organic matter such as corn, sugar cane, trees, and grasses. Explain some of the benefits of using biofuels over fossil fuel.

Go to your *e*ssentials ONLINE to learn about the Garthwaite Center for Science and Art at the Cambridge school of Weston.

TSA chapter requires a group of at least 10 students, and a teacher interested in serving as an advisor. (See **Figure 15.7**.)

Junior Engineering Technical Society (JETS) The Junior Engineering Technical Society (www.jets.org) has several programs that provide students with information about engineering careers. One available resource is a free newsletter. Each issue focuses on an engineering discipline, and several years of past issues are available. Another feature of the JETS website is an interest inventory that can help students determine how their interests and skills relate to various engineering disciplines and college majors. JETS also sponsors an annual team-based engineering competition on two levels (9th and 10th grades and 11th and 12th grades). A new contest theme is provided each year, and competitions are held at the state and national levels. (See **Figure 15.8**.)

American Society for Engineering Education (ASEE) The American Society for Engineering Education is an organization for high-school and university engineering teachers. ASEE also has a Web site specifically designed for high-school students interested in engineering and STEM careers. The Web site (www.egfi-k12.org/) includes a magazine titled *Engineering, Go For It* that contains articles about what engineers do, suggestions for selecting an engineering major, and articles about projects completed by young engineers. Throughout the magazine there are also links to video clips. A free weekly newsletter focusing on engineering innovations is also available at the eGFI website.

Engineer Girl! Engineer Girl! (www.engineergirl.org) is a website sponsored by the National Academy of Engineering. The mission of Engineer Girl! is to promote interest in engineering among young women, and to address the need for more women engineers. To do this, the site provides information about the achievements of historical and currently **practicing** female engineers. (A practicing engineer is one who is currently working in the profession.) A unique feature of this site is the opportunity to ask questions about engineering. It has a section for Frequently Asked Questions (FAQs), and an archive of questions and answers. Each year Engineer Girl! sponsors an essay contest and publishes the winning essays. The site also includes many useful links.

Discover Engineering / Engineering Week The Discover Engineering website (www.discoverengineering.org) offers career **profiles**, or brief career descriptions, information about individual engineering disciplines, and links to engineering-related games and videos. Discover Engineering is sponsored by National Engineers Week. National Engineers Week is supported by some of the leading engineering firms in the United States. National Engineers Week also has its own website (www.eweek.org) with information about the types of engineering, information about Engineers Week activities, and many other useful links.

Design Squad Design Squad (http://pbskids.org/designsquad) is a fast-paced public television program available throughout the United States. Each episode of Design Squad features high school students working in teams and using the engineering design process to solve real engineering problems as they compete for a college scholarship. The Design Squad website contains resources such as a detailed explanation of the

PROJECT CONNECTIONS

The Sloan Career Cornerstone Center website is a comprehensive source for information about careers in engineering, engineering technology, and science. Visit the site to learn more about a career related to your culminating project.

Fig. 15.8 Competition Prep
The JETS website details the competition specifications for the year. *What are some resources available free to students who visit the JETS website?*

engineering design process, hands-on engineering activities, short video clips of young engineers describing their work, and full versions of past episodes.

Try Engineering Try Engineering (www.tryengineering.org) offers an extensive listing of summer programs for prospective engineers, a database of engineering programs throughout the world, profiles of practicing engineers and engineering students, and links to games that challenge students to use their skills to solve engineering problems.

Organizations for Minorities

Several national organizations offer programs that encourage minority students to attend college and pursue careers in engineering and related areas. These organizations include the Society of Women Engineers, the National Action Council for Minorities in Engineering, the American Indian Science and Engineering Society, the National Society of Black Engineers, and the National Society of Hispanic Professional Engineers. (See **Figure 15.9**.)

Society of Women Engineers (SWE) The Society of Women Engineers (http://societyofwomenengineers.swe.org) was founded in 1950 to assist women interested in pursuing a career in engineering. SWE is a national organization, and many colleges and universities with engineering programs have local chapters. The services offered by SWE include scholarships, a website with extensive resources such as a calendar of events taking place all over the U.S. designed to interest girls in engineering, information on competitions and summer camps, and links to hands-on activities.

National Action Council for Minorities in Engineering (NACME) The National Action Council for Minorities in Engineering (www.nacme.org) is leadership organization that seeks to increase the representation of minorities in STEM-based careers. NACME offers scholarships, provides mentors for high school and college students, and publishes a guide to engineering careers in both English and Spanish.

American Indian Science and Engineering Society (AISES) The American Indian Science and Engineering Society (www.aises.org) encourages Native American students to prepare for and pursue careers in the STEM disciplines, including engineering. AISES supports science

Fig. 15.9 Encouraging Minorities Students visit an engineering society booth at a college activities fair. *What are some other ways in which organizations might encourage women and minorities to consider an engineering career?*

fairs, virtual showcases of student research, and summer camp programs designed to interest high school students in engineering and science careers.

National Society of Black Engineers (NSBE) With more than 450 chapters, the National Society of Black Engineers (www.nsbe.org) is one of the largest student-run organizations in the U.S. Its mission is to increase the number of African American engineers. Alumni members volunteer to mentor potential engineering students and NSBE offers hands-on activity programs during the summer and academic year.

Society of Hispanic Professional Engineers (SHPE) The Society of Hispanic Professional Engineers (http://oneshpe.shpe.org/wps/portal/national) was formed to provide role models for Hispanic students. SHPE has chapters throughout the U.S. and internationally. College student chapters sponsor many events for potential engineering students.

Other Organizations

Sloan Career Cornerstone Center The Sloan Career Cornerstone Center (www.careercornerstone.org) is an extensive online collection of resources on STEM careers. The site is continually updated and includes information about more than 150 technical careers through podcasts, links, interviews, and documents that describe engineering careers in detail. Detailed suggestions for career planning while in high school are also provided.

Accreditation Board for Engineering and Technology (ABET) ABET (www.abet.org) is the organization that accredits college and university programs in engineering and related fields. Currently there are more than 600 colleges with nearly 3,000 approved programs. Accreditation indicates that approved programs meet the quality standards of the profession. This is important, since employers and graduate schools look for graduates from accredited institutions. To assist you in finding accredited programs, the website offers an online directory.

Reading Check **Explain** how engineering societies, student organizations, and organizations for minorities help engineers develop their careers.

Visualization

Technical Graphics Technical graphics can be implemented in many ways. Artistic renderings and animations can be used to show clients what a final project will look like. They can also be used in advertising and sales.

Group Workspace

Sketch missing views of objects and list the steps needed to create the objects with 3D modeling software.

Go to your **e**ssentials ONLINE to learn more about developing your abilities to sketch missing views and plan the creation of 3D models.

Check Your Understanding

SECTION **15.2**

After You Read Perform the following tasks.

1. **Identify** the recommended math and science classes that prepare high school students to study engineering in college.

2. **Explain** how the Technology Student Association and the Junior Engineering and Technical Society contribute to the development of engineers.

3. **Outline** the common goals of three organizations that focus on the development of minorities in engineering.

Review and Assessment

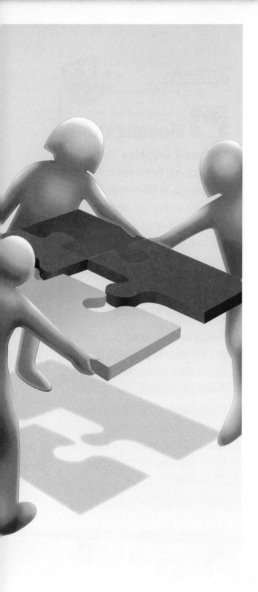

Problem-Solving Process

Identify

The American Society for Engineering Education has called for the early introduction of engineering concepts. They want high school students to create lessons for elementary students. Develop a pre-engineering lesson for elementary students using the following criteria:

- Focus the lesson on a concept like structural forces.
- Describe engineering projects that may be involved in the field.
- Include information about a related career or occupation.
- Develop a small activity that will reinforce the topics covered.

Set Up

1. Research what type of learning is most appropriate for elementary students and how content can be communicated effectively.
2. Gather information. Analyze pre-engineering activities for elementary students. Develop methods for assessing activities.
3. Brainstorm potential lessons. Discuss various pre-engineering topics and related activities that you may present to the students.
4. Choose a solution. Consider the criteria and constraints and the requirements of stakeholders. Discuss ideas with the team.

Execute

5. Plan the lesson with your group. Review the steps needed to explain the topic. Compile a list of resources for the activity.
6. Continue to revisit and evaluate your ideas. They may be used to improve the overall design and delivery of your presentation.
7. Prepare your presentation. Develop a multimedia presentation, and a list of materials. Consider the age of your audience.
8. The team should refine and develop the best solution. Discuss the lesson with an elementary teacher to understand your audience.

Evaluate

Test your presentation. Deliver it to an elementary school, or younger siblings. Ask objective questions to assess your delivery and content.

Share

Develop a website with a digital copy of the presentation as well as guidelines and resources for the activity to share your work with others. Provide an example of the delivery process, as well as any tips and tricks.

Critical Thinking

Key Concepts

1. **Identify** three main types of skills that are common to successful engineers.

2. **Summarize** why communication is a vital skill for engineers interested in management positions.

3. **Compare and contrast** the roles of engineering societies and organizations for minorities.

4. **Evaluate** the role of student organizations in recruitment and development of new engineers.

5. **Predict** how the growth of engineering education in high schools will affect the quality of practicing engineers in the future.

Teamwork

6. **Explain** how engineering organizations benefit the engineering team.

7. **Discuss** with a classmate the potential benefits of having so many professional engineering organizations.

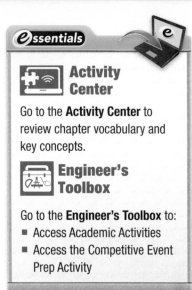

essentials

Activity Center

Go to the **Activity Center** to review chapter vocabulary and key concepts.

Engineer's Toolbox

Go to the **Engineer's Toolbox** to:
- Access Academic Activities
- Access the Competitive Event Prep Activity

---

essentials — **DISCOVERY PROJECT**

Solve an Engineering Problem of Your Choosing

In this chapter's Discovery Project, you will work in teams to identify and solve an engineering problem that is related to one or more of the disciplines and topics that you have studied. After the problem is approved by your teacher, your team will use the engineering design process to develop and document an original solution to the problem.

Go to your ✈ **essentials** ONLINE to collaborate with your team on this Discovery Project.

CHAPTER 16

Future Challenges

ESSENTIAL QUESTION How is engineering changing to meet the challenges of the 21st century?

Engineers today are poised to help solve a number of significant challenges worldwide. Environmental and energy needs are among those challenges, as are calls to assist communities in the developing world and protect us all from the threat of terrorism. As today's engineers work to solve this wide-ranging list of problems, they do so in an employment environment that is increasingly focused on innovation and rapid advances in technology.

*e*ssentials

DISCOVERY PROJECT

Go to your *e*ssentials ONLINE for Discovery Project details.

Design and Build a Mars Landing Vehicle

 21st Century Skills Why do engineers need to be able to work with colleagues in other countries and societies?

In this chapter's Discovery Project, your team will design and build a model space vehicle that includes the systems needed to transport a crew from a spacecraft orbiting Mars to the surface of the planet. You will also include the systems needed to enable the lander to return the astronauts to the orbiting spacecraft.

As you study this chapter, consider the following:

- **Summarize** the challenges that are unique to space travel.
- **List** the areas of engineering that are involved in developing a habitable environment away from Earth.
- **Develop** the components for this project using sketching, drawing, and modeling.

 ### Group Workspace

Discuss how the changing world of technology affects the engineering challenges of traveling into space.

 ### Engineer's Toolbox

Go to the Engineer's Toolbox to:
- Access Note-Taking Activities
- Access Graphic Organizers
- Access Academic Standards met by this chapter

READING GUIDE

Before You Read What are the most important global challenges that face engineers today?

Objectives

- **Identify** the challenges facing engineers in the 21st century.
- **Summarize** engineering opportunities in developing countries.
- **Analyze** how engineers help protect society against terrorism.
- **Relate** the need for sustainable energy sources to the career opportunities that this need will open up.
- **Examine** why socially responsible engineering benefits the engineer working on such projects.

Main Idea

Engineering is a field that is constantly changing to face the world's challenges and benefit the world as a whole.

Vocabulary

Content Vocabulary

- carbon dioxide
- combustion
- nitrogen cycle
- desalination
- drip irrigation
- pandemic
- infectious
- terrorism
- cyberterrorism
- green engineering
- socially responsible engineering

Academic Vocabulary

- concentrate
- infrastructure
- levees
- global
- colleagues

Note-Taking Activity

Draw this table for each section. Write key terms and phrases under **Cues**. Write main ideas under **Note Taking**. Summarize the section under **Summary**.

Cues	Note Taking
• • •	• •
Summary	

Graphic Organizers

Use graphic organizers to write and organize information as you read.

Go to your **essentials** ONLINE for downloadable graphic organizers.

Future Trends in Engineering

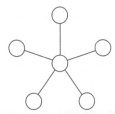

ACADEMIC

Technology

ITEEA STL05 Students will develop an understanding of the effects of technology on the environment.

Mathematics

NCTM Problem Solving Apply and adapt a variety of appropriate strategies to solve problems.

Science

NSES F Develop understanding of personal and community health; population growth; natural resources; environmental quality; natural and human-induced hazards; science and technology in local, national, and global challenges.

ITEEA *International Technology and Engineering Educators Association*
NCTM *National Council of Teachers of Mathematics*
NSES *National Science Education Standards*

College & Career
R E A D I N E S S

Writing Draw evidence from literary or informational texts to support analysis, reflection, and research.

Speaking and Listening Prepare for and participate effectively in a range of conversations and collaborations with diverse partners, building on others' ideas and expressing their own clearly and persuasively.

21ST Century Engineering Challenges

The Challenges for Engineers

In Chapter 1, you learned that the National Academy of Engineering recently brought together a group of distinguished engineers to recognize great engineering achievements of the twentieth century. More recently, the National Academy used a similar process to develop a list of significant global challenges that can be addressed in part through engineering.

National Academy of Engineering Grand Challenges

1. **Make solar energy economical**

2. Provide energy from fusion

3. Develop carbon sequestration [capture] methods

4. Manage the nitrogen cycle

5. Provide access to clean water

6. **Restore and improve urban infrastructure**

7. Advance health informatics [information systems]

8. Engineer better medicines

9. **Reverse engineer the brain**

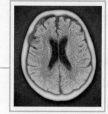

10. Prevent nuclear terror

11. Secure cyberspace

12. Enhance virtual reality

13. Advance personalized learning

14. **Engineer the tools of scientific discovery**

Fig. 16.1 Grand Challenges
These global challenges face engineers today. *Which of these challenges will require the most cooperation among professionals in multiple areas of engineering?*

(See **Figure 16.1**.) In this section, the challenges will be grouped into six categories and possible engineering solutions will be discussed.

Affordable and Sustainable Energy

About 85% of the energy consumed in the United States comes from fossil fuels. New sustainable sources of energy are needed, because eventually the supply of coal, oil, and natural gas will run out.

Wind Power

Wind power is an attractive option that works well in certain areas of the U.S. A large-scale wind turbine can produce enough electricity to power several hundred homes. Wind farms with several hundred turbines have been constructed, and more are being planned. Recent engineering improvements to wind turbines include the development of larger turbines that can generate more power, and the elimination of gear boxes, which are difficult to repair because they are located at the top of towers that can exceed 350 feet in height. (See **Figure 16.2**.)

Since steady winds are more important than strong winds, selecting the right locations for wind turbines is critically important. Sites being considered are studied for several years before a final decision about construction is made. Concerns about the appearance of wind turbines and the noise that they can generate are additional factors that must be considered when choosing sites for turbines in many communities. Those sites are no longer limited to land; locating turbines offshore has proven successful in Europe and is an approach being considered by several U.S. utility companies.

Wind turbine

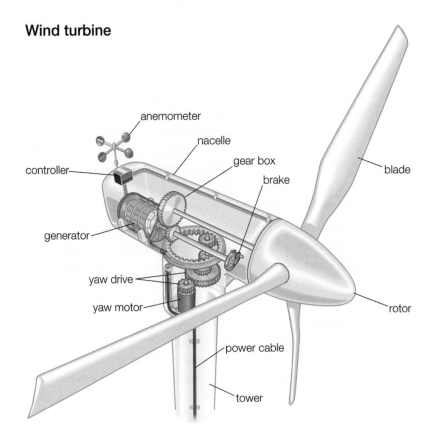

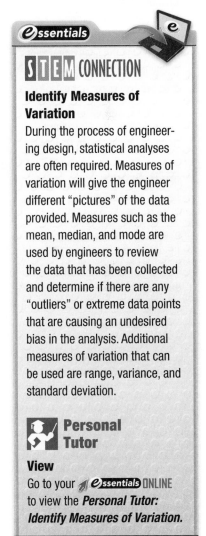

PROJECT CONNECTIONS

Investigate the kinds of power systems that have been used for NASA projects, including various spacecraft and the International Space Station. Decide if these systems will be sufficient for a voyage to Mars or if additional systems will be needed.

essentials   e

STEM CONNECTION

Identify Measures of Variation
During the process of engineering design, statistical analyses are often required. Measures of variation will give the engineer different "pictures" of the data provided. Measures such as the mean, median, and mode are used by engineers to review the data that has been collected and determine if there are any "outliers" or extreme data points that are causing an undesired bias in the analysis. Additional measures of variation that can be used are range, variance, and standard deviation.

Personal Tutor

View
Go to your *essentials* ONLINE to view the *Personal Tutor: Identify Measures of Variation.*

Fig. 16.2 Wind Power The interior of a wind turbine contains a gearbox as a central part of its mechanism. *What is the most important factor engineers must consider before starting a wind power project?*

Solar Energy

There is a lot of interest in solar power as an unlimited source of free and clean energy. However, there are a number of engineering challenges that must be overcome before solar energy can make a significant contribution to our overall energy needs.

Photovoltaic solar cells convert light directly into electricity. Recent advances have made it possible to produce solar cells that are much more efficient than those made only a few years ago. However, electricity produced from those efficient solar cells still costs two to three times as much as electricity produced in fossil fuel generating plants. Research is under way to develop less expensive materials for the next generation of solar cells. Another concern is that millions of solar cells will need to be disposed of or recycled after their useful lifetimes.

Solar thermal plants offer another possible solution. These plants use mirrors to concentrate the sun's rays to heat a fluid that produces the steam needed to operate a turbine and generator similar to those used in conventional power plants.

Protecting the Environment

Reducing the amount of **carbon dioxide**, a gas produced by burning and breathing, that is discharged into the atmosphere is one of the most important steps needed to protect our environment. The burning of fossil fuels releases large amounts of carbon dioxide. Because it will be some time before solar and wind power technologies significantly reduce fossil fuel use, engineers are working on several different approaches to reducing and storing carbon. One possible solution is to clean up the **combustion** (burning) process at power plants. This might be done by using chemicals to absorb carbon dioxide before it is discharged into the atmosphere. Another method that could be used at a coal-fired power plant would be to burn the coal in pure oxygen. This would leave pure carbon dioxide gas that could be safely collected.

Collecting carbon dioxide gas presents another challenge. Where is the best place to store it? Some of the gas can be stored in depleted natural gas and oil fields. Another possibility would be to inject the carbon dioxide into sedimentary rocks deep in the earth or below the ocean floor. Several small-scale carbon capture research projects are now under way, as scientists and engineers work together to develop additional methods for storing large quantities of carbon dioxide.

Controlling the impact of human activity on the **nitrogen cycle** is another environmental concern with possible engineering solutions. The use of fertilizer and the planting of certain crops have disrupted the natural nitrogen cycle (the circulation of nitrogen from the air to the soil to plants and animals, and back into the air). The nitrogen in fertilizer produces nitrous oxide. This byproduct is broken down by sunlight into nitric oxide, which damages the Earth's ozone layer. Dealing with the nitrogen cycle is challenging because fertilizer is a key element in addressing global hunger. Engineers need to develop new kinds of fertilizer and new application techniques that will boost food production while having less of an impact on the environment.

Green reSource

Green Building Certification

The National Association of Home Builders (NAHB) offers a green home certification program for homebuilders and remodelers. It calculates the level of sustainability in a project and certifies it as bronze, silver, or gold.

Go to your *essentials* ONLINE to learn about the Macallan Building and its green features.

Group Workspace

The NAHB program is similar to the LEED ratings offered by the U.S. Green Building Council. Both offer a way to quantify the sustainability of a construction project. Explain why a builder would want to gain green certification.

Reading Check **Identify** how the amount of carbon dioxide entering the atmosphere can be reduced.

Maintaining and Improving the Nation's Infrastructure

As you learned in Chapter 7, the term infrastructure refers to the systems that support a community, such as roads, bridges, and systems for wastewater treatment and drinking water supply. There is general agreement that our national infrastructure needs improvement. In recent years, many infrastructure projects have been postponed or canceled for economic reasons. Below are brief descriptions of some of the major infrastructure problems currently facing the U.S. Similar problems exist around the globe.

Dams

Several thousand dams in the U.S. are in need of repair. Billions of gallons of water are wasted every day because of leaking pipes, and too often wastewater is discharged into waterways from aging and malfunctioning water treatment plants. Another infrastructure problem became evident in 2005 during Hurricane Katrina, one of the costliest and deadliest natural disasters in U.S. history. There are thousands of miles of levees that are inadequate for protecting public health and safety. All of these engineering challenges can be solved if communities recognize the problems and allocate the necessary funding. (See **Figure 16.3**.)

Fig. 16.3 Levees Many communities depend on levees to protect them from flooding. *What stands in the way of repairing aging levees?*

Fig. 16.4 Intermodal Transportation Hub This single facility connects multiple forms of transportation. *What types of public and private transportation are available in your community?*

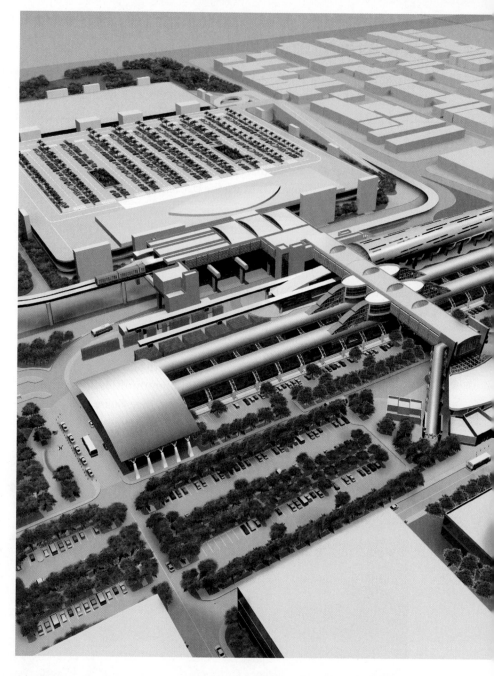

Career Center

Architect and Writer Think about the buildings you spend time in, such as your home and your school. Determine how many square feet are in these buildings. Calculate how much of the space you actually use. Consider the possible differences between what you want and what you need in the space you occupy. Watch the video in which Sarah Susanka discusses her "quality-over-quantity" design philosophy.

Go to your *e*ssentials ONLINE to learn more about the education, career paths, and future of an architect and writer.

Reading Check **Identify** the risks that are posed by aging dams and levees.

Transportation

Transportation problems are evident throughout the U.S. Commuters in areas throughout the country face daily traffic jams due to highway congestion. Air travelers face increasing delays because the air traffic control system is in need of modernization. More than a quarter of the bridges in the U.S. have structural problems, and nearly a third of our roads are in poor condition. For transporting bulk goods, freight trains are several times more efficient than trucks, but U.S. rail systems have been neglected for years. Modern high-speed rail systems, such as those used in Europe, would be beneficial. A possible engineering solution to these problems in urban areas would be to build transportation hubs that integrate parking, bus, rail, and walking systems. These systems could serve as models for the many new urban areas that are expected to develop in the future. (See **Figure 16.4**.)

Improving Life in Developing Countries

There are numerous ways in which engineers can play a part in the improvement of life in developing countries. Three of the most important ways involve water, agriculture, and power.

Water

One critical problem facing developing countries is the lack of clean water. Each week, thousands of children die from diseases caused by drinking contaminated water. One problem is that rivers and streams are used for sewage disposal and as a source of drinking water. Drinking water is also contaminated by naturally-occurring pollutants such as arsenic. In many countries, people spend a major portion of every day walking from their homes to water sources such as streams or ponds to get water for their families, water that too often is not clean.

Engineers can help overcome these problems. Regions near oceans can build **desalination** plants (facilities that remove salt from seawater). Many desalination plants are in operation in the Middle East. Unfortunately, they are expensive to build and operate. Desalination technologies that are more affordable are currently being developed. Another possible solution is to build inexpensive, small-scale distillation plants to meet the drinking water needs of small communities.

PROJECT CONNECTIONS

When future astronauts travel to Mars, they will need reliable sources of power and clean drinking water. Explain how NASA has taken care of this need on past missions. Determine if there are resources on Mars that can help maintain a human habitat.

Virtual Lab: The Fourteen Grand Challenges for Engineers

The National Academy of Engineering (NAE) has identified fourteen grand challenges for engineers. These are the challenges that are expected to drive engineering in the next decade and beyond. How engineers and the other professionals who work with them address these challenges will have long-term implications for sustainability, health, vulnerability, and joy of living.

View Go to your *essentials* ONLINE to view the *Virtual Lab: The Fourteen Grand Challenges for Engineers.*

Agriculture

Developing countries use most of their water for agriculture. For that reason, another way to improve life in those areas is to increase food production by developing more efficient methods of watering crops. One way is to use **drip irrigation**, which is based on the use of small-diameter tubes that deliver water to individual plants. This technique can greatly reduce the quantity of water wasted during crop irrigation. Recycling water so that it can be used for crop irrigation represents another possible engineering solution.

Power

Another challenge that people in many developing countries face is the lack of a central source of electricity and a power grid that can deliver electricity to remote communities. Homes in some remote communities are lit by kerosene lamps, which produce soot and sometimes cause fires. One solution may be the use of renewable energy sources, such as solar and wind energy. A one-watt light-emitting diode (LED) powered by a rechargeable battery and a small solar cell can provide enough light for a person to complete tasks such as a homework assignment. Similarly, relatively small wind turbines combined with the use of batteries for storing power can take care of the basic electricity needs for a small village.

Improving Health and Health Care

During this century, biomedical engineering will continue to develop and refine technologies with the potential to improve human health. Some of the expected changes include improved health information systems, better diagnostic techniques, new medicines, and advanced preparation against pandemics. A **pandemic** is a disease such as influenza that affects a large number of people in a particular area.

The widespread use of health information systems will enable physicians to maintain records that can be instantly shared over global networks with other physicians. In addition to speeding up health care delivery, new information systems will make it possible to monitor the health of individuals remotely with sensors and wireless technologies. For example, a person with diabetes could be reminded to eat a meal to help maintain his or her proper blood sugar level. Improved communication will also make it possible for public officials to gather the information needed for combating large-scale heath emergencies.

New diagnostic techniques will enable physicians to identify diseases and other health problems earlier than ever before. Biomedical engineers will continue to develop new medications, including some designed specifically for individual patients. New vaccines to prevent emerging **infectious** diseases (those that can be passed from one living organism to another) will be created. New manufacturing processes that speed up the production of vaccines will reduce the number of people affected by influenza and reduce the overall impact of pandemics.

PROJECT CONNECTIONS

Investigate how NASA has monitored the health of astronauts on past missions. Describe what kinds of medical equipment should be included on a Mars-bound spacecraft.

Reading Check **Identify** what engineers can do to help guard against the threat of pandemics.

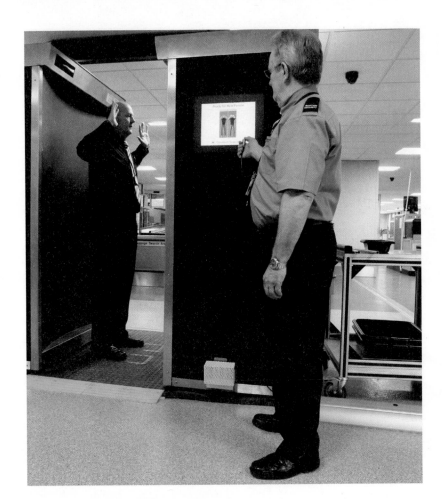

Fig. 16.5 Airport Security This machine scans all incoming airplane passengers for weapons or other restricted items. *How have engineers contributed to increased airport security?*

Combating Terrorism

Since the terrorist attacks of 2001, there has been increasing concern about various forms of terrorism—the use of violence or threat of violence to achieve a particular aim—that are designed to disrupt the lives of ordinary citizens. In the U.S., the Transportation Safety Administration was created to develop systems to ensure the safety of airline passengers. Other countries have established similar agencies. New scanners and bomb detection devices have been developed. Computer engineers are also developing new information systems designed to identify known terrorists before they are able to board an airplane, as well as advanced passenger screening systems. (See **Figure 16.5**.)

Much of the electricity produced throughout the world is generated in nuclear plants. These plants have a good safety record, but there are concerns about terrorists taking over the plants and using spent fuel from the plants to create weapons. Engineering can reduce some of these concerns by developing better security systems for nuclear facilities and systems for keeping track of all nuclear materials, including those used for health care. Many thousands of containers of merchandise arrive in the U.S. every day. Systems that can detect nuclear materials inside the containers are being tested and improved. Similar detection systems are also being developed to identify biological materials that could be used for weapons. Engineers are also helping produce systems to safeguard our food and water supplies.

Fig. 16.6 Cyberterrorism Officials in numerous government agencies have turned their attention to the threat of cyberterrorism. *What electronic networks are most at risk of cyberattacks?*

Cyberterrorism is the use of computers and information technology to cause physical or financial harm. It impacts those who have their computers disrupted by viruses and their financial well-being affected by computer-based identity theft. Since cyberterrorists are constantly modifying their techniques, engineers must continue to develop software to prevent computer viruses and other intrusions into home computers and large computer networks. Engineers need to give particular attention to preventing terrorists from gaining access to vital networks such as government record systems, banking, the electric power grid, and the air traffic control system.

SECTION 16.1

Check Your Understanding

After You Read ▶ Perform the following tasks.

1. **Identify** sustainable sources of electric power.
2. **List** ways in which engineers can help improve the lives of people in developing countries.
3. **Assess** the contributions of engineers to the prevention of terrorist activities.

Engineering in the 21st Century

Addressing the challenges described in Section 1 of this chapter will provide a wide range of opportunities for people interested in engineering and related technical careers. U.S. government projections indicate that there will be good opportunities for engineers and related professionals during the first half of the 21st century. Opportunities for women and other underrepresented groups should be particularly good. Some of the other factors that will affect engineering careers include the trends described below.

Pace of Technological Change

The rapid development of new technologies that occurred during the last century is expected to continue and accelerate. Technological advancement will affect our daily life as well as all of the engineering disciplines that have been described in this book. Key developments such as the expanding use of computers and robotics for a wide range of purposes will continue. Microcomputers will enhance the value of many ordinary products. The Internet will continue to play an increasingly important role in daily life as well as in engineering activities. In the past, there were large gaps of time between important inventions. That has changed and will continue to change.

Creativity and Innovation

To maintain the place of the U.S. in an increasingly competitive world, the nation's engineers will need to continue to develop creative solutions to address new and more complex engineering problems. A more diverse workforce should stimulate creative thinking within engineering teams. Because of increased competition, the teams will also need to be particularly innovative as they work to improve existing products and processes.

Today continuous innovation in areas such as consumer electronics has made it possible to introduce new generations of video games, smart phones, computers and electronic books on a regular basis. One result is that large numbers of people are interested in obtaining the latest versions of these products as soon as they are introduced. **(Figure 16.7)**

PROJECT CONNECTIONS

Describe the role of creativity in designing the Mars lander.

✓ **Reading Check** **Describe** how the pace of technological change has developed in the past century.

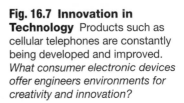

Fig. 16.7 Innovation in Technology Products such as cellular telephones are constantly being developed and improved. *What consumer electronic devices offer engineers environments for creativity and innovation?*

Fig. 16.8 Global Input This airplane contains design features from engineers in multiple countries. *How do engineers worldwide cooperate today?*

Globalization

Engineering firms now compete on a global basis. U.S.-based companies compete with firms from other counties for both domestic and international projects. Engineers will need to become more familiar with the languages and customs of global colleagues and competitors. Many undergraduate engineering programs now offer summer courses and short courses in other countries to help future engineers develop skills in these areas. Airliners and other products that require complex engineering will be designed with the help of software that makes it easy for engineers in various locations to work together using the engineering design process in a global fashion. (See **Figure 16.8**.)

Sustainability

The number of engineers engaged in **green engineering** is expected to increase in the coming century. "Green engineering" refers to the development and use of products and processes that protect human health and the environment by conserving resources, reducing waste, and achieving sustainability. Critical environmental issues of the 21st century that will involve the work of engineers include:

- Energy
- Pollution
- Transportation
- Agriculture
- Land use

The need to address these issues should create excellent career opportunities for environmental engineers and engineers in other disciplines who want to use their skills to prevent and solve environmental problems.

Socially Responsible Engineering

Socially responsible engineering refers to the use of engineering skills to help others. While much of the engineering field is driven by consumer desires, many engineers are interested in using their technical knowledge to help develop solutions to problems facing communities in the U.S. and around the world. Major companies often encourage their engineers to become involved in community service projects. Undergraduate engineering programs also encourage students to participate in projects that will improve lives by addressing the challenges described in the first section of this chapter. Through their participation in such programs, engineers and engineering students can develop the skills needed to advance their careers while making a positive difference in communities.

For example, first-year engineering students at one university were challenged to work as a team to develop playground equipment for disabled students attending a New York City public school. The team visited the school and met with teachers and students to develop an understanding of the students' needs. As they learned to apply the engineering design process, they successfully developed a swing for students who use wheelchairs.

*e*ssentials

Virtual Lab:
Future Trends in Engineering

Engineering trends will have profound effects on how we live in the next century. As the development of new technologies continues and accelerates, the ensuing developments will affect engineering disciplines across the board. In addition, globalization, sustainability, and socially responsible practices will influence how engineers design, develop, and implement solutions.

View Go to your *essentials* ONLINE to view the *Virtual Lab: Future Trends in Engineering.*

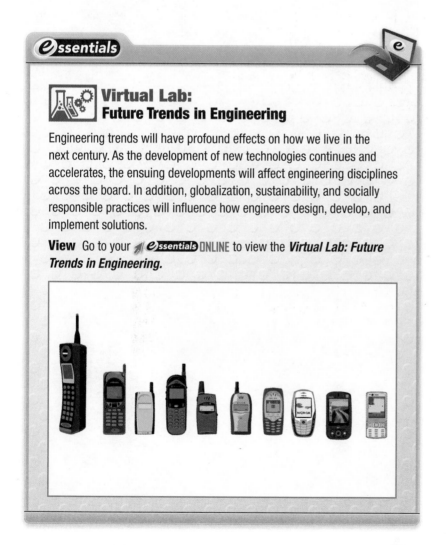

Misleading Results

When engineers analyze results, it is important for them to determine if the results are free from bias and if the results have been collected properly. If an engineer finds any discrepancies in the process or final results, it may be necessary to repeat the data collection. Engineers must always think from a problem-solving perspective to insure that data analyses are used properly. If additional data is required, the engineer must be willing to communicate these results to the stakeholders.

Personal Tutor

View

Go to your **essentials** ONLINE to view the *Personal Tutor: Misleading Results.*

Engineers Without Borders

Engineers Without Borders (EWB) is an international organization that connects professional and student engineers to communities that need help with challenges that can be met through engineering. Major engineering firms and other organizations donate the funds required to complete the projects. EWB student chapters are located throughout the U.S. Students in these chapters work in teams, along with their professors and practicing engineers, to develop appropriate solutions to problems in the areas of water, sanitation, education, renewable energy, and disaster recovery.

Fig. 16.9 Contributing to Society
Engineering projects can help communities in many ways. *What kinds of engineering projects could produce both profit and community benefits?*

Fig. 16.10 Engineers Without Borders These volunteer engineers and engineering students are installing solar power at a home on the Ramah Navajo Reservation in New Mexico. *How do engineers themselves benefit from participating in such projects?*

At the beginning of a project, a team of students from the participating chapter travels to the project location to assess community needs. During the next several years, teams from the same university return to implement the project and evaluate the results. EWB teams continue to be involved for at least five years, to help ensure long-term sustainability. Students who participate in EWB projects find that they provide an excellent opportunity for them to enhance their engineering skills and make a difference in the lives of others. Many high school engineering programs have started similar programs within their local communities. (See **Figure 16.10**.)

✓ **Reading Check** **Define** the term "green engineering."

Check Your Understanding

After You Read Perform the following tasks.

1. **Identify** how globalization has had an effect on the ways in which engineers work.

2. **Summarize** the areas in which sustainability in engineering can have an impact.

3. **Appraise** some of the benefits of socially responsible engineering.

Review and Assessment

Problem-Solving Process

Identify

Many agricultural operations and farms utilize vast amounts of water and fertilizer to grow their crops. Much of this water, along with nitrogen from fertilizer, ends up in waste treatment plants or lakes and streams. In an effort to reduce the amount of nitrogen released into the ecosystem, the EcoGrow company wants to produce a small hydroponic (soil-free) system that will allow water and fertilizer to be reused until it is absorbed by the plants. The project has the following criteria and constraints:

- Use off-the-shelf components.
- Sustain 4–6 medium sized plants.
- The system must be self-contained.

Set Up

1. Ground yourself in information about the various subsystems of a hydroponic system. Research the nutrients needed to grow plants in a hydroponic system. Analyze the environmental factors needed to grow plants indoors.

2. Brainstorm potential solutions. Develop sketches for the various components of the hydroponic system.

3. Choose the best solution. Be sure to use the criteria and constraints as guides in deciding which is the best idea.

Execute

4. Plan the building of the solution with your team. What types of materials can be obtained locally and inexpensively? What techniques can be used in producing the prototype?

5. Sketch and record your ideas.

6. Prepare models of the system using various production methods.

7. Discuss the project's progress with your team after each session.

Evaluate

Determine which design is the most effective by testing the system in a simulated environment. Introduce several plants of the same size and variety, and record their growth. Compare the amounts of water and nutrients needed for each system and the resulting progress of the plants.

Share

Share your work in a report on the system and its effectiveness.

Critical Thinking

Key Concepts

1. **List** the systems that make up the nation's infrastructure and the ways in which they are in need of improvement.

2. **Identify** the ways in which engineers can make a positive difference in developing countries.

3. **Analyze** the different types of terrorist threats and the ways in which engineers are working to counter them.

4. **Explain** the critical environmental issues of the 21st century that will involve the work of engineers.

5. **Examine** what aspects of health care can be improved in the future by engineers.

Listening  21st Century Skills

6. **Share** with your project team what you have learned about the future directions of engineering and how that information relates to your Discovery Project. Ask your team members what they have learned.

7. **Discuss** what you have learned about the growing need for creativity and innovation in engineering. How will you use this information in your Discovery Project?

essentials

Activity Center

Go to the **Activity Center** to review chapter vocabulary and key concepts.

Engineer's Toolbox

Go to the **Engineer's Toolbox** to:
- Access Academic Activities
- Access the Competitive Event Prep Activity

---

essentials

DISCOVERY PROJECT

Design and Build a Mars Landing Vehicle

In this chapter's Discovery Project, your team will design and build a model space vehicle that includes the systems needed to transport a crew from a spacecraft orbiting Mars down to the surface of the planet. You will also include the systems needed to enable the lander to return the astronauts to the orbiting spacecraft.

Go to your **essentials ONLINE** to view the video about what life on Mars could be like for human explorers. Then collaborate with your team on this Discovery Project.

Critical Thinking

Key Concepts

1. **Identify** the professionals and team members who work with engineers.

2. **List** the communication skills that engineers must develop in order to work successfully with others.

3. **Discuss** how an engineer's technical skills should increase as she gains more experience.

4. **Relate** the need for sustainable energy sources to the career opportunities that this need will create.

5. **Describe** the role of engineering societies in continuing education.

6. **List** at least three organizations that focus on minorities in engineering.

7. **Identify** the major types of challenges facing engineers in the 21st century.

Leadership — 21st Century Skills

8. **Discuss** how socially responsible engineering benefits the engineer working on such projects.

9. **Analyze** with your classmates how engineers are needed to help protect society against terrorist threats.

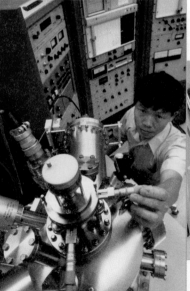

Design and Model a Mars Habitat

Project Process

IDENTIFY

1. Research the Mars environment. Investigate factors such as atmosphere, gravity, winds, radiation, sunlight, and length of the day.

2. Identify the systems that the habitat would require for a one-year mission.

3. Research architectural designs that will include the required elements of the habitat. Record your ideas.

SET UP

4. Choose the materials for your design.

5. Prepare alternate sketches for all the systems and architectural elements.

6. Use a decision matrix to choose the best design for each of the essential systems and of the habitat.

EXECUTE

7. Create detailed, scale drawings of the habitat. Describe key systems and architectural features in your notes.

8. Begin construction of the model habitat. After each session, make notes summarizing your progress.

9. Verify that the model includes all of the systems needed to sustain life for the crew as well as the features that will help them enjoy an extended stay.

10. Complete the model habitat. Compare it to the detailed drawings, to determine if any changes are needed.

SHARE

11. Present your model to the class.

EVALUATE

 Group Workspace

12. Write about the research, design, and construction of your Mars habitat. Describe what changes you would make if you continued the project.

Project Evaluation Chart

 Go to the Engineer's Toolbox to access the Project Evaluation Chart.

Go to your **essentials** ONLINE for Challenge Project details.

NSPE Code of Ethics Appendix

Preamble

Engineering is an important and learned profession. As members of this profession, engineers are expected to exhibit the highest standards of honesty and integrity. Engineering has a direct and vital impact on the quality of life for all people. Accordingly, the services provided by engineers require honesty, impartiality, fairness, and equity, and must be dedicated to the protection of the public health, safety, and welfare. Engineers must perform under a standard of professional behavior that requires adherence to the highest principles of ethical conduct.

I. Fundamental Canons

Engineers, in the fulfillment of their professional duties, shall:

1. Hold paramount the safety, health, and welfare of the public.
2. Perform services only in areas of their competence.
3. Issue public statements only in an objective and truthful manner.
4. Act for each employer or client as faithful agents or trustees.
5. Avoid deceptive acts.
6. Conduct themselves honorably, responsibly, ethically, and lawfully so as to enhance the honor, reputation, and usefulness of the profession.

II. Rules of Practice

1. Engineers shall hold paramount the safety, health, and welfare of the public.
   a. If engineers' judgment is overruled under circumstances that endanger life or property, they shall notify their employer or client and such other authority as may be appropriate.
   b. Engineers shall approve only those engineering documents that are in conformity with applicable standards.
   c. Engineers shall not reveal facts, data, or information without the prior consent of the client or employer except as authorized or required by law or this Code.
   d. Engineers shall not permit the use of their name or associate in business ventures with any person or firm that they believe is engaged in fraudulent or dishonest enterprise.
   e. Engineers shall not aid or abet the unlawful practice of engineering by a person or firm.
   f. Engineers having knowledge of any alleged violation of this Code shall report thereon to appropriate professional bodies and, when relevant, also to public authorities, and cooperate with the proper authorities in furnishing such information or assistance as may be required.

2. Engineers shall perform services only in the areas of their competence.
   a. Engineers shall undertake assignments only when qualified by education or experience in the specific technical fields involved.
   b. Engineers shall not affix their signatures to any plans or documents dealing with subject matter in which they lack competence, nor to any plan or document not prepared under their direction and control.
   c. Engineers may accept assignments and assume responsibility for coordination of an entire project and sign and seal the engineering documents for the entire project, provided that each technical segment is signed and sealed only by the qualified engineers who prepared the segment.

3. Engineers shall issue public statements only in an objective and truthful manner.
   a. Engineers shall be objective and truthful

in professional reports, statements, or testimony. They shall include all relevant and pertinent information in such reports, statements, or testimony, which should bear the date indicating when it was current.

b. Engineers may express publicly technical opinions that are founded upon knowledge of the facts and competence in the subject matter.

c. Engineers shall issue no statements, criticisms, or arguments on technical matters that are inspired or paid for by interested parties, unless they have prefaced their comments by explicitly identifying the interested parties on whose behalf they are speaking, and by revealing the existence of any interest the engineers may have in the matters.

4. Engineers shall act for each employer or client as faithful agents or trustees.

a. Engineers shall disclose all known or potential conflicts of interest that could influence or appear to influence their judgment or the quality of their services.

b. Engineers shall not accept compensation, financial or otherwise, from more than one party for services on the same project, or for services pertaining to the same project, unless the circumstances are fully disclosed and agreed to by all interested parties.

c. Engineers shall not solicit or accept financial or other valuable consideration, directly or indirectly, from outside agents in connection with the work for which they are responsible.

d. Engineers in public service as members, advisors, or employees of a governmental or quasi-governmental body or department shall not participate in decisions with respect to services solicited or provided by them or their organizations in private or public engineering practice.

e. Engineers shall not solicit or accept a contract from a governmental body on which a principal or officer of their organization serves as a member.

5. Engineers shall avoid deceptive acts.

a. Engineers shall not falsify their qualifications or permit misrepresentation of their or their associates' qualifications. They shall not misrepresent or exaggerate their responsibility in or for the subject matter of prior assignments. Brochures or other presentations incident to the solicitation of employment shall not misrepresent pertinent facts concerning employers, employees, associates, joint venturers, or past accomplishments.

b. Engineers shall not offer, give, solicit, or receive, either directly or indirectly, any contribution to influence the award of a contract by public authority, or which may be reasonably construed by the public as having the effect or intent of influencing the awarding of a contract. They shall not offer any gift or other valuable consideration in order to secure work. They shall not pay a commission, percentage, or brokerage fee in order to secure work, except to a bona fide employee or bona fide established commercial or marketing agencies retained by them.

III. Professional Obligations

1. Engineers shall be guided in all their relations by the highest standards of honesty and integrity.

a. Engineers shall acknowledge their errors and shall not distort or alter the facts.

b. Engineers shall advise their clients or employers when they believe a project will not be successful.

c. Engineers shall not accept outside employment to the detriment of their regular work or interest. Before accepting any outside engineering employment, they will notify their employers.

d. Engineers shall not attempt to attract an

engineer from another employer by false or misleading pretenses.

  e. Engineers shall not promote their own interest at the expense of the dignity and integrity of the profession.

2. Engineers shall at all times strive to serve the public interest.

  a. Engineers are encouraged to participate in civic affairs; career guidance for youths; and work for the advancement of the safety, health, and well-being of their community.

  b. Engineers shall not complete, sign, or seal plans and/or specifications that are not in conformity with applicable engineering standards. If the client or employer insists on such unprofessional conduct, they shall notify the proper authorities and withdraw from further service on the project.

  c. Engineers are encouraged to extend public knowledge and appreciation of engineering and its achievements.

  d. Engineers are encouraged to adhere to the principles of sustainable development in order to protect the environment for future generations.

3. Engineers shall avoid all conduct or practice that deceives the public.

  a. Engineers shall avoid the use of statements containing a material misrepresentation of fact or omitting a material fact.

  b. Consistent with the foregoing, engineers may advertise for recruitment of personnel.

  c. Consistent with the foregoing, engineers may prepare articles for the lay or technical press, but such articles shall not imply credit to the author for work performed by others.

4. Engineers shall not disclose, without consent, confidential information concerning the business affairs or technical processes of any present or former client or employer, or public body on which they serve.

  a. Engineers shall not, without the consent of all interested parties, promote or arrange for new employment or practice in connection with a specific project for which the engineer has gained particular and specialized knowledge.

  b. Engineers shall not, without the consent of all interested parties, participate in or represent an adversary interest in connection with a specific project or proceeding in which the engineer has gained particular specialized knowledge on behalf of a former client or employer.

5. Engineers shall not be influenced in their professional duties by conflicting interests.

  a Engineers shall not accept financial or other considerations, including free engineering designs, from material or equipment suppliers for specifying their product.

  b. Engineers shall not accept commissions or allowances, directly or indirectly, from contractors or other parties dealing with clients or employers of the engineer in connection with work for which the engineer is responsible.

6. Engineers shall not attempt to obtain employment or advancement or professional engagements by untruthfully criticizing other engineers, or by other improper or questionable methods.

  a. Engineers shall not request, propose, or accept a commission on a contingent basis under circumstances in which their judgment may be compromised.

  b. Engineers in salaried positions shall accept part-time engineering work only to the extent consistent with policies of the employer and in accordance with ethical considerations.

  c. Engineers shall not, without consent, use equipment, supplies, laboratory, or office facilities of an employer to carry on outside private practice.

7. Engineers shall not attempt to injure, maliciously or falsely, directly or indirectly, the professional reputation, prospects,

practice, or employment of other engineers. Engineers who believe others are guilty of unethical or illegal practice shall present such information to the proper authority for action.

  a. Engineers in private practice shall not review the work of another engineer for the same client, except with the knowledge of such engineer, or unless the connection of such engineer with the work has been terminated.

  b. Engineers in governmental, industrial, or educational employ are entitled to review and evaluate the work of other engineers when so required by their employment duties.

  c. Engineers in sales or industrial employ are entitled to make engineering comparisons of represented products with products of other suppliers.

8. Engineers shall accept personal responsibility for their professional activities, provided, however, that engineers may seek indemnification for services arising out of their practice for other than gross negligence, where the engineer's interests cannot otherwise be protected.

  a. Engineers shall conform with state registration laws in the practice of engineering.

  b. Engineers shall not use association with a nonengineer, a corporation, or partnership as a "cloak" for unethical acts.

9. Engineers shall give credit for engineering work to those to whom credit is due, and will recognize the proprietary interests of others.

  a. Engineers shall, whenever possible, name the person or persons who may be individually responsible for designs, inventions, writings, or other accomplishments.

  b. Engineers using designs supplied by a client recognize that the designs remain the property of the client and may not be duplicated by the engineer for others without express permission.

  c. Engineers, before undertaking work for others in connection with which the engineer may make improvements, plans, designs, inventions, or other records that may justify copyrights or patents, should enter into a positive agreement regarding ownership.

  d. Engineers' designs, data, records, and notes referring exclusively to an employer's work are the employer's property. The employer should indemnify the engineer for use of the information for any purpose other than the original purpose.

  e. Engineers shall continue their professional development throughout their careers and should keep current in their specialty fields by engaging in professional practice, participating in continuing education courses, reading in the technical literature, and attending professional meetings and seminars.

Footnote 1 "Sustainable development" is the challenge of meeting human needs for natural resources, industrial products, energy, food, transportation, shelter, and effective waste management while conserving and protecting environmental quality and the natural resource base essential for future development.

As Revised July 2007

"By order of the United States District Court for the District of Columbia, former Section 11(c) of the NSPE Code of Ethics prohibiting competitive bidding, and all policy statements, opinions, rulings or other guidelines interpreting its scope, have been rescinded as unlawfully interfering with the legal right of engineers, protected under the antitrust laws, to provide price information to prospective clients; accordingly, nothing contained in the NSPE Code of Ethics, policy statements, opinions, rulings or other guidelines prohibits the submission of price quotations or competitive bids for engineering services at any time or in any amount."

Statement by NSPE Executive Committee

In order to correct misunderstandings which have been indicated in some instances since the issuance of the Supreme Court decision and the entry of the Final Judgment, it is noted that in its decision of April 25, 1978, the Supreme Court of the United States declared: "The Sherman Act does not require competitive bidding."

It is further noted that as made clear in the Supreme Court decision:

1. Engineers and firms may individually refuse to bid for engineering services.
2. Clients are not required to seek bids for engineering services.
3. Federal, state, and local laws governing procedures to procure engineering services are not affected, and remain in full force and effect.
4. State societies and local chapters are free to actively and aggressively seek legislation for professional selection and negotiation procedures by public agencies.
5. State registration board rules of professional conduct, including rules prohibiting competitive bidding for engineering services, are not affected and remain in full force and effect. State registration boards with authority to adopt rules of professional conduct may adopt rules governing procedures to obtain engineering services.

6. As noted by the Supreme Court, "nothing in the judgment prevents NSPE and its members from attempting to influence governmental action . . ."

Note: In regard to the question of application of the Code to corporations vis-a-vis real persons, business form or type should not negate nor influence conformance of individuals to the Code. The Code deals with professional services, which services must be performed by real persons. Real persons in turn establish and implement policies within business structures. The Code is clearly written to apply to the Engineer, and it is incumbent on members of NSPE to endeavor to live up to its provisions. This applies to all pertinent sections of the Code.

National Society of Professional Engineers
1420 King Street
Alexandria, Virginia 22314-2794
703/684-2800 • Fax:703/836-4875
www.nspe.org
Publication date as revised: July 2007 • Publication #1102

Content standards for a particular discipline are concepts that have been determined by experts as essential to understanding the field, or discipline. Standards can be written by national, state, or local institutions and educators are required to create lessons that cover these very important ideas.

Engineers must be knowledgeable in many content areas, including math, science, technology, and language arts. The standards found on the following pages provide a broad outline of key concepts for these important areas.

National English Language Arts Standards

NCTE 1 Students read a wide range of print and nonprint texts to build an understanding of texts, of themselves, and of the cultures of the United States and the world; to acquire new information; to respond to the needs and demands of society and the workplace; and for personal fulfillment. Among these texts are fiction and nonfiction, classic and contemporary works.

NCTE 2 Students read a wide range of literature from many periods in many genres to build an understanding of the many dimensions (e.g., philosophical, ethical, aesthetic) of human experience.

NCTE 3 Students apply a wide range of strategies to comprehend, interpret, evaluate, and appreciate texts. They draw on their prior experience, their interactions with other readers and writers, their knowledge of word meaning and of other texts, their word identification strategies, and their understanding of textual features (e.g., sound-letter correspondence, sentence structure, context, graphics).

NCTE 4 Students adjust their use of spoken, written, and visual language (e.g., conventions, style, vocabulary) to communicate effectively with a variety of audiences and for different purposes.

NCTE 5 Students employ a wide range of strategies as they write and use different writing process elements appropriately to communicate with different audiences for a variety of purposes.

NCTE 6 Students apply knowledge of language structure, language conventions (e.g., spelling and punctuation), media techniques, figurative language, and genre to create, critique, and discuss print and nonprint texts.

NCTE 7 Students conduct research on issues and interests by generating ideas and questions, and by posing problems. They gather, evaluate, and synthesize data from a variety of sources (e.g., print and nonprint texts, artifacts, people) to communicate their discoveries in ways that suit their purpose and audience.

NCTE 8 Students use a variety of technological and informational resources (e.g., libraries, databases, computer networks, video) to gather and synthesize information and to create and communicate knowledge.

NCTE 9 Students develop an understanding of and respect for diversity in language use, patterns, and dialects across cultures, ethnic groups, geographic regions, and social roles.

NCTE 10 Students whose first language is not English make use of their first language to develop competency in the English language arts and to develop understanding of content across the curriculum.

NCTE 11 Students participate as knowledgeable, reflective, creative, and critical members of a variety of literacy communities.

NCTE 12 Students use spoken, written, and visual language to accomplish their own purposes (e.g., for learning, enjoyment, persuasion, and the exchange of information).

Standards are listed with permission of the National Council of Teachers of English (NCTE). NCTE *does not endorse the content or validity of these alignments.*

National Council of Teachers of Mathematics Standards for Grades 9–12

Number and Operations

Understand numbers, ways of representing numbers, relationships among numbers, and number systems.

Understand the meanings of operations and how they relate to one another.

Compute fluently and make reasonable estimates.

Algebra

Understand patterns, relations, and functions.

Represent and analyze mathematical situations and structures using algebraic symbols.

Use mathematical models to represent and understand quantitative relationships.

Analyze change in various contexts.

Geometry

Analyze characteristics of two- and three-dimensional geometric shapes and develop mathematical arguments about geometric relationships.

Use visualization, spatial reasoning, and geometric modeling to solve problems.

Specify locations and describe spatial relationships using coordinate geometry and other representational systems.

Apply transformations and use symmetry to analyze mathematical solutions.

Measurement

Understand measurable attributes of objects and the units, systems, and processes of measurement.

Apply appropriate techniques, tools, and formulas to determine measurements.

Data Analysis and Probability

Formulate questions that can be addressed with data and collect, organize, and display relevant data to answer them.

Select and use appropriate statistical methods to analyze data.

Develop and evaluate inferences and predictions that are based on data.

Understand and apply basic concepts of probability.

Problem Solving

Apply and adapt a variety of appropriate strategies to solve problems.

Solve problems that arise in mathematics and in other contexts.

Build new mathematical knowledge through problem solving.

Monitor and reflect on the process of problem solving.

National Science Standards

Content Standard 1 Students should develop an understanding of science unifying concepts and processes: systems, order, and organization; evidence, models, and explanation; change, constancy, and measurement; evolution and equilibrium; and form and function.

Content Standard A Students should develop abilities necessary to do scientific inquiry, understandings about scientific inquiry.

Content Standard B Students should develop an understanding of the structure of atoms, structure and properties of matter, chemical reactions, motions and forces, conservation of energy and increase in disorder, and interactions of energy and matter.

Content Standard C Students should develop understanding of the cell; molecular basis of heredity; biological evolution; interdependence of organisms; matter, energy, and organization in living systems; and behavior of organisms.

Content Standard D Students should develop an understanding of energy in the earth system, geochemical cycles, origin and evolution of the earth system, origin and evolution of the universe.

Content Standard E Students should develop abilities of technological design, understandings about science and technology.

Content Standard F Students should develop understanding of personal and community health; population growth; natural resources; environmental quality; natural and human-induced hazards; science and technology in local, national, and global challenges.

Content Standard G Students should develop understanding of science as a human endeavor, nature of scientific knowledge, historical perspectives.

Reprinted with permission from National Science Education Standards, *1996 by the* National Academy of Sciences, *Courtesy of the* National Academies Press, *Washington, D.C.*

International Technology And Engineering Educators Association Standards for Technological Literacy

The Nature of Technology

Standard 1. Students will develop an understanding of the characteristics and scope of technology.

Standard 2. Students will develop an understanding of the core concepts of technology.

Standard 3. Students will develop an understanding of the relationships among technologies and the connections between technology and other fields of study.

Technology and Society

Standard 4. Students will develop an understanding of the cultural, social, economic, and political effects of technology.

Standard 5. Students will develop an understanding of the effects of technology on the environment.

Standard 6. Students will develop an understanding of the role of society in the development and use of technology.

Standard 7. Students will develop an understanding of the influence of technology on history.

Design

Standard 8. Students will develop an understanding of the attributes of design.

Standard 9. Students will develop an understanding of engineering design.

Standard 10. Students will develop an understanding of the role of troubleshooting, research and development, invention and innovation, and experimentation in problem solving.

Abilities for a Technological World

Standard 11. Students will develop abilities to apply the design process.

Standard 12. Students will develop abilities to use and maintain technological products and systems.

Standard 13. Students will develop abilities to assess the impact of products and systems.

The Designed World

Standard 14. Students will develop an understanding of and be able to select and use medical technologies.

Standard 15. Students will develop an understanding of and be able to select and use agricultural and related biotechnologies.

Standard 16. Students will develop an understanding of and be able to select and use energy and power technologies.

Standard 17. Students will develop an understanding of and be able to select and use information and communication technologies.

Standard 18. Students will develop an understanding of and be able to select and use transportation technologies.

Standard 19. Students will develop an understanding of and be able to select and use manufacturing technologies.

Standard 20. Students will develop an understanding of and be able to select and use construction technologies.

Glossary

How to Use this Glossary

Content vocabulary terms in this glossary are words that relate to this book's content. They are highlighted yellow in your text.

Words in this glossary that have an asterisk (*) are academic vocabulary terms. They are **boldfaced blue** in your text. They help you understand your school subjects and are used on tests.

Page numbers refer to where the term is defined or explained in the text, and not necessarily to first use in the text.

A

absorption n. a material's ability to absorb anything (for example, light waves) *(p. 111)*

* **adjustments** n. changes made to achieve a desired result *(p. 213)*

aggregate n. pieces of broken or crushed stone used in making concrete *(p. 133)*

* **aids** v. helps *(p. 101)*

alloys n. metals made by combining two or more metals *(p. 74)*

* **alternative** adj. relative to a choice between two or more possibilities *(p. 171)*

analog adj. relating to a signal that changes continually *(p. 164)*

animations n. the computerized generation of a series of images that seem to show motion *(p. 80)*

anthropometric data n. information relating to the sizes of humans and the specific distances between parts of the body *(p. 60)*

* **aspects** n. specific parts of a process or job *(p. 260)*

* **assembled** v. put together *(p. 187)*

automation n. the use of control systems to regulate equipment and perform processes *(p. 195)*

B

biomaterials n. natural or synthetic materials used in medical applications *(p. 214)*

biomechanical adj. relating to an area of engineering that deals with the mechanics of the body *(p. 206)*

biomedical adj. relating to both biology and medicine *(p. 19)*

* **bonds** n. forces or links that unite or combine *(p. 106)*

byproducts n. waste products left over from production processes *(p. 222)*

C

capacitor n. a device that filters out electrical interference, blocks the flow of direct current, and stores energy in a circuit *(p. 152)*

carbon dioxide n. a gas with no color or odor produced by burning and breathing *(p. 290)*

castability n. the ease with which a molten material can be cast into a given form by being poured into a mold *(p. 112)*

cathodic protection n. the use of an electrochemical process to protect a metal against corrosion *(p. 119)*

chemical reaction n. a process in which one or more substances are changed into other substances *(p. 155)*

circuit n. in electricity and electronics, a series of electrical components through which electricity may flow *(p. 90)*

closed-loop system n. a system that responds to changing conditions *(p. 93)*

coefficient of thermal expansion n. the value that describes the change in a material as a result of a change in its temperature *(p. 110)*

* **colleagues** n. fellow-workers in the same profession or business *(p. 298)*

combustion n. the burning of something *(p. 290)*

* **communicate** v. to share or exchange information *(p. 65)*

* **complex** adj. complicated *(p. 179)*

* **components** n. parts or elements of a larger whole *(p. 133)*

composite adj. made from two or more distinct materials that remain distinct after processing *(p. 106)*

* **compounds** n. substances composed of two or more elements *(p. 46)*

compressive strength n. the resistance of a material to breaking under compression (being pushed together) *(p. 108)*

computed tomography (CT, CAT) n. an x-ray technique that produces a three-dimensional image of a part of the body *(p. 209)*

computer simulations n. mathematical analyses that are used instead of physical models *(p. 80)*

computer-aided design (CAD) n. the use of special computer software to design parts, products, or structures *(p. 71)*

computer-aided manufacturing (CAM) n. the use of computer software to control machine tools *(p. 195)*

computer-integrated manufacturing (CIM) n. the use of computers to control the entire manufacturing process *(p. 195)*

* **concentrate** v. to gather together, to focus *(p. 290)*

* **concepts** n. ideas *(p. 7)*

conductance n. the ability to conduct an electrical current *(p. 153)*

conductivity n. the degree to which a material is able to conduct electricity or heat *(p. 110)*

conductors n. materials containing mobile (or free) electrons, through which electrons can move easily *(p. 151)*

* **conflicts** n. serious disagreements *(p. 275)*

* **constant** adj. unchanging *(p. 225)*

* **constraints** n. limitations, restrictions *(p. 10)*

* **construction** n. large scale, on-site fabrication *(p. 113)*

consultants n. individuals or companies engaged to provide expert advice or assistance *(p. 21)*

contaminants n. substances that make another substance unclear or impure *(p. 138)*

continuous manufacturing n. the manufacturing of products without interruption *(p. 189)*

* **coordination** n. the organization of elements to make them work together efficiently *(p. 244)*

corrosion n. a process of disintegration by chemical action; one form of corrosion is oxidation (rusting) *(p. 107)*

* **criteria** n. principles on which something is planned or judged (singular: criterion) *(p. 57)*

cryptography n. the process of writing and deciphering coded messages *(p. 245)*

current n. in electricity and electronics, the flow of electricity *(p. 90)*

custom manufacturing n. the manufacturing of items to fill a specific, individual order *(p. 189)*

cyberterrorism n. the use of computers and information technology to cause physical or financial harm *(p. 296)*

D

dead load n. the weight of a structure, including the materials used to build it and the permanent equipment that is part of the structure *(p. 132)*

decision matrix n. a mathematical tool used to narrow options and compare criteria in order to identify a solution *(p. 62)*

deflection n. the measure of how much a structural element bends under stress *(p. 109)*

deinking n. the process in which inks and dyes are removed from paper *(p. 224)*

derivatives n. in mathematics, measures of how a function changes when its input changes *(p. 38)*

desalination adj. relating to the removal of excess salt from water *(p. 293)*

* **design** v. to decide on the look and function of a device, structure, or other object, usually by making plans or drawings *(p. 6)*

* **deviations** n. departures from a norm; in statistics, the differences between the value of an observation and the mean of the population *(p. 29)*

* **device** n. something made for, or adapted to, a particular purpose *(p. 70)*

* **differentiate** v. to make a difference between or among two or more things *(p. 273)*

digital adj. relating to a signal that is either high or low, on or off *(p. 164)*

diluted v. made thinner or weaker by adding water *(p. 230)*

* **dimensions** n. marks used to indicate the size of an object and its various parts *(p. 74)*

diode n. an electrical component that normally allows current to flow in only one direction *(p. 160)*

disclosure n. the act of making information known *(p. 55)*

dispersion n. the separation of a light wave into colors *(p. 111)*

dissolved v. mixed with liquid to make a solution *(p. 228)*

distillation n. the process of purifying a liquid by successive evaporation and condensation *(p. 226)*

* **distribution** n. the action of sharing something out among several recipients *(p. 157)*

* **diversity** n. variety *(p. 101)*

* **drafting** n. the process of preparing working drawings of an item *(p. 72)*

draftsperson n. a person who produces technical plans or drawings, by hand or using a computer *(p. 258)*

drip irrigation n. a way of watering plants that uses small-diameter tubes from which water slowly leaks *(p. 294)*

ductility n. the maximum extent to which a material can be stretched without fracturing *(p. 109)*

dyes n. liquids containing dissolved coloring matter *(p. 228)*

dynamic loads n. loads on a structure that change over time *(p. 132)*

dynamics n. the study of how forces affect moving objects *(p. 173)*

E

* **economics** n. the social science that deals with the supply of and demand for goods and services *(p. 239)*

elasticity n. the tendency of a material to return to its original shape after a stress is removed *(p. 109)*

electrification n. the process of making electricity readily available within a region or country *(p. 12)*

electrochemical cell n. a device in which a chemical reaction produces electricity *(p. 155)*

electromagnetic adj. relating to electromagnetism (the magnetism produced by an electric current) *(p. 39)*

electromagnetic force (EMF) n. an interaction of the electric and magnetic fields of charged particles *(p. 151)*

electronic adj. based on or operated by the flow of electrons *(p. 6)*

* **elements** n. component parts *(p. 92)*

* **emerging** adj. coming into being *(p. 241)*

emissions n. gases discharged into the air, for example from an automobile *(p. 96)*

* **emphasize** v. to give special importance to something *(p. 270)*

* **energy** n. the strength or power required to perform an activity *(p. 8)*

engineering n. the branch of science and technology that deals with the design, construction, and maintenance of engines, machines, structures, and systems *(p. 9)*

engineering technician n. a person who combines the responsibilities of engineer and technician in his or her daily work *(p. 256)*

engineering technology n. an area of engineering that focuses mostly on practical applications; a college-level program that involves a less rigorous study of mathematics and science than a general engineering program *(p. 236)*

entropy n. a reduction in the availability of energy, which is the subject of the Second Law of Thermodynamics *(p. 225)*

* **environmental** adj. relating to an organism's surroundings *(p. 220)*

environmental engineering n. a branch of engineering that applies engineering principles to improve the natural environment *(p. 241)*

enzymes n. proteins from living cells that cause chemical reactions *(p. 226)*

equilibrium n. a state of balance *(p. 225)*

ergonomics n. the study of how people interface and interact with various items, such as a desk or a machine *(p. 60)*

esthetically adv. in a manner that is appealing to the eye *(p. 271)*

* **expertise** n. expert knowledge or skill *(p. 192)*

extensively adv. in a broad or widespread way *(p. 274)*

extracurricular adj. relating to activities or studies that are not part of the standard academic curriculum *(p. 276)*

extrusion n. a process in which a material blank is pressed through a die and forced into the desired shape *(p. 115)*

F

fabrication n. the manufacturing or construction of various items *(p. 113)*

* **factors** n. elements, features, or conditions that bring about a particular result *(p. 193)*

fatigue n. weakness in a material caused by being repeatedly subjected to stress *(p. 109)*

feedback n. the evaluation of the results or output from a system or process *(p. 92)*

filtration n. the process of removing particles by passing a liquid or gas through a filter *(p. 226)*

* **flexible** adj. easily changed or modified *(p. 60)*

flexible manufacturing n. a manufacturing method in which changes in the process are easy to make *(p. 190)*

fluid mechanics n. the study of fluids and the forces that act on them *(p. 45)*

force n. anything that causes a free body to change or move *(p. 42)*

* **format** n. the way something is arranged or set out *(p. 274)*

forming n. the shaping of a material by various processes, including forging, rolling, extruding, pressing, bending, shearing, compressing, drawing, and stamping *(p. 114)*

* **foundations** n. the lowest areas of a building, usually located below ground level *(p. 141)*

G

* **global** adj. worldwide *(p. 298)*

* **goal** n. aim, purpose *(p. 54)*

green engineering n. the development and use of products and processes that conserve resources, reduce waste, and achieve sustainability *(p. 298)*

H

homeostasis n. an organism's ability to regulate its internal environment *(p. 202)*

Hooke's Law of Elasticity n. a law describing the relationship between a force applied to a spring and the amount that the spring stretches when that force is applied *(p. 109)*

hydraulics n. machinery or systems that use oil or another liquid to transfer force *(p. 176)*

hydrocarbons n. molecules that consist only of hydrogen and carbon atoms *(p. 47)*

hydroelectric adj. relating to electrical power generated from the movement of water *(p. 156)*

hydrology n. the study of water and its occurrence, circulation, and distribution on earth *(p. 45)*

I

I-beam n. a structural member in the shape of a capital I *(p. 134)*

* **image** n. a visual representation of something *(p. 208)*

implementation n. the carrying out of a plan or procedure *(p. 243)*

* **incentive** n. anything that motivates or encourages a person to do something *(p. 135)*

* **indicator** n. anything used to predict performance or outcome *(p. 26)*

industrial robots n. devices that can be programmed to perform many industrial tasks that are dangerous or difficult for humans to perform consistently *(p. 195)*

inertia n. the property of an object remaining at rest *(p. 172)*

infectious adj. relating to a disease or other condition that can be passed from one living organism to another *(p. 294)*

information security systems n. systems that protect personal and private data sources *(p. 245)*

* **infrastructure** n. the systems that support a community, such as roads, bridges, and systems for wastewater treatment and drinking water supply *(p. 291)*

* **input** n. anything that is included into a system or process, often at the very beginning *(p. 92)*

* **integrated** adj. combined together *(p. 164)*

intellectual property n. a work or invention that results from the use of creative thought, such as a manuscript or a design *(p. 55)*

* **interact** v. to act on each other *(p. 90)*

intermittent manufacturing n. the manufacturing of products in lots or batches *(p. 189)*

inverse adj. relating to an image in which less dense materials appear darker and more dense material appears lighter *(p. 208)*

* **investigations** n. careful searches or examinations *(p. 141)*

isometric adj. relating to a sketch that shows an object in a three-dimensional view *(p. 75)*

isotopes n. various types of atoms from the same chemical element that differ in nuclear mass but not in nuclear number *(p. 210)*

iteration n. a succession of approximations used to develop accuracy; a repetition *(p. 34)*

J

just-in-time (JIT) manufacturing n. a manufacturing method based on the idea that all necessary resources should be available exactly when they are needed *(p. 190)*

K

kinetic energy n. active energy, based on the movement of an object from a stationary position *(p. 40)*

L

lean manufacturing n. manufacturing whose goal is to eliminate waste in all aspects of the process *(p. 190)*

LED (light-emitting diode) n. a semiconductor that glows when an electric current passes through it *(p. 90)*

* **levees** n. raised areas built along rivers to prevent flooding *(p. 291)*

* **license** n. a legal document that gives permission to practice a professional skill *(p. 130)*

live loads n. loads on a structure that are not part of the structure itself *(p. 132)*

logistics n. in industry, the detailed planning of production, inventory control, distribution, storage, shipping, and routing *(p. 240)*

M

machinability n. the ease with which a material can be worked to an acceptable surface finish on a machine *(p. 112)*

magnetic resonance imaging (MRI) n. the use of strong magnetic fields and radio waves to produce an image *(p. 209)*

malleability n. the maximum extent to which a material can be compressed without fracturing *(p. 109)*

manufacturer n. an individual or company that makes goods or articles, usually on a large scale, by using machinery *(p. 20)*

mathematics n. the study of the relationships among numbers, shapes, and quantities *(p. 9)*

mechanical advantage n. the increase in force gained by using a machine *(p. 176)*

mechanics n. a branch of physics involving the study of motion and movement *(p. 171)*

mechanism n. a system made up of a number of parts, which may be simple machines *(p. 179)*

minimalization n. making as minor or insignificant as possible *(p. 241)*

minimally invasive surgery n. a surgical procedure in which only very small incisions are made into the body *(p. 204)*

mockup n. a physical representation of an item or structure *(p. 81)*

molding n. a process in which a material (usually plastic) is heated and then injected, blown, or pressed into a mold. *(p. 114)*

momentum n. the product of the mass and velocity of a moving object *(p. 172)*

municipal adj. relating to a city or town *(p. 137)*

musculoskeletal adj. relating to the system in the human body that includes bones, joints, tendons, ligaments, and muscles *(p. 204)*

N

nitrogen cycle n. the circulation of nitrogen from the air to the soil to plants and animals, and back into the air *(p. 290)*

* **nuclear** adj. relating to the creation or use of atomic energy *(p. 174)*

O

open-loop system n. a system that does not respond to changing conditions *(p. 93)*

optimization n. making the best or most efficient use of a situation, product, or resource *(p. 236)*

optimize v. to improve to the maximum extent *(p. 79)*

orthographic adj. relating to a sketch that shows what an object looks like from a front, top, right, cross-sectional, or other view *(p. 73)*

* **output** n. the results produced by a system or process *(p. 92)*

P

pandemic n. an outbreak of disease that infects a large number of people in a particular area *(p. 294)*

* **parameters** n. limits or boundaries that define the scope of an activity *(p. 81)*

particulate adj. relating to fine particles, or tiny pieces of matter, in a substance that remain separate from that substance *(p. 138)*

patent n. a government document that establishes the inventor of a new device or process *(p. 55)*

* **perspective** adj. relating to a type of pictorial drawing that shows an object in a realistic, three-dimensional way *(p. 77)*

pharmaceuticals n. products of the medical drug industry *(p. 220)*

photovoltaic adj. relating to devices that use solar radiation to create electricity *(p. 157)*

* **physical** adj. in this context, relating to the branch of science known as physics *(p. 221)*

physical security systems n. systems that protect physical spaces such as residences, commercial offices, and other facilities, or even entire countries *(p. 245)*

pigments n. insoluble substances that become a paint or ink when suspended in a liquid *(p. 228)*

pneumatics n. machinery or systems that use air or another gas to transfer force *(p. 176)*

polarization n. the orientation of light waves in a particular direction *(p. 111)*

potential energy n. stored energy, based on an object's position (*p. 40*)

practicing adj. pursuing a particular profession, career, activity, or interest (*p. 281*)

* **primary** adj. earliest in time or first in order (*p. 138*)

* **principles** n. generally applicable theorems or laws (*p. 156*)

probability n. the number of times an event occurs divided by the total number of occurrences in the sample (*p. 28*)

* **process** v. to apply a treatment to something in order to change or preserve it (*p. 6*)

* **professional** adj. relating to a highly trained individual in the work environment (*p. 220*)

profiles n. brief descriptions or outlines (*p. 281*)

project management n. planning, organizing, and managing physical and human resources to complete a project (*p. 130*)

project manager n. a professional responsible for planning and carrying out a project in any field (*p. 237*)

* **promotional** adj. relating to the advertising of a company, product, performance, or service, to increase sales or public interest (*p. 192*)

propulsion n. the act of moving something forward (*p. 99*)

prospective adj. possible, likely (*p. 278*)

prosthetic adj. relating to any artificial body part, such as an artificial arm, leg, or heart (*p. 19*)

prototype n. a model made to test a new design (*p. 63*)

Q

quadratic adj. relating to a polynomial function involving a square of unknown value (*p. 31*)

quality control (QC) n. a procedure or set of procedures intended to ensure that a product or service meets established standards (*p. 191*)

quality control adj. relating to the process of ensuring quality in a product or service through testing and review (*p. 20*)

R

* **ratio** n. a comparison of two numbers, most commonly expressed as a fraction (*p. 26*)

* **rational** adj. based on reasoning; in math, relating to a number that can be expressed by a ratio of two integers (*p. 26*)

reactivity n. the extent to which a material reacts to chemical processes such as corrosion (*p. 107*)

* **refined** adj. free of impurities (*p. 221*)

reflectivity n. the degree to which a light wave "bounces" off of the surface of a material (*p. 111*)

reflector n. a curved sheet of metal or plastic that reflects light back (*p. 90*)

refraction n. the "bending" of a light wave when it passes through a material (*p. 111*)

* **relevant** adj. closely connected or appropriate to the subject at hand (*p. 58*)

* **reliability** n. dependability, trustworthiness (*p. 58*)

remediated adj. improved and made usable by removing pollutants (*p. 241*)

rendering n. a realistic drawing of an item or structure (*p. 77*)

* **research** n. systematic study (*p. 18*)

resin n. a sticky natural or synthetic substance used in various chemical applications, including the creation of plastics (*p. 224*)

resistor n. an electrical component that can be used to optimize current flow and control the voltage applied in a circuit (*p. 160*)

* **resources** n. a stock or supply of materials, people, or other assets that can be used to accomplish something (*p. 7*)

reverse engineering n. the analysis of a device, object, or system, often by taking it apart, to determine how it has been made or operates (*p. 61*)

* **revolutionized** v. completely and fundamentally changed, usually for the better (*p. 187*)

risk assessment n. the evaluation of the level of risk that is likely to attach to a situation or course of action (*p. 262*)

robotic surgery n. a procedure in which a surgeon uses a robotic surgery system to perform an operation (*p. 204*)

* **roles** n. the parts played by people or things (*p. 254*)

rolling n. a process in which a material is drawn through rollers that press it and make it thinner. (*p. 115*)

S

scale n. a ratio of size ("full scale" means full size) (*p. 72*)

schematic diagram n. a drawing that uses symbols to represent specific components (*p. 159*)

science n. the systematic study of the physical and natural world (*p. 7*)

security engineering n. a branch of engineering that applies engineering principles to the planning, operation, and maintenance of security systems *(p. 245)*

simple machine n. a tool that uses a basic power system to make work easier *(p. 177)*

socially responsible engineering n. the use of engineering skills to help others *(p. 299)*

space n. the three-dimensional extent of an object or area *(p. 34)*

specialized adj. adapted for a particular purpose *(p. 270)*

stakeholders n. the people, companies, or institutions that have a special interest in anything *(p. 56)*

static loads n. loads on a structure that are at rest at a given point in time *(p. 132)*

statics n. the study of how forces affect non-moving objects *(p. 173)*

* **statistical analysis** n. the collection, study, and interpretation of numerical data *(p. 60)*

* **statistics** n. the science of collecting and mathematically analyzing data *(p. 239)*

strain n. the change in a material's size or shape when stress is applied; also called deformation *(p. 108)*

* **stress** n. the amount of force exerted on a certain area *(p. 107)*

* **structure** n. the organization or arrangement of parts of a whole *(p. 220)*

subsystem n. a smaller system that is part of a larger system *(p. 95)*

* **sustainable** adj. capable of being maintained or continued with no major negative effects on the environment *(p. 119)*

synthetic adj. made by combining two or more components to form a new material *(p. 106)*

systems engineering n. a branch of engineering that applies engineering principles in designing and managing large and complicated projects *(p. 244)*

systems n. sets of things or parts that form a connected whole *(p. 90)*

T

technician n. a person who often works with, and reports to, engineers on projects *(p. 256)*

* **techniques** n. ways of carrying out a particular task *(p. 135)*

* **technologists** n. people who have received training in engineering technology and specialize in engineering applications rather than theory *(p. 236)*

technology n. the use of resources to solve problems and create things that people need and want *(p. 7)*

tempering n. a strengthening process in which a metal or glass is brought to a high temperature and then cooled very quickly (glass can also be chemically tempered) *(p. 117)*

tensile strength n. the resistance of a material to breaking under tension (being stretched or pulled apart) *(p. 107)*

terrorism n. the use of violence or threat of violence (usually by a group) to achieve a particular aim *(p. 295)*

thermal adj. relating to heat *(p. 110)*

thermodynamics n. the study of the relations among heat and other forms of energy *(p. 173)*

tissue engineering n. an area of biomedical engineering that uses cells and special materials to repair or replace body tissues *(p. 210)*

tolerance n. an acceptable margin of error *(p. 74)*

* **transfer** v. to move from place to place *(p. 180)*

transformer n. a device that steps voltage up or down *(p. 157)*

transistor n. a device used to switch or amplify electronic signals in a circuit *(p. 161)*

* **transmission** n. a process or mechanism that sends something from one place to another *(p. 170)*

transplant n. a procedure in which a person with a failed bodily organ receives a functioning organ from a donor *(p. 211)*

turbine n. an engine that is powered by water, steam, or combustion gases *(p. 175)*

U

ultrasound imaging n. a procedure in which high-frequency sound waves are sent into the body and reflected back by soft tissue to produce an image *(p. 209)*

universal systems model n. a model used to describe how any system works, which uses a standard set of elements (need, input, process, output, and feedback) *(p. 92)*

V

* **variables** n. elements, features, or factors that can change *(p. 81)*

* **vehicle** n. any device used to transport items, animals, or people *(p. 180)*

viable adj. practical, usable *(p. 62)*

* **virtual** adj. produced by a computer, not real *(p. 283)*

* **visible** adj. that can be seen *(p. 161)*

voltage n. the rate at which electricity is drawn from a source, measured in volts *(p. 90)*

W

waveforms n. the shapes and forms of signals moving through a solid, liquid, or gas *(p. 36)*

working drawing n. a drawing made to scale that shows the complete plans for an engineered product *(p. 72)*

Y

yield strength n. the point at which a material begins to deform permanently *(p. 109)*

Index

Credits

Cover © Linda Bucklin/iStockPhoto; **iii** (t) Courtesy of Henry R. Harms, (b) Courtesy of David A. Janosz, Jr; **vii** John Miller/Robert Harding World Imager/Getty Images; **ix** (l) Ilene MacDonald/Alamy, **ix** (r) Bill Cobb / SuperStock; **x** (l) Klaus Tiedge/Blend Images/Getty Images, **x** (r) Monty Rakusen/Getty Images; **xii** Tim Matsui/Liaison; **xiv** John Henderson/Alamy; **xvi** Photo courtesy of USDA Natural Resources Conservation Service; **xix** (tl) Bruce Forster 2007/Viewfinders, (tr) LUSH PIX/age Fotostock, (bl) Justin Sullivan/Getty Images, (br) MoMo Productions/The Image Bank/Getty Images; **xx** (tl) Andersen Ross/Blend Images/Getty Images, (tr) © Robert Sorbo/Reuters/Corbis, (bl) H.J. Martin/Corbis, (br) Michele Wassell/age Fotostock; **xxi** (tl) Tetra Images/age Fotostock, (r) Dan Kitwood/Getty Images News/Getty Images, (bl) Rich LaSalle/Riser/Getty Images; **xxix** Joho/Cultura/Getty Images; **xxx** IDREAMSTOCK/age Fotostock; **xxxi** Stockbyte/Getty Images; **xxxii** Comstock Images/Getty Images; **xxviii** AP Images; **4** Learn360; **6** Ryan McVay/Getty Images; **7** AP Images; **9** (t) Corbis, (c) Antony Nettle/Alamy; **10** John Miller/Robert Harding World Imager/Getty Images; **11** Science and Society/SuperStock; **16** Tony Hertz/Alamy; **17** Paul Rapson/Photo Researchers, Inc; **19** © UpperCut Images/Alamy; **20** H.J. Martin/Corbis; **23, 24** Learn360; **33** (bl) © The Gallery Collection/Corbis, (bc) Glowimages/Getty Images, (br) SEYMOUR/Photo Researchers, Inc; **35** Getty Images; **44** AP Images; **45** Jupiterimages/Comstock Images/Getty Images; **46** Eye Ubiquitous/SuperStock; **49** AP Images; **51, 52** Learn360; **56** Phil Degginger/Alamy; **59** Bill Cobb/SuperStock; **65** Ilene MacDonald/Alamy; **67, 68** Learn360; **78** Artpartner-images.com/Alamy; **80** Dan Kitwood/Getty Images; **82** Dorling Kindersley/Getty Images; **85** Learn360; **88** Engineering News-Record; **93** Jay S Simon/Stone/Getty Images; **96** Monty Rakusen/Getty Images; **99** Daniel Acker/Bloomberg via Getty Images; **101** Klaus Tiedge/Blend Images/Getty Images; **103** Engineering News-Record; **104** Learn360; **105** Tetra Images/ageFotostock; **107** Peter Titmuss/Alamy; **108** CSA Plastock/CSA Images/Getty Images; **109** (t) Photononstop/SuperStock, (c) IndexStock/SuperStock, (b) Kim Steele/Getty Images; **110** MoMo Productions/The Image Bank/Getty Images; **112** Science Faction/SuperStock; **113** LUSH PIX/age Fotostock; **114** (t) Exactostock/SuperStock, (b) E. L. Mustee & Sons, Inc; **115** Bruce Forster 2007/Viewfinders; **122** Learn360; **128** Learn360; **131** (tl) Last Refuge/Robert Harding World Imagery/Getty Images, (tr) Gail Shotlander/Flickr/Getty Images, (cl) Image Source Pink/SuperStock, (c) Jason's Travel Photography/Flickr/Getty Images, (cr) Banana Stock/PunchStock, (bl) SambaPhoto/Cassio Vasconcellos/Getty Image, (br) Arterra Picture Library/Alamy; **132** Michele Wassell/age Fotostock; **133** Fotoccompli/David Griffiths; **136** Paul Conklin/Taxi/Getty Images; **137** Steven Puetzer/Iconica/Getty Images; **141** Michael Doolittle/Alamy; **142** Stocktrek Images/Getty Images; **143** Rich LaSalle/Riser/Getty Images; **144** Jim West/Alamy; **145** Getty Images News/Getty Images; **147** Learn360; **148** Engineering News-Record; **152** (l) GIPhotoStock Z/Alamy, (t) David J. Green - electrical/Alamy, (r) sciencephotos/Alamy; **156** Tim Matsui/Liaison/Getty Images; **157** (l) XSPhoto/Alamy, (c) Ingram Publishing/SuperStock, (r) Stockbyte/Punchstock Images; **163** (l) David J. Green - electrical/Alamy, (c) Charles Nesbit/Photodisc/Getty Images, (r) Lyroky/Alamy; **164** (l) Gaertner/Alamy, (r) RalphWilliam/Alamy; **165** Stockbyte/Getty Images; **167** Engineering News-Record; **168** Learn360; **170** (b) Walter Geiersperger/Corbis, (inset) Steve Dunwell/Getty Images; **184** Engineering News-Record; **186** David Joel/Getty Images; **187** Matt Cardy/Getty Images; **187** Monty Rakusen/Getty Images; **188** Stratasys for Business Wire via Getty Images; **190** Royalty-Free/CORBIS; **191** Zigy Kaluzny-Charles Thatcher/Stone/Getty Images; **194** Ralph Mercer/Stone /Getty Images; **195** John Henderson/Alamy; **196** Courtesy of the Industrial Engineering Program, Kettering University; **197** Chris Sattlberger/age Fotostock; **199** Engineering News-Record; **200** Eliene Augenbraun, MP Axle, Inc; **202** Henry Westheim Photography/Alamy; **204** © 2010 Intuitive Surgical, Inc; **205** Photo courtesy of Instron®; **209** Stockbyte/PunchStock; **210** Photograph courtesy Siemens Medical Solutions USA, Inc - www.siemens.com/healthcare; **213** AP Images; **214** SSPL/Getty Images; **215** Tim Boyle/Getty Images; **217** Eliene Augenbraun, MP Axle, Inc; **218, 233** Learn360; **234** Engineering News-Record; **237** AP Images; **238** (tl) John Coletti/The Image Bank/Getty Images, (tr) Photo courtesy of USDA Natural Resources Conservation Service, (cr) Royalty-Free/CORBIS, (b) Graeme Norways/Stone/Getty Images; **244** Engineering News-Record; **252** Learn360; **254** JGI/Daniel Grill/Blend Images/Getty Images; **256** Royalty-Free/CORBIS; **258** Steve Dunwell/The Image Bank/Getty Images; **260** Bruce Ayres/Stone/Getty Images; **261** Bloomberg via Getty Images; **265** Andersen Ross/Blend Images/Getty Images; **267** Learn360; **268** Getty Images; **270** Image courtesy of PTC; **272** James Law Cybertecture; **273** Polka Dot Images/Masterfile; **276, 277** Images; **280** Heinrich van den Berg/Gallo Images/Getty Images; **281** JETS TEAMS 2010, jets.org; **282** MARK RALSTON/AFP/Getty Images; **285** Getty Images; **288** (t) Stockbyte/Getty Images, (tc) Banana Stock/PunchStock, (b) Getty Images, (bc) Miriam Masio/SPL/Getty Images; **289** Universal Images Group Limited/Alamy; **291** Justin Sullivan/Getty Images; **292** The MIC is a program of the Florida Department of Transportation. Images provided by AECOM; **295** AP Images; **296** Getty Images; **297** Tim Hawley/Photographer's Choice/Getty Images; **298** © Robert Sorbo/Reuters/Corbis; **300** Jim West/age Fotostcok; **301** AP Images; **381** Emmanuel Lattes/Alamy.